**Electron-Beam Technology
in Microelectronic Fabrication**

CONTRIBUTORS

J. P. BALLANTYNE

GEORGE R. BREWER

BERNARD FAY

JAMES S. GREENEICH

RICHARD C. HENDERSON

DONALD R. HERRIOTT

JACQUES TROTEL

Electron-Beam Technology in Microelectronic Fabrication

Edited by

GEORGE R. BREWER

HUGHES RESEARCH LABORATORIES
MALIBU, CALIFORNIA

 1980

ACADEMIC PRESS
A Subsidiary of Harcourt Brace Jovanovich, Publishers
New York   London   Toronto   Sydney   San Francisco

CHEMISTRY

6369-3628

ACADEMIC PRESS, INC.
111 Fifth Avenue, New York, New York 10003

United Kingdom Edition published by
ACADEMIC PRESS, INC. (LONDON) LTD.
24/28 Oval Road, London NW1 7DX

Library of Congress Cataloging in Publication Data
Main entry under title:

Electron-beam technology in microelectronic fabrication.

　　Includes bibliographies and index.
　　1.　Microelectronics.　2.　Lithography, Electron
beam.　I.　Brewer, George Raymond
TK7874.E48　　　621.381'7　　　79−8856
ISBN　0−12−133550−X

PRINTED IN THE UNITED STATES OF AMERICA

80 81 82 83　　9 8 7 6 5 4 3 2 1

Contents

1   High Resolution Lithography

GEORGE R. BREWER

2   Electron-Beam Processes

JAMES S. GREENEICH

List of Contributors

Numbers in parentheses indicate the pages on which the authors' contributions begin.

J. P. BALLANTYNE* (259), Bell Laboratories, Murray Hill, New Jersey 07971

GEORGE R. BREWER (1, 141), Hughes Research Laboratories, Malibu, California 90265

BERNARD FAY (309), Service de Microlithographie, Thomson-CSF, Domaine de Corbeville, 91401 Orsay, France

JAMES S. GREENEICH (59), Burroughs Corporation, San Diego, California 92127

RICHARD C. HENDERSON (217), Hughes Research Laboratories, Malibu, California 90265

DONALD R. HERRIOTT (141), Bell Laboratories, Murray Hill, New Jersey 07971

JACQUES TROTEL (309), Service de Microlithographie, Thomson-CSF, Domaine de Corbeville, 91401 Orsay, France

* Present address : Bell Laboratories, 2525 N. 11th Street, Reading, Pennsylvania 19604.

Preface

Those who have been involved in the microelectronics field over the past two or three decades have witnessed an exciting evolution in this technology. In the 1940s, when modern electronics received its first major impetus, electronic operations were performed by electron tubes. Such systems required power levels and occupied volumes that look incredible by modern standards. By contrast, we can now buy on the commercial market integrated circuits of a complexity approaching 100,000 transistors on a chip of silicon a few square millimeters in area with a power consumption of only a few tenths of a watt.

This great advance in microelectronics has been made possible by the invention of solid state devices, greater understanding of the physics of operation of these devices, cleverness in integrating them into complex circuits, and evolutionary improvements in the technology of their fabrication. These performance growth trends are continuing; present-day integrated circuits can perform more functions faster, with less power, and in a smaller volume than such circuits could just a few years ago. Furthermore, an important contribution to the improved performance in these modern circuits has been the reduction in size of the constituent components; and it turns out that the smaller size makes them cheaper to fabricate than the older, larger, circuits. As a result, microelectronics is pervading our lives to the extent that the worldwide market for integrated circuits alone is now approaching five billion dollars per year, and growing rapidly.

Microelectronic fabrication technology is based on the use of photolithography to create the very small features and patterns that make up a device or a circuit. During the past 20 years tremendous improvements have been made in the optical machines and techniques used in photolithography. The microelectronics field owes its very existence to this process. However, as the desired size of features is reduced to less than about 1 μm, some fundamental limits restrict the usefulness of this photolithographic process because the features to be exposed become comparable in size with the wavelength of light.

Presently, the only known way to draw these submicrometer features with arbitrary shape is by the use of a fine, focused electron beam that is controlled by a computer. This new technology of electron beam lithography has been developed over the past decade in several industrial laboratories and has matured sufficiently that it is now beginning to be applied in the production of microelectronic devices and integrated circuits. Judging from the history of microelectronic technology, further advances in performance and reductions in cost could be paced by the effectiveness of the fabrication tools that are available. Electron beam lithography is such a microelectronic fabrication tool; it should provide the means for continued advances in this field.

The intent of this book is to present a unified description of the technology of high resolution lithography in such a way as to be of most value to students and to engineers who will want to learn its unique features so that they can apply it in research, development, or production of the next generation of microelectronic devices and circuits. The topics treated here include the physics of interaction of the electrons with the polymer resist in which the patterns are drawn, the machines that generate and control the beam, and ways of applying electron-beam lithography, for example, in device fabrication and in the making of masks for photolithographic replication. While electron beams can be focused to a size that is at least an order of magnitude smaller than the wavelength of light, and can therefore create correspondingly smaller features, this technology presently suffers from some fundamental limits of its own, such as machine throughput and pattern resolution. These limits, and their technical and economic implications, are discussed in some detail. An integral part of high resolution lithography is the means to match replicate patterns with submicrometer dimensions as a possible way to higher throughput; one chapter is devoted to this subject. While these high resolution lithography techniques can be used to create submicrometer patterns in the resist, the translation of these patterns into useful semiconductor features requires the use of new etching, material deposition, etc., processes that preserve the resolution of the original patterns. These compatible fabrication processes, an essential part of this technology, are also treated here. The emphasis throughout is on the understanding and use of these technologies in practical situations.

Finally, since the technologies of high resolution lithography are still somewhat evolving, a unanimity of opinion on the ultimate form they will take has not yet emerged. Therefore, in order to present as broad a view as possible, this book has been written by seven authors employed by four industrial organizations. These individuals have all been heavily involved over the past decade in the development of high resolution lithography. I wish to express my sincere appreciation to these authors, who have contributed so well to make this book possible.

**Electron-Beam Technology
in Microelectronic Fabrication**

1

High resolution lithography

GEORGE R. BREWER

HUGHES RESEARCH LABORATORIES
MALIBU, CALIFORNIA

1

I. INTRODUCTION

During the past two decades, there has been an extremely rapid growth in both the technology and the application of microelectronics, to the point that it now pervades virtually all aspects of commercial and military business. Microelectronics,* particularly integrated circuits, have already made profound changes in such diverse fields as computers, industrial control systems, military electronics, wrist watches, automobiles, and cameras. The size and performance of microelectronic devices has been improved substantially, especially in the past few years; for example, transistor circuits can now operate at clock rates greater than 1 GHz, whereas 10 MHz was a goal just a few years ago.

Despite this rapid evolution, many of the applications of microelectronics need even higher levels of performance (particularly lower power requirements and higher speed) and higher functional density; all of them seek higher reliability and lower cost. In order to accommodate these needs, the microelectronics industry is finding it necessary to apply a new generation of processing, fabrication, and control techniques in the manufacture of these devices. One of the more promising ways to achieve the desired goals is to make the devices smaller, i.e., to evolve integrated circuits with higher functional density. The operating frequency of these circuits can be made higher and the power lower; yield improvement, resulting from smaller chips that still contain many functions, will result in lower cost and presumably higher reliability. Therefore, higher functional density integrated circuits are, in general, a desirable goal of technology development.

The contemporary photolithography process of pattern definition is the cornerstone of modern integrated circuit fabrication. However, among the several processing steps used in the manufacture of integrated circuits, photolithography is the lowest yield step in present production lines. Also the performance levels and density demanded of the new generations of microelectronic devices cannot be achieved by using photolithography for pattern definition. Therefore, a new pattern definition process is needed, and this in turn requires new complementary fabrication processes. Sophisticated diagnostic techniques, together with computer control of automated production processes, are also needed in order to achieve customer expectations for performance, cost, and reliability.

Energetic beams, specifically electron beams, ion beams, and laser

---

* The term microelectronics is used here in i s most general context, to denote discrete semiconductor devices, integrated circuits, and various forms of microwave solid state devices.

beams, form a powerful set of tools with which to attack these problems.* That is, ion beams can be used to implant dopant atoms into a semiconductor, to complement or replace diffusion. Electron beams can create surface patterns in resist, a process now carried out by photolithography. Laser and electron beams can anneal damaged wafers with better results than by present furnace annealing. The real advantage of beams, especially charged particle beams, as process and diagnostic tools is that they can perform basically the same functions as the corresponding contemporary processes, but they carry out these functions in qualitatively different ways. Therefore a significant change would be expected in the quality of the process they carry out; and indeed this expectation is realized. For example, laser beams and ion beams are already used successfully in production processing, e.g., for resistor trimming and ion implantation. Electron beams can be used to make patterns that are smaller and that show better edge resolution than can the best photolithography. Limited data suggest that the crucial yield determinant, pattern defect density, can be reduced and that machines can be made to effect economical device production. This newer electron-beam technology is emerging from the laboratory to form the next generation of lithography and quality control tools for the production of microelectronic devices.

The purpose of this book is to describe the processes and the machine technology of high resolution lithography for microelectronic device fabrication, together with some of its applications to semiconductor device processing. This chapter provides an introduction to this new technology, with emphasis on the main technical and economic issues on which its practical realization depends.

II. THE NEED FOR AN IMPROVED LITHOGRAPHY

A. Historical Trends in Microelectronics

Establishing the need for a new manufacturing process and projecting an advance in technology to fill this need are, at best, uncertain endeavors. However, some insight into the need can be gained by examining past historical trends as a guide to the future. Two of the more important parameters that can be used to evaluate microelectronics are the number of components that can be fabricated on a chip, and the product of power

---

* Review articles on this subject include Broers and Hatzakis (1972), Brewer (1971, 1972a,b), Broers (1976, 1978), and Thornton (1979).

and time delay in an integrated circuit. These parameters are measures of the economics and technical performance, respectively, of integrated circuits, where electron-beam lithography will ultimately have its greatest impact.

Figure 1.1 shows a plot of the growth trend in the number of components per chip over a 14-year period (Moore, 1975). This trend corresponds to a doubling of the number of components per chip every year, for a total growth of over four orders of magnitude. Of this total growth, Moore attributed a factor of 32 to improvements in photolithography, a factor of 20 to the use of larger chips, and the remaining factor of 100 to improved circuit design and layout. During this time period, the cost per chip has remained roughly constant, so that the cost per component or function has dropped dramatically. Presuming that future growth will come by further improved lithography and larger chip area, Moore predicts a growth curve for the future as shown by the upper dashed line. The speed–power product of more-or-less conventional devices shows a drop by a factor of 10 during this same time period. Examples of recent tech-

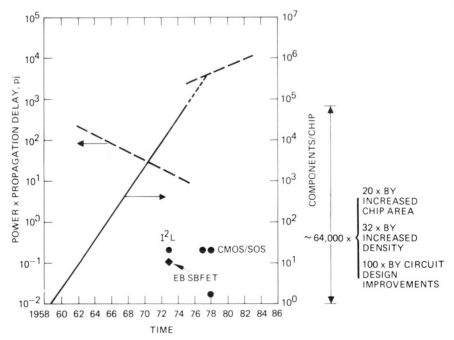

FIG. 1.1   Growth trend in the number of components in an integrated circuit that can be fabricated on a chip, for both silicon bipolar and MOS technologies. The corresponding decrease in the speed–power product and the factors that resulted in the growth in component density are also shown.

nology advances are shown, viz., the I²L (integrated injection logic) CMOS/SOS technologies and an electron-beam fabricated field effect transistor. It is seen that the corresponding speed–power products resulting from use of these new device and lithography technologies are about two orders of magnitude lower than the dashed trend curve. Thus future gains can also result from the use of revolutionary new device fabrication technologies and new device structures, such as I²L, that are themselves inherently integrated.

This historical trend can serve as an indicator of the future need for new technology in the microelectronics industry. There have been, of course, valid economic reasons for the advances made so far. As pointed out above, the cost per function has been reduced substantially, allowing integrated circuits to be used in more applications than would have otherwise been economically possible. The economic basis of these prior advances is unlikely to vanish in the near future; therefore, there will be pressure to continue the established trend. Furthermore, a manufacturing technology is becoming available that allows further growth at an affordable cost. But this argument does not show that a new technology is needed. Why not continue to push the fabrication and design technologies that are now available? This is being done, of course. There is a strong downward historical trend on linewidth in production devices (Bossung and Muraski, 1978), but the answer is that these technologies are reaching rather fundamental limits. Innovative device and circuit improvements will certainly continue to be made, as evidenced by the I²L point* on Fig. 1.1. More sophisticated use of computer aided circuit design will allow more compact circuits. The use of projection photolithography extends feature sizes down to around the 1 μm regime. The trend to larger chips may be limited unless the defect density of the lithography steps can also be reduced. However, the improvements in these areas will not be nearly as dramatic as in the past. Therefore, it appears that the principal way the number of components per chip can be increased significantly is by making the devices with submicrometer dimensions and by locating them closer together. But this step requires smaller linewidths and device dimensions, and the necessary submicrometer geometries are beyond the capabilities of photolithography, for reasons that will be described later.

A second view of the historical trend in microelectronics technology is shown in Fig. 1.2. This graph illustrates the dramatic shrinkage in size,†

---

* This point represents the speed–power product, but the I²L technology also permits higher device packing density than either conventional MOS or bipolar technologies.

† An interesting and imaginative view of the ever-present desire to make things smaller was given a number of years ago by Dr. Richard P. Feynmann in a chapter entitled *There's Plenty of Room at the Bottom, in* "Miniaturization," (ed. H. D. Gilbert), Reinhold, New York, 1961.

GEORGE R. BREWER

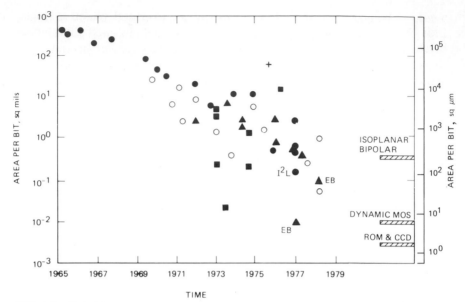

FIG. 1.2 Trend in area per bit of memory and logic type integrated circuits. The shaded bars indicate the limits to bit density calculated for the classes of devices indicated. +, Bubble ram; ■, MOS by EB; ▲, charge coupled device; ●, bipolar; ○, MOS; ▭, lower limit (THEO).

as expressed by the area required to store or process one bit of information. The points represent several types of devices, viz., MOS, bipolar, and CCDs, used mostly as memories, but a few points represent logic circuits. Most of the round points prior to 1971 were taken from a paper by Vadasz *et al.* (1971); they represent commercially available semiconductor memories made by photolithographic techniques. The points subsequent to 1971 represent both off-the-shelf and developmental devices made by photolithography and electron-beam lithography, as indicated in the figure. The general downward trend in area per bit, covering almost four orders of magnitude, is clear. Developmental devices made by electron-beam lithography are represented by the square points and the triangle so marked. However, there is a limit on the minimum size to which devices can be scaled. The horizontal bars show the theoretical lower limits as calculated by Hoeneisen and Mead (1972a,b) for several semiconductor technologies, viz., isoplanar bipolar transistor, dynamic MOS transistors, read only memories (ROM), and charge coupled devices. These limits are imposed principally by breakdown in the oxide or at the collector junction. The limitation in device and circuit size imposed by the resolution of photolithographic fabrication methods was mentioned above. The bars in Fig. 1.2 show that there are also fundamental limits imposed by the device physics. These subjects are discussed more fully later; however, a projection of future possibilities can be made. The area per bit varies approximately with the square of the minimum feature size. Such experimental data suggests that bit densities of 10^2 bits/mil^2 or better should be achievable at ~ 0.25 μm design rules if lithographic resolution were the only limiting factor. This value corresponds roughly with the lowest limit bars in Fig. 1.2, suggesting that the trend to smaller design rules for these types of devices can continue down to ~ 0.25 μm.

B. The Photolithography Process

Since the photolithography pattern definition process forms a limitation on further progress in microelectronic devices and circuits, it is important to understand the technical factors causing these limitations. In this replication process, a pattern is created in a mask, for example, in a photographic emulsion film or in a chromium film on glass. This mask is pressed against, or held in very close proximity to, a semiconductor wafer that has been coated with a light-sensitive polymer called a resist. Light passing through the transparent portions of the mask will expose corresponding regions of the resist, causing a change in the polymeric material so that it can be dissolved selectively by a chemical developer (if it is a positive-acting resist). The open regions in the resist define areas of access to the substrate for subsequent processing, such as metal deposition, etching, etc. Similarly, the exposed regions of a negative-acting resist becomes less soluble and remain after development. If the lines in the mask are relatively wide, for example, several micrometers, the pattern in the resist and subsequently in the substrate, forms a reasonably faithful reproduction of the pattern in the mask. However, when higher resolution is demanded, and the linewidth is reduced to the point that it is comparable to the wavelength of the light used for exposure, diffraction effects from the mask openings and reflection effects within the resist degrade the quality of the replicated image of the mask.

In order to appreciate the former effect, consider an elementary example of diffraction from a single knife edge spaced a distance from a surface and illuminated with collimated light. Because of the diffraction from the edge, light will extend a certain distance into the geometrical shadow region. When the linewidth in the mask (viewed here as a narrow slit aperture) becomes less than 1 μm, such diffraction effects are significant. These effects are illustrated in Fig. 1.3. Referring to this figure, it is seen that in addition to the diffraction or spreading effect of the light rays, there will be multiple reflections between the upper and lower surfaces of the

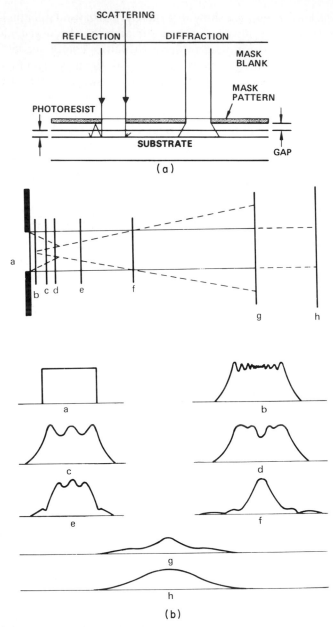

FIG. 1.3 Illustrations of the several effects that can result in a broader line in optically exposed resist than that in the mask; (a) is from Sullivan and Hause (1976). The curves in (b) were calculated for light diffracted from a 2-μm-wide slit (Heim, 1977).

resist that result in changes in light intensity and further lateral spreading of the light. These effects are enhanced if the wafer to be exposed is not planar, i.e., if there are steps (e.g., windows in an oxide) in which the resist is farther from the mask than it is in other regions. In addition, reflections from the top and bottom of the resist can create standing waves in the resist that can result in uneven exposure as a function of depth (Finnila et al., 1974). Figure 1.3b shows the calculated light intensity patterns due to diffraction from a 2-μm-wide transparent slit in the mask, as a function of mask-to-resist spacing (Heim, 1977). Positions b, c, and d correspond to separation distances typical of proximity printing. It is noted that both intensity and width are affected by diffraction. The mask must be pressed very close (~ 1 μm) to the resist in order to obtain a reasonably faithful reproduction of the 2 μm line in the resist. In order to achieve this close spacing, the mask must be pressed against the resist. Under this pressure, the irregularities on the resist surface cause damage to the mask surface. These mask defects will result in corresponding defects in the next resist-coated wafer that is exposed with this mask, and additional mask defects are caused by the second exposure, and so on. This is obviously a cumulative process that results in increasingly more defects in the exposed resist (and therefore in the devices that are produced) as the same mask is used repeatedly, and therefore limits the number of times a mask can be used (to, e.g., about 10 times for an emulsion working mask). This effect is usually the principal cause of low yield in the production of integrated circuits, accounting for typically 70% of the chip yield loss experienced in production. Despite these problems with contact photolithography, this process has formed the basis of microelectronic fabrication to date and excellence in this area is responsible for the tremendous growth in the microelectronics business over the past two decades.

A solution to some of the above problems of contact photolithography lies in the use of projection photolithography and shorter wavelength radiation to expose the resist, which reduces diffraction effects. Short wavelength replication techniques will be discussed later. In the projection replication process, the mask forms the object in an optical system that projects an image, either in real size or demagnified, onto the resist-coated wafer. To the degree that this optical system is stigmatic, the diffraction effects discussed above will not cause line broadening in the resist. However, there will be spherical aberration effects in any lenses used in the optical system, and diffraction from the object aperture, that will limit the resolution of this replication process. Because of these effects, the projection technique provides good resolution only over a limited area, so that step-and-repeat exposure or a scanning slit, which also limits the instantaneous exposure area to a small fraction of the total wafer area, must be used to cover an entire wafer. Both methods are slower than would be possible if the entire wafer could be exposed at one time. The use of short wavelength (≤ 2000 Å) light in a projection system with reflection optical elements can provide better resolution. Linewidth of ~ 0.8 μm has been demonstrated in laboratory tests (Elliott and Hockey, 1978) with 4350 and 4050 Å light, and 0.5 μm bars with 0.25 μm gaps printed in PMMA resist by Lin (1975) using contact lithography (2000–2600 Å wavelength). It is clear that projection photolithography provides considerable improvement in resolution over the contact process, and because there is no contact between mask and resist, the yield is higher vis-à-vis contact photolithography. However, 1 μm feature size is probably the lower limit of the projection process in production.

In addition to the resolution-area limitation, optical lithography suffers from the limit on depth of focus obtainable. In diffraction-limited optical systems, the resolvable linewidth is related to the diameter of the Airy disk, which is given by $2\lambda F$ (F is the numerical aperture of the system and λ the wavelength of radiation used). Both a short wavelength and a small numerical aperture must be used to obtain narrow lines. However, the total depth of focus of this diffraction limited system is given by $2 \times 2.44\lambda F^2$. Therefore, the steps that are taken to allow narrow lines to be exposed result in a decrease in the depth of focus. For example, the depth of focus of a 4× projection system to print 0.8 μm lines is limited to ~ 3 μm (Elliott and Hockey, 1978) so that nonflatness of the wafer (typically up to 10 μm bow) limits exposed resolution.

C. Resolution Comparison

A summary of the resolution capabilities of several lithography processes is shown in Fig. 1.4. This figure shows the narrowest linewidth or feature size that has been obtained with each of the lithography processes shown, under two or three different situations. The cross-hatched bar indicates the approximate minimum feature size in production, the bar at the end of the heavy line shows the narrowest linewidth (either feature size or developed resist dimension) that has been demonstrated under reasonably practical laboratory R&D conditions, and the triangle at the end of the dashed line shows the narrowest dimension in resist that has been created using special precautions (e.g., a very thin substrate in the electron-beam lithography case). The electron-beam lithography mask data refers to masks for photolithographic replication.

It will be shown later that realistic needs exist for device features well below 1 μm, and eventually these devices must be produced in quantities.

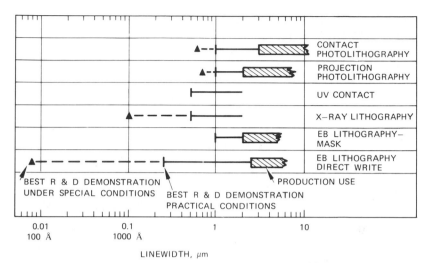

FIG. 1.4 Summary of the resolution capabilities of contact and projection photolithography and electron-beam and x-ray lithography.

It is clear from Fig. 1.4 that the lithography process on which the microelectronics industry has depended will not satisfy this need.

There are other considerations than resolution that establish the need for improved mask-making capabilities even at modest (1–2 μm) resolution. The total fabrication time for a mask made by contemporary photographic processes is typically up to six weeks. This long turnaround time severely limits the rate of progress in iterative device development programs and represents a costly delay in initiating production runs. Other factors such as linewidth control, edge smoothness, and mask-to-mask registration accuracy are important criteria for judging lithographic processes; electron-beam lithography also offers significant advantages in these areas.

III. ELECTRON-BEAM LITHOGRAPHY

A. Pattern Creation by an Electron Beam

The use of electron-beam lithography provides a means to alleviate the critical technical (e.g., resolution) and economic (e.g., yield, mask generation cost) problems that can limit progress in microelectronics. It can do this because it is a fundamentally different process of lithography, not

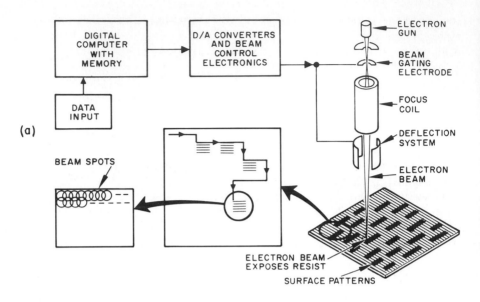

(a)

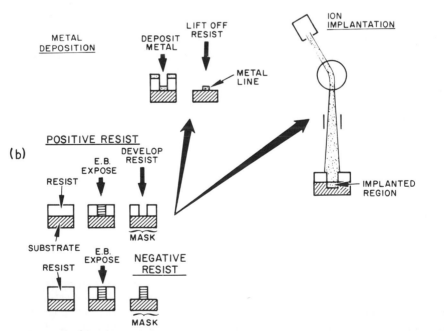

(b)

FIG. 1.5   The processes of electron beam lithography. (a) Schematic of the electron beam system. (b) The ways of using a resist mask to create patterns and implanted regions.

subject to the same types of physical limitations that affect photolithography. There are, of course, some fundamental limits on the electron-beam process as well, but the resolution limits, which will be discussed later, are sufficiently small that at least an order of magnitude extension in minimum linewidth is possible.

The way in which an electron beam is used in microelectronic fabrication is to create a mask in resist that can be employed in any of several ways to create a pattern on the substrate (e.g., a silicon wafer or a mask blank). This process is illustrated schematically in Fig. 1.5. The basis of this technology is a finely focused electron beam that is both deflected over a surface and blanked on and off under computer control. The electron beam exposes the resist where it strikes, i.e., the electrons break (or join) the molecules of the resist and so locally change its characteristics in such a way that subsequent development can either remove selectively the exposed part (positive resist) or remove the unexposed part (negative resist), as shown in Fig. 1.5b. This resist pattern constitutes a mask in direct contact with the substrate and it can be used for any of the subsequent processes in device fabrication that require pattern definition. For example, metal deposition onto the positive resist can be used to form a narrow metallic line as illustrated in Fig. 1.5. After deposition, the resist is dissolved and the excess metal is lifted off to leave a desired line that conforms accurately to the opening created in the resist by the electron beam. The openings in resist can also be used for micromachining of the substrate by ion beam or plasma etching, or under limited conditions, for selective ion implantation into the substrate. This process for creating a metallic line by the use of either positive or negative resist is shown in more detail in Fig. 1.6. In the negative resist case, the remaining resist protects the desired metal areas against the etching which removes the undesired regions of metal. The resist can be exposed in this manner over an area of one scan field of the electron beam (typically $1-40$ mm^2). Larger areas, for a given resolution, can be exposed by a precisely controlled stepwise movement of the target and repetition of the electron-beam-formed pattern. Figure 1.6 suggests that a line can be exposed by one pass of the beam. This exposure strategy is certainly possible, but requires adjustment of the spot size or shape to fit the desired linewidth. A more typical exposure strategy involves several (three to five) passes of a small diameter beam to expose a line of $0.5-1$-μm width; this method also produces better edge resolution.

The process of generating a high resolution pattern in resist described above is fundamental to electron-beam microfabrication. This process can be applied to two generic classes of structures, viz., to fabricate masks for subsequent replication or to fabricate the devices or circuits

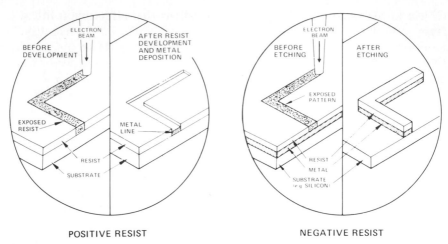

FIG. 1.6   Use of an electron beam to create a metallic line by the use of positive or negative resist.

directly. The diagram of Fig. 1.7 depicts the spectrum of ways to use electron-beam systems for microfabrication and diagnostics. Electron-beam diagnostics shown in the far right-hand column is indispensable in electron-beam lithography. Scanning electron microscopy (including compositional analysis) is the only way to examine critically the device structures that have the high resolution that can be created by electron-beam microfabrication.* The direct exposure process is shown in the center column of Fig. 1.7. The utility of direct device exposure with present electron-beam machines lies in experimental device development where flexibility and the capability for rapid design changes are important, in the fabrication of the highest performance specialty devices and circuits (e.g., microwave solid state devices) where the ultimate in resolution is required, and in low to modest volume production of devices and integrated circuits. As the throughput of electron-beam machines is increased, this direct exposure process may prove useful in higher volume production of submicrometer large scale integrated circuits.

The fabrication of photolithographic master (1×) masks by electron beams is an attractive way to provide fast turnaround and higher quality masks; this subject is discussed in Chapter 5. It is seen that the electron-beam generation of patterns is fundamental to all high resolution lithographies. In the generation of complex integrated circuit patterns, the

---

* Scanning electron microscopy as a high resolution diagnostic tool is described fully in the book "Scanning Electron Microscopy" by O. C. Wells *et al.*, McGraw-Hill, New York, 1974.

electron-beam system can be made interactive with computer aided design (CAD) programs, as shown.

A dramatic illustration of the relative resolution capabilities of electron beams and photolithography is shown in Fig. 1.8. In this example, a conventional microcircuit with ~ 5-μm-wide metallization was coated with resist and a series of 0.2-μm-wide metal lines were created by the use of an electron beam, metal deposition, and liftoff. The comparative edge definition of the metallizations that were defined by photolithography and chemical etching and that were defined by electron-beam lithography and liftoff is clear in Fig. 1.8b. This photograph illustrates another important, but subtle, feature of electron-beam lithography, viz., the depth of focus of the electron beam, which can create the pattern continuously over the ~ 1-μm-thick metallization.

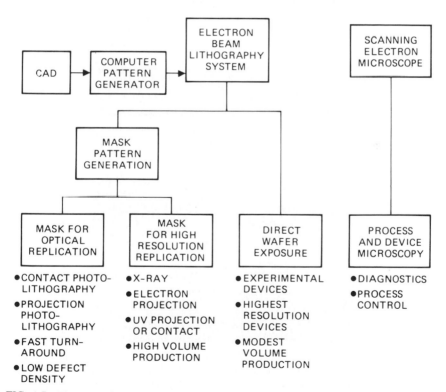

FIG. 1.7 The several ways in which electron-beam lithography can be applied to create masks and patterns directly on the wafer. Electron microscopy (right side) must be used to examine these high resolution patterns accurately.

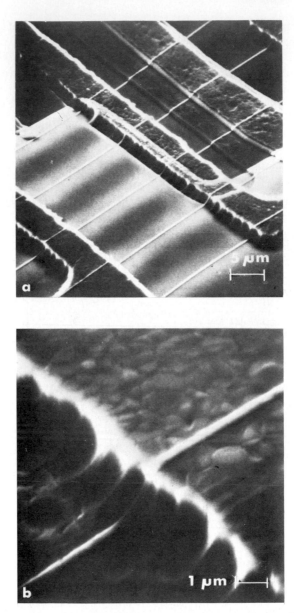

FIG. 1.8 A comparison of metal lines created by conventional photolithography and electron-beam lithography. The large aluminum pattern is 5-μm wide and 1-μm thick; the narrow (EB) gold line is 0.2-μm wide. (From Hughes Research Laboratories.)

B. Replication Techniques

While modest quantities (by present production standards) of high performance devices and integrated circuits can be made effectively by direct electron-beam exposure, it may be possible to make larger production quantities of complex devices more economically by replication using an electron-beam fabricated mask. It is clear, however, that the replication technique employed must be capable of about the same resolution as the original electron-beam exposure. Figure 1.9 illustrates four of the most promising high resolution replication techniques under development. One of these replication approaches uses very short wavelength radiation, where diffraction effects are negligible, to obtain higher resolution (Fig. 1-9c). Noncontacting replication of a high resolution mask onto a wafer

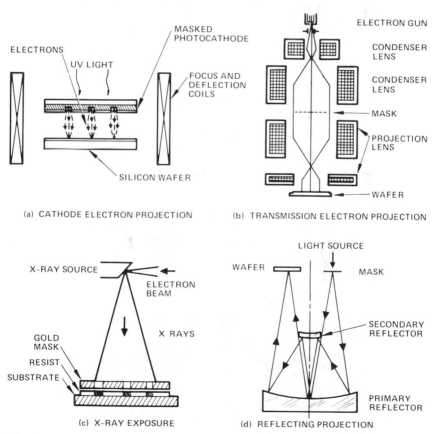

(a) CATHODE ELECTRON PROJECTION

(b) TRANSMISSION ELECTRON PROJECTION

(c) X-RAY EXPOSURE

(d) REFLECTING PROJECTION

FIG. 1.9 Schematic illustration of four techniques of high resolution replication of a pattern from a mask onto the resist-coated wafer.

has been demonstrated using both electrons (Figs. 1.9a and 1.9b) and x rays (Fig. 1.9c). The electron-imaging technique (Fig. 1.9a) has been shown to produce lines as narrrow as 0.5 μm over a 74 mm field in laboratory systems (Livesay, 1978); x-ray lithography has demonstrated 0.1 μm lines in laboratory equipment (Feder *et al.* 1976). These masks, with submicrometer patterns, must be fabricated by electron-beam lithography.

C. Compatible Processes

The creation of high resolution patterns in resist by electron-beam exposure is but the first step in the fabrication of devices or masks with high resolution surface structures. After the pattern is created in the resist on the wafer, the subsequent processes of doping, selective oxide removal, delineation of metallization patterns, etc., must be carried out by appropriate techniques that are compatible with the high resolution pattern, i.e., they must not significantly degrade the resolution of the original lithographic step. Therefore, in general, for each contemporary process step, there must exist a corresponding high resolution process, especially for those with inherently low resolution such as some chemical etching steps. For example, properly applied plasma etching will remove oxide or metal while reproducing the pattern in the resist with less undercutting than usually present in wet chemical etching; the edge resolution can be as good as the pattern in the resist. Ion implantation can be used to create doped regions with less (but still not negligible) lateral spread than with diffusion. The conventional processes of wet etching and diffusion are still employed in the fabrication of high resolution devices; but in general, they are restricted to the low resolution steps in the process. Therefore, high resolution microelectronic fabrication technology must include a complete series of compatible high resolution processes. These subjects are described more fully in Chapters 2 and 4.

IV. TECHNICAL BENEFITS OF HIGH RESOLUTION LITHOGRAPHY

Three types of benefits should accrue to the manufacturers and users of devices made by the use of high resolution lithography, viz., improved technical performance (higher frequency of operation, lower power, etc.), higher functional density, and better yield, which will be translated into lower costs and presumably higher reliability. At this stage in the development of this technology, there have been many demonstrations of device performance improvement by the use of electron-beam lithography, but very little yield data is yet available to substantiate the latter claim. The technical benefits are discussed here; the yield and other economic issues are treated in a subsequent section.

A. Appropriate Types of Devices

The use of high resolution lithography can improve those types of devices for which the performance is dependent on the arrangement and size of surface patterns since the important characteristics of these devices generally become better as these patterns are made smaller. Examples of the principal resolution-dependent microelectronic devices are shown in Fig. 1.10. The ability to define surface patterns, e.g., metallic electrodes,

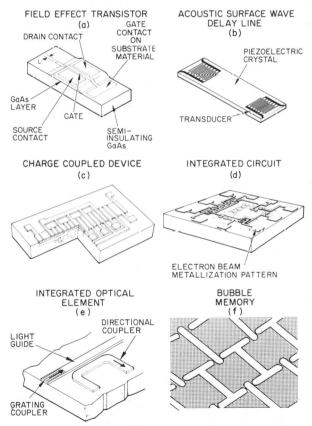

FIG. 1.10 Types of microelectronic devices for which the performance depends strongly on surface structure. These devices can benefit substantially by the use of high resolution lithography.

implantation and etching masks, interconnect lines, etc., with good edge resolution and high location precision means that these structures can be made smaller and be placed closer together. Small size results in reduced capacitance. Since most of the power required by a memory or logic circuit is due to the charging of the device capacitance ($P \propto fCV^2$), the required power and its attendant dissipation and temperature rise problems are reduced. The use of closely spaced electrodes reduces the transit time of the carriers through the active region of devices, and the use of shorter interconnect lines reduces the propagation time and power loss of signals between devices. Both of these latter effects result in lower device and circuit propagation delay (τ_p). Therefore, higher resolution fabrication results in lower values of the speed–power product ($P\tau_p$), which is an important measure of device and circuit performance. The lower propagation delay also raises the upper limit of operating frequency.

The changes in device performance that result from changes in the critical device dimensions can be determined by means of a scaling analysis. Dennard *et al.* (1974) have presented the results of such an analysis for the MOSFET by letting all dimensions (lateral and depth) of the new device (L') be related to the corresponding old dimensions (L) by $L' = L/k$, the applied voltage by $V' = V/k$, and the doping density in the channel by $N_a' = kN_a$. Under these scaling rules, the electric field in the channel is constant. By applying these scaling relations in the appropriate equations for the operating characteristics of the MOSFET, the scaling laws shown in Table 1.1 are derived. It is seen, for example, that the speed–power product for three-dimensional scaling (lateral and depth dimensions) is reduced as k^{-3}, and the upper frequency limit (inverse delay time) increases as k. Other aspects of device scaling are discussed later.

TABLE 1.1

	Three-dimensional scaling		Three-dimensional scaling
Device dimension			
t_{ox}	$1/k^a$	Delay time VC/I	$1/k$
L	$1/k$	Power dissipation VI or fCV^2	$1/k^2$
W (width)	$1/k$	Power density VI/A	1
Doping concentration N_a	k^a	Threshold voltage V_T	$1/k$
Voltage V	$1/k$	Interconnect line current density	k^a
Current I	$1/k$	Electric field V/L	1
Capacitance $\epsilon A/t$	$1/k$	$P \cdot \tau$	$1/k^3$

^{a} Problem area.

B. Performance Dependence on Feature Size

The dependence of certain important performance characteristics on the appropriate critical feature or electrode dimension is shown in Fig. 1.11 for several of the devices illustrated in Fig. 1.10. The high frequency limit of the microwave field effect transistor (Fig. 1.10a) is ultimately limited by the carrier transit time between source and drain, as well as certain parasitic resistances and capacitances associated with the device. In short gate length devices, the field will generally be high enough that the carrier velocity is the saturated level (v_s), so that the maximum or cutoff frequency is given to first order by $f_{max} = v_s/\pi L$ (Sze, 1969). The symbol L is used in Fig. 1.11 to represent the length of the critical dimension for each type of device; in the case of the FET, L represents the gate length. The dependence of f_{max} on L is shown by the upper two lines in Fig. 1.11, corresponding to carrier velocities at the peak of the GaAs carrier–velocity plot, and the high field saturation level which is valid for both GaAs and Si. It is seen from these theoretical curves (which neglect device parasitic effects) that FET cutoff frequencies greater than 100 GHz appear possible by making the gate < 0.7 μm or so. A number of points representing performance data reported in the literature (Liechti et al., 1972; Hooper et al., 1971; Baechtold, 1971; Baechtold et al., 1972, 1973) are shown. The solid dots and the inverted triangles represent GaAs and Si microwave field effect transistor performance, respectively. The ordinate position shows the maximum or cutoff frequency, usually obtained by extrapolation of the maximum available gain data. These devices were all made by photolithographic pattern definition techniques. The smallest gate length (0.5 μm) was achieved by the use of a special technique that pushed photolithography to its limit. It is seen, by the progressively greater deviation of these points from the transit time limit lines as L is reduced, that parasitic effects are also important determinants of device performance at these small dimensions.

The principal upper frequency limitation of an acoustic surface wave delay line (Fig. 1.10b) is governed by the achievable spacing of the electrodes which form the interdigital transducer. In the fundamental (π) mode, the frequency of operation of the transducer will be given by $f = v/p$, where v is the acoustic surface wave velocity and p is the pitch of the electrode ($p = \lambda$, the wavelength on the crystal). For the simple case of $p = 4L$, where L denotes the electrode width and gap, $f = v/4L$; this relation is plotted in Fig. 1.11 for wave velocities corresponding to LiNbO$_3$. The points plotted near this line represent a pulse compression filter containing 650 electrodes 0.5-μm wide, fabricated using serial electron-beam lithography (Weglein et al., 1973); a nondispersive 2.5

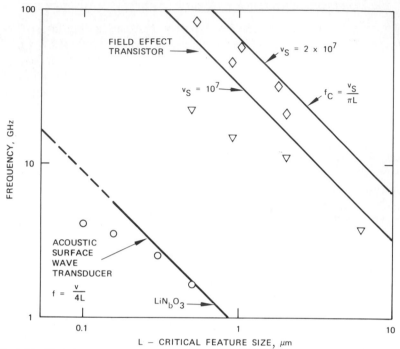

FIG. 1.11   The dependence of one measure of device performance, viz., frequency of operation, on minimum dimension, for the microwave field effect transistor and the surface acoustic wave filter. ◇, GaAs FET; ▽, Si FET; ○, acoustic surface wave device.

GHz delay line (Lean and Broers, 1970); and transducer patterns that were fabricated for operation at 3.5 (Lean and Broers, 1970) and 4.1 GHz (Wolf, 1972). The points are off the straight line because the electrode width actually fabricated was less than a quarter-wavelength.

Reduced power and propagation delay of transistors and integrated circuits with smaller dimensions have also been demonstrated (Fig. 1.12). In this graph, L represents the critical performance-determining dimension, viz., the gate length for FETs. The three points in Fig. 1.12 denoted by the diamond symbol represent the stage propagation delay of ring oscillators made of 11 silicon insulated gate field effect transistors (IGFET) that were fabricated with different gate lengths by electron-beam lithography (Fang et al., 1973). Silicon Schottky barrier FETs (MESFET) were also fabricated by electron-beam lithography into a NAND circuit which exhibited a propagation delay of ~100 ns (Picquendar, 1972, 1973). Both of these devices operated at a speed–power product of ~0.1 pJ. The solid curve marked CMOS/SOS represents the stage propagation delay of a series of ring oscillators made with different gate lengths by the use of x-ray

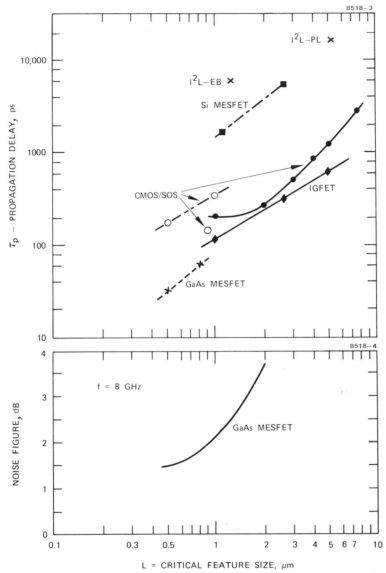

FIG. 1.12 Experimental data on propagation delay and noise figure vs. gate length (for FET devices) and minimum line dimension for the I²L device.

lithography (Stover *et al.*, 1979). The open circles also denote data on CMOS/SOS ring oscillators; those connected by a dashed line were fabricated at two gate lengths by photolithography (Ipri, 1978); the single point represents an EB device (Mayer and Perkins, 1979). The silicon MESFET data is from Darley *et al.* (1978). Two points (*x*) represent integrated injection logic (I²L) devices made by the use of electron beam and photolithography, respectively (Evans *et al.*, 1978). The crosses represent GaAs MESFET ring oscillators made at 1.0 and 0.5 μm gate length by electron-beam lithography (Greiling *et al.*, 1979). These latter devices exhibited a power–delay product of 1.4 pJ. It is noted that most of these data exhibit a slope that is close to L^{-1}, as expected.

The noise figure of an FET is to first order inversely proportional to the cutoff frequency f_T, which in turn is inversely proportional to L; therefore, the noise figure decreases with shorter gate length (Pucel *et al.*, 1975). This effect has been demonstrated experimentally. The lower graph in Fig. 1.12 shows noise figure data on GaAs microwave MESFETs at a frequency of 8 GHz (Butlin *et al.*, 1977). Thus, the GaAs FET with 0.5 μm gate length is a very attractive device for use in the input portion of a low noise microwave receiver, being surpassed in noise figure only by the more complex parametric amplifier.

As illustrated also in Fig. 1.10e, an electron beam can be used to create integrated optical elements such as light guides and passive circuitry (directional couplers, hybrids, etc.). Narrow lines and good edge smoothness (< 500 Å) are possible by direct exposure of the resist and have proven to be valuable features best attainable by electron-beam techniques.

In addition to the devices shown in Figs. 1.10 and 1.11, other types of devices can benefit by smaller surface feature sizes, including I²L, CCD, bipolar transistors, superconducting Josephson junction devices, etc. For example, in the charge coupled device (Fig. 1.10d) the gap between electrodes should be made small for fast charge transfer. The maximum frequency can be shown to vary approximately as $1/L^2$ (where L is the electrode pitch). The clocking power required depends on the area of the CCD; therefore, the speed power product will decrease approximately as L^4 (if only lateral scaling is effected).

V. LIMITATIONS ON ELECTRON-BEAM LITHOGRAPHY

It appears from the preceding discussion that some of the more critical limitations of contemporary microelectronics technology can be overcome by the use of electron-beam lithography and associated high resolution processes. The features and virtues of these new fabrication technologies have been extolled here and elsewhere. Therefore the potential user may believe that this new process can solve all of his problems quickly and economically. He might envision, for example, that this new process will create 0.1 μm patterns, placed with 50 Å precision, over a 3 in. wafer in a few seconds. In fact, of course, electron-beam lithography suffers from some fundamental limits of its own; it cannot, for example, achieve the above performance. To be most effective, therefore, electron-beam lithography must be applied so as to take advantage of its unique features, but with full knowledge of its limitations. Those physical effects that can limit the performance of electron-beam lithography as applied to microelectronic fabrication are reviewed here briefly. These limits are due to the resist material and to the electron beam and control electronics of the electron-beam machine. In addition, the physical principles of operation of some types of devices may limit their ability to perform at very small dimensions. The economic implications of the electron-beam process and its limiting factors are discussed in the next section. These effects not only determine the ways in which electron-beam lithography can be used to make devices, but establish the design criteria for electron-beam lithography machines.

A.   Resist Related Limits

When an electron beam strikes a target, it deposits a charge, given by the current multiplied by the time of exposure. The useful effect of a beam on a target surface can be expressed in terms of the number of electrons deposited per unit area that are necessary to produce the desired effect. Thus, each resist is characterized by a value of this sensitivity factor S, measured in coulombs per square centimeter. The time necessary to expose a spot of diameter d_s with a beam providing a current density J_s at the surface is then simply $\tau_s = S/J_s$. For example, in order to expose an electron resist material that exhibits a value of $S = 8 \times 10^{-5}$ C/cm^2, approximately 5×10^{14} electrons/cm^2 are required to break (or link) the chemical bonds of the polymer so that it can be developed to the desired degree of contrast. The smaller the value of S, the more sensitive the process; that is, fewer electrons are required to effect the desired change in the resist. Therefore, the sensitivity of the resist is a strong determinant of writing speed of the electron-beam lithography process. As shown in Chapter 2, the value of S varies widely for different resists and is quite dependent on the resist development process.

A serious limitation on resolution is due to the broadening of the written line in the resist by electron scattering so that the linewidth is greater than the spot diameter. It is well known that electrons impinging on a solid material can be scattered through large angles by elastic collisions with the atomic nuclei of the material. This scattering is approximately proportional to the atomic number (Z) (Wells, 1974a; Everhart,

1960). The electron range in a resist is usually much greater than the thickness of the resist layers; therefore, the electrons penetrate the resist and continue into the substrate (e.g., silicon) where the atomic number is usually higher than in the resist. For these reasons, most of the scattering occurs in the substrate. A large fraction of the electrons that are scattered through $\sim 180°$ return to the resist with sufficient energy to expose it, thus creating an exposed volume of resist that is wider than the diameter of the impinging electron beam. This effect presently forms the principal ultimate limit on minimum linewidth attainable by electron-beam lithography. Also, some resists change shape, i.e., swell or contract on development, thereby changing feature sizes.

In addition to the electron-scattering limit described above, there is another effect that sets a minimum linewidth that can be written (Everhart, 1968); this effect is dependent on the resist sensitivity and basically results from the statistical nature of the electron stream. While this subject will be treated in more detail in Chapter 2, a qualitative description will be useful here. It was pointed out above that exposure of a resist can be characterized by the number of electrons impinging per unit area, i.e., S (C/cm^2) $= eN_e/A$, where N_e is the number of electrons striking area A. To consider a quantitative example, if $A = (0.1 \text{ cm})^2$ and $S \cong 10^{-7}$, $N_e = 6 \times 10^9$ electrons. However, if $A = (0.01 \ \mu\text{m})^2$, $N_e \cong 0.6$ electrons for this same resist. Therefore, the concept of a constant resist sensitivity is not valid when the discrete area to be defined is very small. A certain minimum number of electrons must be deposited on each minimum defined area (i.e., each pixel element). This number can be determined roughly as follows. Electrons are emitted from a cathode as random events in time, not as a series of emission events equally spaced in time. Because the number of electrons that strike a surface in time t ($N_s = Jt/e$) is large, the uncertainty in this number is $\sqrt{N_s}$. That is, the number actually striking can vary over the range $Jt/e \pm \sqrt{Jt/e}$. Therefore, the ratio of the desired number to the uncertainty is $N_s/\sqrt{N_s} = \sqrt{N_s}$; this value has a rough analogy to signal-to-noise ratio. To be reasonably certain that the resist is exposed, this ratio should be high, e.g., 10, which indicates that the minimum number of electrons that will certainly expose an area is of the order $N_m = 10^2$. Therefore, in the region of small dimensions, the minimum linewidth can be related to the conventional sensitivity factor by

$$(L_{\min})^2 = N_m e/S \qquad (1.1)$$

where $L_{\min}$ is the minimum pixel size for a resist of sensitivity S. This relation shows that very sensitive resists cannot be used to create very high resolution structures unless considerably more than the minimum number of electrons is used to expose the smaller area. The implications of this limit are described in Chapters 2 and 3.

B. Machine Related Limits

In addition to the inherent sensitivity and resolution limits imposed by the resist material, there are a number of fundamental and technology related limits that are due to the electron-beam machine. These machine related limits include those due to the electron optics of beam formation and deflection and the mechanical and electronic limits on scan area and scan rate.

The spot current density J_s is equal to the ratio of the total current in the beam to the area of the spot at the target. The diameter of an undeflected spot is limited by three principal effects: the spherical and chromatic aberrations of the focusing lenses and the transverse velocity of the electrons (and in some cases by diffraction). Each of these effects can be considered to give rise to a minimum value of beam diameter, usually called the *disk of least confusion*, which is larger than the value that would be produced by a perfect lens. These effects are treated extensively in the literature on electron optics (see, for example, Grivet, 1965) and are discussed more fully in Chapter 3. Briefly, spherical aberration results from the fact that the focusing fields of a lens are almost always stronger at the outside of the beam than on the axis; electrons entering the lens at different radii are therefore directed toward a focus at different points along the axis (the outer electrons cross the axis closer to the lens). Chromatic aberration is a measure of the sensitivity of the lens to electron energy; since the electrons always have a spread in energy, due to such factors as thermal velocity of emission, power supply ripple, etc., this effect will also defocus the beam. The deflection system which serves to move the beam on the target can also distort the size and shape of the spot.

In addition to beam distorting effects caused by the electric or magnetic fields used to focus or deflect beams, the beams themselves contain, in a sense, the cause of two other forms of distortion. The first of these is the beam expansion resulting from the beam space charge. However, this space charge expansion effect is usually not the limiting factor in determining spot size, since the current values are too low and the beam voltage too high in all but the highest current beams of interest in lithography machines.

A second property of the charged particles in a beam that usually causes a first-order effect on both spot size and current density is the transverse random component of velocity due to the emission of the electrons from a hot surface. Electrons emitted from a cathode at temperature T_c will, in general, possess a Maxwellian velocity distribution $[f(v_r) = k \exp(-mv_r^2/2kT_c)]$. In passing through the subsequent acceleration and focusing systems, this transverse velocity distribution is transformed into a gaussian distribution of current density in the focused spot. If the convergence half-angle of the beam toward this focus is denoted by α, it can be shown [Eq. (3.4)] that the maximum possible current density J_m at this spot is related to the emitter current density J_c by the following equation, which represents the Langmuir limit on current density (Langmuir, 1937; Moss, 1968):

$$J_m \sim J_c(11,600V_0\alpha^2/T_c) = 4I_0/\pi d_G^2 \tag{1.2}$$

where d_G is the "Gaussian" spot diameter; that is, the diameter if the spot is limited by this transverse thermal velocity effect. The corresponding equations relating the diameter to the beam to the lens parameters, attributable to the three effects described above, viz., spherical aberration, chromatic aberration, and diffraction, are given in Chapter 3 [Eqs. (3.11), (3.14), and (3.20)]. All of these equations depend on the convergence angle of the beam. The beam diameter is usually represented by the rms sum of these four equations (Wells, 1974b). A plot of beam diameter versus α (see Fig. 3.11) typically shows that the effect of diffraction is negligible and that of chromatic aberration less important than the thermal velocity and spherical aberration effects, which are dominant in most of the electron-optical systems considered here. This figure also shows that the beam will attain a minimum diameter for $\alpha \sim 5-10 \times 10^{-3}$ rad, and this diameter, for representative values of the parameters, is in the range 100–400 Å for beam currents of $10^{-12}-10^{-10}$ A (refer also to Fig. 1.14). These characteristics are observed experimentally in good electron-beam machines. Since these spot dimensions are small compared with either the desired device resolution (in the near term at least) or the wavelength of light, it is clear that high quality electron-optical systems can create a useful beam. That is, the ultimate pattern resolution attainable is not presently limited by the spot diameter, but rather by the electron-scattering effect. However, Eq. (1.1) shows implicitly that there is a dependence of spot diameter on beam current; this dependence will be shown later to give rise to a tradeoff between writing time and resolution.

The dependence of current density, and therefore exposure time, on the electron-optical parameters of the system can be derived from the above referenced equations. If the effects of chromatic aberration and diffraction are neglected, so that the spot diameter is determined only by transverse thermal velocities and spherical aberration, the optimal convergence angle that will produce a minimum spot diameter d can be determined (Broers, 1972). From this latter equation, the exposure time per spot τ under optimum beam conditions can be shown (see Chapter 3) to be

$$\tau_{opt} = S/J_s \cong 0.5SC_s^{2/3}/d^{2/3}B \tag{1.3}$$

where C_s is the spherical aberration coefficient of the final lens. It is seen from Eq. (1.3) that to first order, to achieve a given linewidth, resist sensitivity, source brightness B [refer to Eq. (3.6)], or the spherical aberration of the final lens can be varied to decrease τ. The time T to expose a large area is $T = n_s\tau$, where n_s is the total number of spots (pixels) used.

Although electron beams can produce fine patterns, with linewidth and edge resolution considerably finer than possible with photolithography, the area of pattern that can be written is limited, and is related, as in the photolithographic process, to the resolution. In photolithography the resolution is degraded with distance from the optical axis by lens aberrations and diffraction. Similarly, there are two principal limitations on the area over which an electron beam can be scanned.

One limit on pattern area results from the electron-optical distortion suffered by a beam of electrons in passing through the complex electric or magnetic fields used to deflect them. That is, if a limit is placed on maximum allowable spot distortion, the scan distance is effectively limited. It is well known that the fields used to deflect an electron beam will cause a distortion of an initially round beam into a noncircular spot. This effect is due to astigmatism and sometimes coma in the noncylindrically symmetric fields of the deflection system (Amboss, 1975; Thomson, 1975; Grivet, 1965). Also, as electrons are deflected through different angles, they will be brought to a focus at different distances from the gun; thus, the spot size on the target will change with deflection angle. Fortunately, the most significant of these aberrations, viz., astigmatism and deflection focus change, can be corrected. Further, if deflecting current is applied so as to try to create a rectangular pattern, this pattern can appear distorted. These effects are described more fully in Chapter 3. A quantitative measure of the scan field–resolution tradeoff is illustrated at the top of Fig. 1.13, which shows data on typical electron beams in a microfabrication system with and without dynamic focus correction. It is seen that with dynamic focus correction, a scan field of about 2×2 mm can be scanned by this system before the beam diameter is increased to 0.1 μm. These data correspond to deflection of about 20,000 pixels or spot diameters with tolerable distortion. It appears, therefore, that with a high quality electron-optical system, a deflection distance up to $\approx 10^4$ spot diameters can be achieved with low to moderate beam currents. With high beam currents, the distortion is greater, resulting in a limitation on scan field size to about 7000 lines. For reference, the deflection of a typical television raster is 500 lines. The upper curve represents the outer envelope of the deflection distortion curves of some high performance electron-beam fabrication and display systems; this curve represents an approximate upper limit to the scan field–resolution tradeoff; no single deflection

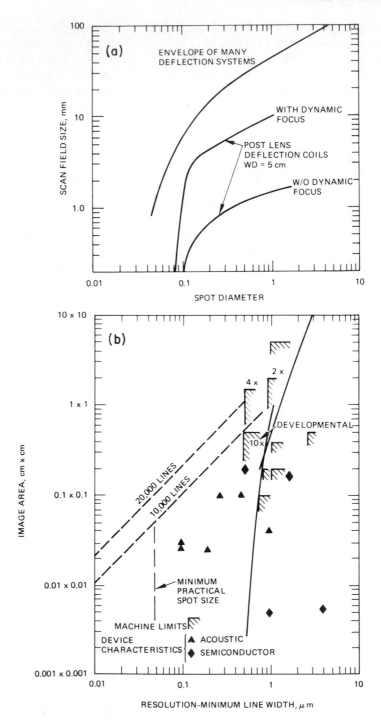

system would be expected to follow this curve. In addition to the distortion of the spot, deflection of the electron beam results in distortion of the pattern written. That is, if rectangular grid pattern data were fed to the deflection system, the beam would not trace a perfectly rectangular replica of the pattern data (illustrated in Chapter 3). Measurements of this form of deflection distortion show about ± 2.5 μm deviation in position at the extremities of a 5 mm scan field, corresponding to a position resolution of 2000 lines (Chang and Viswanathan, 1978).

The second limit on pattern area results from the finite resolution of the digital-to-analog (D/A) converter that drives the deflection amplifier. The digital signals from the controlling computer must be converted into analog form in order to drive the beam-deflection amplifier. However, this D/A converter can produce only a finite number of discrete voltage levels; for example, 32,768 for a 15-bit converter and 65,536 for a 16-bit converter. This ultimate resolution is degraded also by linearity and noise effects in the amplifier. Typical linearity is ~ 0.01% of full scale and typical noise contributing to deflection distortion is comparable with the least significant bit of a 16-bit D/A converter. These factors also affect the minimum address size of the writing machine, i.e., the minimum discrete distance that the electron beam can be deflected on the target. There is also a tradeoff between D/A stepping rate (which translates into beam writing speed) and precision (number of bits).

A comparison of the image area versus resolution characteristic of various lithography systems is shown in the lower part of Fig. 1.13. The heavy solid lines on the right show the area resolution limits of contact photolithography due to diffraction and lens aberrations used in the reduction camera; practical fabrication tolerances such as registration, etching, undercutting, light scattering in the resist and diffraction from the mask are not included. The upper segment of these curves is derived from analysis of the best optical lenses by Tibbets and Wilczynski (1969). The area resolution limits of projection exposure systems with $2\times$, $4\times$, and $10\times$ reduction are indicated. The area resolution limits of present electron-beam lithography systems are also shown.

The number of lines representing the ratio of field coverage to linewidth is indicated by the diagonal (dashed) lines in the lower part of Fig. 1.13. While 15-bit D/A converters that are typically used should yield about 30,000 lines, a conservative present day practical limit is around 10,000

FIG. 1.13 (a) The limit on area coverage by an electron beam due to deflection distortions (abscissa is spot diameter). WD = working distance. (b) Comparison of the area coverage vs. linewidth between photolithographic and electron-beam systems with typical developmental devices plotted (upper semiconductor device points represent active chip size).

lines. In general the pattern resolution will be limited more by deflection distortion (even when deflection distortion correction is used) and by power supply stability than by D/A converter resolution (refer to Chapter 3).

Several points plotted in Fig. 1.13 show the area and minimum line-widths that have been representative of laboratory devices fabricated directly by electron-beam lithography. It is seen that electron-beam device patterns have been created with resolution better by as much as an order of magnitude compared with patterns made by photolithography. Furthermore, these electron-beam fabricated devices have not yet been made with linewidth near the ultimate resolution of the electron-beam process. Narrower linewidths have been attained in masks and in demonstration samples; the best reported are 0.02 μm in collodion films (Schief, 1969), and 0.045 μm in PMMA resist (Wolf et al., 1971); Broers et al. (1976) have created 80-Å-wide metallic lines by electron beam exposure of contaminant films (see also Fig. 1.21).

The area of greatest applicability of electron beams for writing high resolution single-field patterns is given roughly by the triangle in Fig. 1.13 formed on the left by the 10,000 pixel lines and on the right by the heavy vertical lines. For a given resolution, larger areas can be exposed by a precision controlled stepwise movement of the target and repeat of the electron-beam formed pattern. The mechanical stage motion can be controlled to a repeatability of ~ 50–100 Å by using a laser interferometer (Pasiecznik, 1977). Computer-controlled electron-beam techniques for the registration of sequential pattern levels to a precision of ± 0.1 μm have been reported (Chang et al., 1976); the ultimate limit on registration accuracy is probably set by machine stability. The direction of further machine and process technology development is represented by movement upward (larger scan field area) and to the left (narrower linewidth) from this triangular region.

Despite improvements in the resolution field coverage for either electron-optical or light-optical exposure systems, the size of a single exposure field in multiple-mask fabrication processes could be limited ultimately by the distortion in the semiconductor wafer induced by the various fabrication processes. For example, if the lateral (in-plane) wafer distortion is nonuniform and of sufficient magnitude, sequential pattern steps may not register accurately at all points over the wafer. Some preliminary distortion measurements on a silicon wafer show ~ 1 μm lateral random dimensional change over a 6-cm-diameter wafer (i.e., about 16 ppm); this data would suggest a maximum exposure field of ~ 6 mm to assure 0.1 μm alignment accuracy. Distortion of this magnitude eliminates the possibility of exposure of all points over a full wafer simultaneously by any high resolution lithography, unless the distortion can be reduced substantially by material or processing changes. In the direct writing electron-beam process, each scan field can be registered on a set of benchmarks applied for that field. In this way, in contrast with whole wafer exposure, the effects of in-plane distortion can be greatly reduced. On the other hand, there are limits on the accuracy with which sequential mask levels can be registered, due basically to the signal-to-noise ratio of the process; this effect will in turn limit the maximum scan field size and the minimum device feature size. This subject is discussed more fully in Chapter 2.

Another machine-dependent factor that strongly affects the economics of the electron-beam lithography process is the speed with which high resolution patterns can be written. This important subject, discussed in detail in Chapter 3, is reviewed here briefly. It was shown above that the time required to expose one pixel of the resist τ_s is $\tau_s = S/J_s$. Therefore, one of the most important machine parameters that determines pattern writing speed is the current density where the electron beam strikes the resist. However, the diameter to which a beam can be focused is dependent on the current, as shown in Fig. 1.14. The solid diagonal lines in this figure are drawn for constant values of a parameter proportional to current density; it is seen that in typical electron-beam machines (dashed lines), the current density is reduced as the spot is focused to a smaller diameter. A

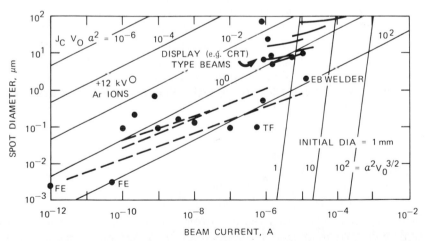

FIG. 1.14 The dependence of electron beam spot diameter on beam current, with the limit due to transverse thermal velocities [Eq. (1.2)] shown as parameter (solid diagonal lines). The approximate limit due to space charge expansion is shown by the near-vertical lines at right. The dashed lines and the points show the current–diameter characteristics of several electron-beam machines.

typical relationship is $I = 2 \times 10^{-5} d^{2.86}$ A (d in μm). This factor is one element in the resolution writing speed tradeoff.

A second major factor affecting pattern writing time is the speed with which the beam can be moved over the substrate. Referring back to Fig. 1.5, there are two practical ways of moving the location of the beam spot on the substrate, viz., to deflect the beam in two orthogonal directions with the substrate fixed, or to deflect the beam in one direction with the substrate moving in the orthogonal direction.* Likewise, there are two ways of employing the deflected beam to expose resist, viz., by positioning the beam at each location to be exposed and holding it there for a time τ_s (point-by-point method), or by deflecting it continuously along a line with a velocity of $\sim d_s/\tau_s$ (analog scan). The point-by-point scan is slower because of the overhead times associated with settling times of the D/A converter and deflection amplifier, and if the addressing is under software control, by the time required to address each new point by computer command. The sum of the first two of these overhead times is about 0.1–0.4 μs, the computer address time is roughly 1–2 μs. On the other hand, the point-by-point method offers higher accuracy in beam placement. These two scan techniques can effectively complement each other, with the point-by-point method used to provide a high precision outline of the area to be covered, and the analog scan used to fill in the center area.

The third element of time required to write a pattern is that needed for registration of the beam to the existing pattern and motion of the substrate between scan fields. It will be shown in Chapter 3 that the stage motion time is a critical factor in machine writing speed, for all but the highest resolution patterns. By using automatic registration techniques the registration time per scan field can be made as short as $\sim 0.25–1$ s; longer time is required to achieve higher accuracy. In addition, there are two factors that influence the time resolution tradeoff which do not depend directly on the machine design, viz., the resist sensitivity and the line broadening due to electron backscattering. Because of the broadening effect, a smaller spot diameter must be used to draw a given linewidth, implying lower current density than if no broadening occurred.

Therefore, the machine and resist limits on writing speed, resolution, and area covered per scan field can be summarized as follows: (a) backscattering limits the ultimate resolution of direct writing electron-beam lithography; (b) resist sensitivity and beam current density strongly affect writing time, principally in the regime below 0.75 μm; and (c) the times re-

---

* Holding the beam stationary and moving the substrate in both directions is too slow and eliminates one of the advantages of charged particles for pattern generation, viz., the ability to deflect them rapidly by the use of electromagnetic fields.

quired for step and repeat and for registration on each scan field form the principal limit for larger linewidths. Implicit in these conclusions are the conditions that the deflection rate can be made fast enough that it does not form a limit (it will eventually — at the larger linewidths), that the number of resolvable spots per scan line is limited to $\leq 10^4$ spots (improved electron-optical systems and lower noise deflection amplifiers could increase this limit), and that the resist can exhibit adequate resolution at the assumed sensitivity to reproduce the narrowest lines.

C. Factors Affecting Exposure Time

As described above, there are four independent beam or resist dependent relationships that affect the exposure time per spot. These relationships contain the key performance parameters of current density, linewidth, beam diameter, and resist sensitivity. The actual exposure time required is determined by the self-consistent solution of these four equations. Since these equations contain in common certain of the key parameters, the self-consistent solution can be illustrated graphically, as shown in Fig. 1.15. In this figure, each of these equations is plotted in a graph occupying one quadrant. Quadrant I represents the relationship $S = Jt$, quadrant II represents Eq. (1.1), quadrant III the linewidth-to-spot-diameter ratio as determined by the number of passes of the beam employed to write the line, and quadrant IV is a plot of Eq. (3.24). The self-consistent solution is a point in quadrant I yielding the exposure time per spot. The minimum value of beam current is reached when the intersection in quadrant II is on the curve representing the minimum number of electrons per pixel, i.e., $N_e = N_m$.

D. Device Related Limits

The limits on device size, as determined by the technology of electron-beam lithography, were discussed above. Resolution is presently limited by backscattering from the substrate. The user of an electron-beam machine may have to wait a long time for the narrowest lines to be written, but for certain special situations this may be satisfactory. After all, there is no other way to write an arbitrary pattern with lines 0.1-μm wide! Beam diameters ~ 200 Å are achieved routinely in scanning electron microscopes; 30 Å resolution has been obtained by Crewe (1968) in a transmission electron-beam machine, and 80-Å-wide lines have been written on a carbon film that was thin enough (100 Å) to prevent backscattering of the electrons (Broers et al., 1976). If the backscattering limit can be circumvented in practice by the use of a very thin substrate or other

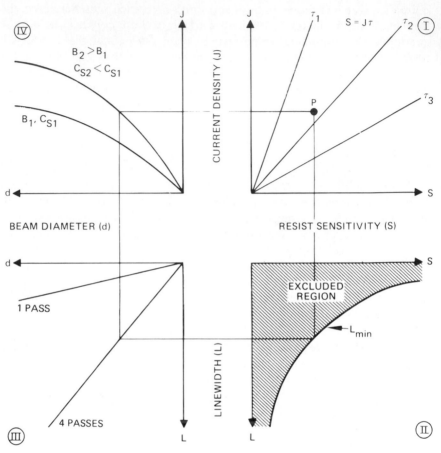

FIG. 1.15 Composite diagram showing the various factors that affect exposure time. The four lines that form a square represent the self-consistent solution; writing time is indicated by the point P.

techniques, lines as narrow as 100–200 Å should be achievable. However, even with this ultrahigh resolution lithography, there will be another type of limitation on device feature size, determined more by the physics of the device operation and materials distortion than by the fabrication technology. The types of fundamental device effects that can result in limitations on the size to which a device can be scaled include breakdown through an oxide or along a surface and in the semiconductor material, electromigration in the interconnect conductors, p–n junction breakdown, statistical doping and carrier fluctuations, minimum depletion layer width, carrier velocity saturation, and power dissipation. Which type of physical effect will form the limit in any specific case will depend on the type of device considered. Analysis of the ultimate limits in microelectronic devices, particularly from the point of view of energy per bit required in bistate devices used in logic operations, have been presented in a series of excellent articles by Keyes (1969, 1972, 1975, 1977). However, only very limited analysis has been carried out on the effects on performance of reducing dimensions of devices. This is a vital subject that should be pursued as a guide to high resolution technology. Therefore, it is of interest to review here briefly some of the known effects, in order to gain some insight into the device limits. It is fruitless to develop high resolution technology that will make devices so small that they will not operate.

The physical factors that limit the operation of both MOSFET and bipolar transistors, as their dimensions are scaled down in three dimensions, have been examined analytically by Hoeneisen and Mead (1972); MOS devices have also been analyzed by Swanson (1974). Hoeneisen and Mead found that breakdown in the oxide will form the principal MOSFET limitation; this breakdown was indicated at a gate length of ~ 0.2 μm. Therefore, they predict that practical gate lengths must be $\sim 0.3-0.4$ μm, still a factor $5\times - 10\times$ smaller than contemporary production devices. For the isoplanar bipolar transistor, they found the limiting factors to be collector junction breakdown and base punchthrough. A minimum base thickness of 0.07 μm was predicted. Achievement of the minimum sized bipolar device, however, is not directly aided by higher resolution surface features; dopant depth control must also be improved. Klaassen (1978) provides scaling rules for MOS and I²L devices. As Keyes points out, the ultimate device limits are generally dependent more on the material properties of breakdown voltage, dielectric constant, and thermal conductivity than on the key performance related property, viz., mobility.

From simple carrier transit time and capacitance considerations, the maximum frequency of an FET (proportional to inverse minimum propagation delay) should vary as the gate length L. The power per device should vary approximately as L^2; thus, the speed–power product $P \cdot t_{pd}$ will vary as L^3. Typical CMOS devices with 5 μm design rules exhibit speed–power product values around 10 pJ. Comparing these data with that of devices with 1 μm gate length, fabricated by the use of electron-beam lithography to yield ~ 0.1 pJ (Fang et al., 1973; Picquendar, 1973), it is seen that a decrease by a factor of $\sim 10^2$ has been achieved, while the three-dimensional scaling law would suggest a decrease by 5^3. Thus, the devices with smaller dimensions exhibit roughly the expected performance gain.

As device dimensions are reduced and limits, e.g., breakdown, are encountered, the parameter scaling will have to be modified. For example, voltage can be scaled down so as to reduce the electric field, but this can result in poorer noise characteristics and incompatibility with interfacing circuits.

The above data have significant implications for the fabrication of high density, high speed integrated circuits. The values of propagation delay observed experimentally for devices made by electron-beam lithography show that the propagation delay of an FET can be made small enough that the devices will not limit the frequency of an IC made with $0.5-1$ μm design rules up to at least 10 GHz. The delays due to interconnect leads and capacitance charging can be reduced by the use of high resolution lithography and very careful circuit design. Because the power per gate varies approximately as fCV^2, power will increase with operating frequency. Therefore, power dissipation could limit the operating frequency to a lower value than these electronic limits. Within the limits possible with three-dimensional scaling of a MOSFET device, the power density is constant (Table 1.1); therefore, power dissipation is not a problem in this situation. In those situations where scaling does result in increased power density, another approach may offer a solution. With 1 μm design rules, a device density of approximately 5×10^6/cm^2 is possible. Assume that each device will dissipate about 1 mW ($\sim$0.1 pJ at 10 GHz), then the power dissipation capability of the IC must be about 5×10^3 W/cm^2. While this value of power density is very high by conventional IC standards, it is less than that of most microwave solid state devices, which typically operate at a power density at the device–heat sink interface of approximately 10^6 W/cm^2. The reason that this high power density can be sustained with tolerable temperature rise is that the heat flow away from the tiny area of the microwave device takes place in the two lateral directions as well as the perpendicular (to the device surface) direction. This well-developed technology used in microwave devices can be applied to high performance integrated circuits. The temperature rise is $\Delta T = Pr$ (where r is the thermal resistance in degrees Celsius per watt). For the one-dimensional heat flow situation $r = kA/l$ and $r = 1/(kD)$ for the two-dimensional flow case. (D = diameter, A = area of the device, k = thermal conductivity, l = thickness.) A typical 10 GHz IMPATT device will have a diameter of $\sim$0.15 mm, for which $r \approx 30^{\circ}$C/W. Over a thousand devices could be fabricated in this area with 1 μm design rules. The power dissipation will be $\sim$1 W and the temperature rise $\sim$30°C. Therefore, an alternative approach to preventing a power dissipation limit on performance could be to fabricate the circuits in small clusters.

The discussion above has provided some general guidelines on the minimum dimensions that can be used in microelectronic devices, as limited by the physics of the device operation. Similarly, some general guidelines on the ultimate performance expected can be derived from theoretical considerations, at least for devices used in logic or bistable switching functions. The expected performance 'improvement, but not the limits, with higher resolution fabrication of microwave devices was suggested in Fig. 1.11. In a comprehensive article on the physical limits in digital electronics, Keyes (1975) points out several device limiting factors; this article will be the basis of much of the following discussion of this subject. The performance of microelectronic devices or circuits that handle digital data, i.e., in which the electrons move in discrete packets, is best represented on a plot of the power required to effect the movement of one bit of data versus the time required to effect this change. Such a graph is shown in Fig. 1.16. Diagonal lines on this plot represent equal amounts of energy per bit, expressed in fractions of a joule. Keyes points out two ultimate limits on the value of the energy per bit required by any digital switching operation (e.g., the minimum energy required to switch a transistor from an output of 0 to 1), one based on information theory and the other on quantum mechanics. The thermodynamic minimum energy required to make a decision between two alternatives is on the order of kT, where k is the Boltzmann constant and T the absolute temperature of the switching structure. The quantum mechanical lower bound of energy required to make a physical measurement (e.g., differentiate between the 0 and 1 states) in a time τ is given by h/τ. These two limits are drawn at the lower left of Fig. 1.16. The vertical line marked Material Limit represents the minimum switching time as limited by breakdown and thermal dissipation (Swanson, 1974). The dash–dot line shows calculated limits for MOS devices with lowest reasonable voltage and oxide thickness (Swanson, 1974). The shaded area in the upper right of this figure represents the general region of performance of present devices (MOS, I²L, etc.); the shaded region at left encompasses data on 1979 developmental GaAs and CMOS/SOS devices. A CCD memory fabricated using 2 μm minimum linewidth is plotted in the lower right. Scaling this device to 0.5 μm minimum linewidth, the power should vary as the area (i.e., as capacitance, or as L^2), to the lower line; the upper frequency limit will also increase (as L^2). In the upper center of this figure, a point represents the demonstrated energy per bit for 1 μm gate length GaAs MESFET. The energy should scale as L^4 (and propagation delay as L), so that a device with 0.1 μm gate length should exhibit the performance of the lower point—if it works at this short gate length!. Analysis of another type of physical limit will illustrate the effect of the circuit that interconnects the devices. Consider a transmission line of characteristic impedance $\sim 100\ \Omega$ that will transfer charge between two very small discrete devices. The energy associated with the charging of this line of length l, viewed as a capacitor with capaci-

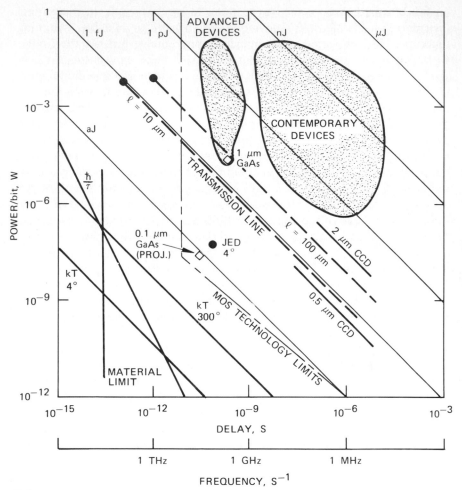

FIG. 1.16 The theoretical limits on power and propagation delay (left curves), compared with present-day devices. Also shown are the effects of smaller device dimensions, derived by scaling, and calculated energy stored in interconnect lines.

tance C' per unit length, is $C'lV^2$. For a line 10 μm long charged to 1V, the energy requirement is ~7×10^{-4} pJ; this line and one for 100 μm length are drawn dashed in Fig. 1.16. The left end of each of these lines designates the propagation delay of this length of transmission line. It is clear that the time delay and energy requirement associated with interconnect lines and other parasitic capacitance can form a significant limitation to the performance of very high speed integrated circuits.

Several conclusions can be drawn by inspection of Fig. 1.16. It is clear that there are still significant performance gains waiting to be realized in microelectronics; smaller dimensions form one method of achieving these goals. However, the theoretical ultimate energy limits, kT or $\hbar/\tau$, probably cannot in practice be approached within one or two orders of magnitude; but there is still a very wide gap between the switching energy required by present-day devices and any theoretical limit. In certain kinds of devices, the energy required to move a bit of information is just that energy needed to charge the capacitance defined by the device; in these cases, the energy per bit will scale as the square of the lithographic design rule. In most applications of integrated circuits, the energy per bit and the functional density are economically more important than the frequency or propagation delay limits. However, there are limits to the reduction by scaling of both energy and density, dictated partly by the means of interconnecting devices. For example, the scaled 0.1 μm device performance may be limited by the transmission line connecting it to the next device. Thus more intimate integration of devices is needed as the devices are made smaller. I^2L and CCD devices are examples of such closer device integration; such device technologies should benefit from the use of higher resolution lithography. An ultimate limit to density and performance will be determined also by the dimensional stability of the various materials, the silicon wafer, masks, etc., used in the pattern delineation. Present photolithographic techniques yield dimensional tolerances in the 10^{-4}–10^{-5} range; a new process must be at least as good if the resulting performance and density is to increase.

There is another type of limit on the minimum dimensions or feature sizes that can be achieved, related to the statistical uncertainty in feature position and size. Consider a simple case of one-line features that must be aligned with respect to another feature on a previous mask level. There will be an uncertainty in the position of each edge due to alignment error and to processing error. Thus, for the two lines there will be a total of eight possible errors. If the alignment and edge processing errors are equal, the alignment accuracy must be better than 625 Å for a 0.5-μm-wide line, or the lines could miss contact completely. Therefore, the minimum feature size will be determined in part by the registration accuracy of the lithography process; or equivalently, the registration accuracy required depends on the linewidth. Wallmark (1979) has examined this issue to determine the ultimate linewidth limit due to fundamental physical laws. He points out that the inability to measure the relative position of a feature edge to an accuracy less than the limit imposed by the Heisenberg uncertainty principle will form an ultimate limit on feature size. Furthermore, as the number of features in a circuit (e.g., on a chip) increases, the minimum linewidth must be increased to avoid a yield reduction due to the statistical probability of misalignment. For a circuit with 10^4 elements his analysis suggests a minimum feature size of ~ 0.07 μm.

VI. ECONOMIC FACTORS

Except in special situations the ultimate consideration as to the practical utility of any technology or process will be one of economics, i.e., the cost of producing the product compared with its value in the market place. The cost of applying any process (e.g., lithography) in the production of a microelectronic device is equal to the cost per hour of running the process facility divided by the product of throughput (devices per hour) and yield (number of good devices out divided by number of starting devices). Each of these factors will be discussed here briefly in order to show how the economics of production of microelectronic devices may be affected by the use of high resolution lithography, and, conversely, how economic considerations will influence the ways of applying high resolution lithography.

A. Yield

The principal yield loss factor in photolithographically fabricated devices is due to the lithographic steps. Furthermore, the yield of a given device through a production line depends strongly on the area A_d of the die containing the device or circuit, the defect density in the lithographic mask (D_k) and in the semiconductor material (D_l), and the number of wafers processed (i.e., the maturity or experience of the production line). The yield dependence on the first three factors is frequently expressed by an equation of the form $Y = (1 + AD)^{-n}$ (where $D = D_k + D_l$, and n is the number of mask levels). Experimental data provides some confirmation of the general form of this distribution, except that in practice the zero-area yield intercept may be less than 100%, because the yield of some of the fabrication processes do not depend on defects in the mask or material. The general shape of this yield dependence on area is shown by the upper curves in Fig. 1.17. Strictly, this dependence assumes constant lithographic design rules, i.e., reduced circuit complexity as area is reduced. The slope of the curve near the origin is proportional to the number of masking steps n and the defect density.

In order to illustrate qualitatively how the yield–area curve is affected by a different lithography process, consider that the upper solid curve in Fig. 1.17 represents a typical series of photolithographic processes using 5

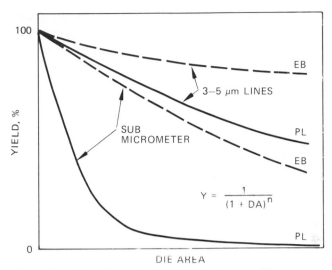

FIG. 1.17 Illustration of the effect of a higher resolution process on production yield.

μm lines, and that these processes are replaced by masking steps in which the masks are perfect and do not contact the resist during exposure (so that no defects are created by the contact itself). These new processes could be electron-beam lithography, projection photolithography, or a noncontacting high resolution replication technique. In the electron-beam case, the pattern is defined by the computer program and can be made defect free (except for unpredictable effects such as electrical transients). In the latter cases, the masks can be fully inspected and only essentially perfect ones chosen for use, and no damage to the mask will be incurred by its use in the projection for replication machine. By changing to these new processes, the yield will be represented by a new, higher curve (shown by the upper dashed line in Fig. 1.17) that exhibits a lower slope, determined principally by the material defect density. Now consider that the device features are made of submicrometer lines, using the same lithographic processes that were compared above. By using normal contact photolithography it is possible to expose satisfactorily a small area (e.g., one transistor), but optical distortion, runout, and alignment errors will result in a rapid decrease in yield as more devices are fabricated on a larger die, as shown in the lower solid curve. On the other hand, the higher resolution process will not be employed beyond its resolution capability, so that the resulting yield will be higher, as shown by the lower dashed curve. The shape and position of these latter curves depends strongly on the type of patterns being reproduced and the size distribution of defects; a given size defect (e.g., a dust particle, resist pin hole) will obviously be more serious with narrow lines and spaces than with coarse geometries. Another factor that will limit yield as the feature size is reduced is the need to improve the pattern alignment accuracy in proportion to feature size. This effect is discussed in Chapter 4. This reduction in yield as the design rules approach the ultimate limit of the lithography process forms a practical limit to the minimum size of microelectronic devices that can be produced economically. Therefore, a new lithography process that is capable of higher ultimate resolution can be used to make the same number of devices as the prior process, but on a smaller chip, so that the new process will be represented by a point higher on the yield curve. That is, a higher resolution noncontacting lithography process will not only allow smaller devices to be fabricated, but will provide higher yield at a given resolution, for the two reasons mentioned above.

B.   Machine Throughput

A second factor that affects the cost of devices is the throughput of the lithography step, i.e., the number of mask levels that can be exposed per hour. While there are several production steps associated with the lithography process other than the actual exposure of the resist (e.g., application of resist, development, handling), the exposure time is the principal factor that is different between the several processes. Details of the dependence of exposure time on resolution and machine characteristics for electron-beam lithography are shown later (Fig. 3.14). Here the several lithography processes will be compared on the basis of exposure time, including where applicable the time required for registration and step-and-repeat of the individual exposures.

A comparison of the lengths of time required to expose the resist on one mask level of a 3-in.-diameter wafer is shown in Fig. 1.18 for several lithography processes. Most of the points represent actual, published, performance data; the lines for x-ray and proton replication are based on calculations. In some cases the published data has been extrapolated (by area) to a 3 in. wafer size. The history of electron-beam machine development is shown by the decrease in exposure time for the diamond symbols; the upper points are circa 1976. The design of more recent machines has emphasized speed more strongly; these are represented by the lower points. Although Fig. 1.18 shows only published data, several of these machines will expose lines that are considerably narrower than the data point indicates. The exposure time for narrower linewidths can be estimated by drawing a line through the data point and parallel to the line A, down to the resolution limit of the machine. The line A has a slope of $\frac{8}{3}$ which is derived from Eq. (3.29), as discussed in Chapter 3, Section

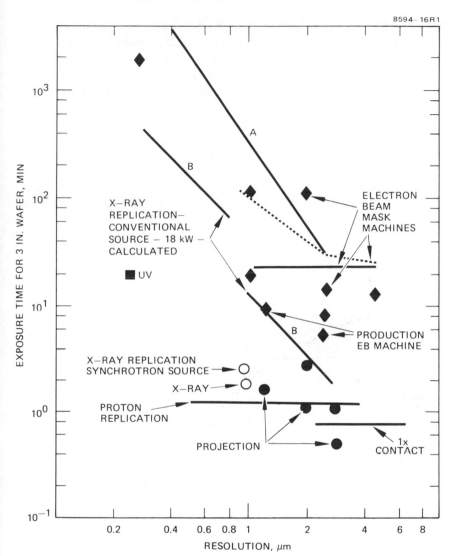

FIG. 1.18 1979 state of the art in exposure times for several lithographic techniques. ●, photolithography; ◆, electron-beam lithography.

III.B. Two diamond symbols in Fig. 1.18 represent electron-beam machines that have been used for the production of circuits by direct writing. One machine uses a 2.5 μm square beam and provides a throughput of 22 2.25 in. (57 mm) wafers per hour (Yourke and Weber, 1976); the other involves a 1.25 μm square beam with 10 57 mm wafers per hour (Weber and

Moore, 1979). These data represent the best reported state-of-the-art in production type electron beam machines. An exposure time by electron projection in a laboratory machine (Fig. 1.9a) of ~60 s for a 2-in. wafer with 2 μm features has been reported (Fuller *et al.*, 1978). Several points are shown for commercial electron-beam mask making machines; the throughput of these machines need not be competitive with direct writing machines in order to be economically viable.

The x-ray replication lines were calculated for two different conditions, viz. full wafer exposure and step-and-repeat. A full wafer exposure system can faithfully reproduce linewidths >1 μm over a 3-in.-diameter wafer (Zaharias, 1979). For such a system an 18 kW source was assumed to be exposing a resist with a sensitivity of 0.02 J/cm². The 18 kW source is assumed to produce a flux at the resist, after passing through a typical mask, of $0.15/D^2$ W/cm² where D is the source-to-mask distance in cm. With a mask-to-wafer gap of 15–20 μm (5 μm uncertainty) the source-to-mask distance should be 75 cm to hold the uncontrolled geometric distortion to 0.25 μm (± 0.13 μm) at the edge of the 3 in. wafer. For linewidths greater than 1 μm the source can be moved closer to the mask; therefore, the exposure time is proportional to the inverse square of the linewidth. However, decreasing the source-to-mask distance increases the amount of geometric distortion and degrades the resolution, unless the mask-to-wafer gap is also reduced. Closer proximity of the mask to the wafer can also reduce the process yield.

For x-ray replication of linewidths less than 0.8 μm it may be desirable to use a step-and-repeat exposure system to achieve greater mask-to-mask alignment accuracy because of wafer distortion. Such a system might expose 2 cm² fields and step 9 times to cover a 3 in. wafer. Using a mask-to-wafer gap of 15–20 μm, the source distance can be reduced to 25 cm to achieve 0.2 μm uncontrolled geometric distortion. For linewidths less than 0.8 μm the source-to-mask distance must be proportionally increased. Also for linewidths <0.8 μm it may not be possible to use high sensitivity resists; for this calculation a resist sensitivity of 0.1 J/cm² was assumed. Although this value is about 10 times more sensitive than PMMA, such resists have been reported to be suitable for 0.5 μm linewidth replication (Hatzakis, 1979). For linewidths between 0.8 and 1.0 μm either of these x-ray lithography techniques might be used.

The general time–resolution dependence for x-ray replication is the result of a finite area source that is placed a sufficient distance from the mask and wafer to reduce the distortions to a small fraction of the linewidth. If the x-rays were perfectly collimated (point source, infinite distance from the mask) then the exposure time would not increase as the linewidth is decreased (refer to Chapter 6). This is the case with synchrotron radiation, which has been used for x-ray replication over a small area to expose 1 μm lines in PMMA resist (Spiller *et al.*, 1976). Lines as narrow as 700 Å were also replicated. Comparison of this point (Fig. 1.18) with the lines calculated above shows the time reduction achievable by the use of a source providing much higher x-ray intensity.

The line marked Proton Replication is an estimate of throughput, based on experimental exposure data, for a new replication process that uses a large area proton beam to expose the resist (Rensch *et al.*, 1979). The patterns are delineated by passing a proton beam through a proximity mask in a manner analogous to x-ray replication. The high sensitivity of the resist (PMMA in this case) to protons makes this a relatively high throughout replication process.

The solid round points in Fig. 1.18, designated Photolithography, represent the time per wafer required for handling, alignment, step-and-repeat, and exposure on optical projection aligners. Lines as narrow as ~0.6 μm can be printed on a 4× aligner, but 1.0–1.5 μm is probably a more practical limit. The 1× line is typical of contact photolithography. In general, exposure times increase as resolution capability is improved by the use of a projection exposure system with greater demagnification, i.e., the time for exposure in a 4× system is greater than in a 1× contact technique. This effect is the result of the reduction in field size with higher resolution, so that more step-and-repeat operations must be carried out with the higher magnification systems.

The principal conclusions from Fig. 1.18 can be summarized as follows. First, all lithography processes exhibit, each for its own reason, a resolution throughput tradeoff. Any given process cannot expose narrow lines as fast as it can expose wide lines (all other parameters constant). Second, the parallel or batch replication processes generally show shorter exposure time than electron-beam direct writing exposure, which is a serial process. However, the photolithographic techniques would be pushed to their limit below about 1 μm linewidth and would not be a reliable production operation. The most advanced high resolution replication process, viz., x-ray lithography, is still unproven in production. While the comparative data in Fig. 1.18 suggests that direct electron-beam writing at high resolution (< 1 μm) may be uneconomical for production of quantities of devices, the exposure time could change markedly with the development of higher throughout electron-beam machine technology and with higher resist sensitivity (refer to Chapter 3, Section IV.D). Furthermore, in general only the highest resolution mask levels need be drawn by the use of electron-beam direct writing; the lower resolution patterns could be exposed by a faster process. Nevertheless, it is in the very high resolution regime that a fast high resolution replication process may be especially useful. It is emphasized that most of the data in this figure are based on data and calculations from machine usage in an R&D environment; virtually no production throughout data is available at this time on any high resolution machine.

More devices, and therefore, for example, more logic functions, can be fabricated on a given size chip by the use of a narrower linewidth. That is, more equivalent gates or charge storage sites can be made per unit area. In those types of integrated circuits for which the higher level of integration is useful, cost comparisons should be made on a per function basis. For example, by changing from a process with 5 μm design rules to one allowing 1 μm design rules, up to 25 times as many functions can be fabricated on a given size chip, or a given circuit complexity can be made on a smaller chip so that the wafer will contain a larger number of chips. While the lithography costs of the higher resolution process will probably be higher, as shown below, these are only a portion of the total wafer cost. Experience in the microelectronics industry has shown that the processing cost per wafer (by photolithography) is roughly invariant with wafer size. Therefore, there has been a strong trend to larger wafers. These cost and functional density factors have been combined into an approximate comparison of relative cost between the several lithographic processes, similar to that given by Broers (1978). This comparison is shown in Fig. 1.19, in which the cost per pixel [pixel area = (linewidth)^2] is plotted versus linewidth for existing and projected electron-beam, x-ray, and optical projection machines. The costs were taken as the sum of the capital acquisition cost (from published or estimated prices, amortized over 5 years), maintenance (higher for electron-beam machines), and one machine operator. The throughput values were taken from the manufacturers data or calculations of expected performance, as shown in the caption. The trend to higher lithography cost with narrower linewidth on a per pixel basis is clear. This cost must be balanced against the higher device performance attainable with smaller features. This higher cost is probably offset also by higher yield from the higher resolution processes, as discussed in the previous section.

C.   A Cost Model

The decision as to which high resolution process to use in any given situation will depend on the relative cost per unit produced, which in turn depends on the production quantities involved and the cost factors. Henderson (1976) has developed a cost model that can form a useful guideline for projecting such costs and making decisions on the optimal lithographic process, for example, between replication and direct writing. Following

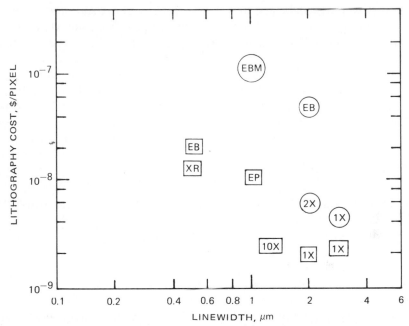

FIG. 1.19 A comparison of the exposure cost per pixel by several lithography processes. EB = direct writing electron beam lithography, XR = x-ray replication, EBM = electron-beam mask maker, EP = electron projection ○, operational; □, projected performance. Three in. wafer, 20% exposed area and two shift operation assumed. Therefore ~8 × 10^8 1-μm pixels on a 3 in. wafer. Capital costs: EB ~ 1.3–1.5M$, photo ~ 140–880K$.

his analysis, the cost of fabricating N_W finished wafers by direct electron-beam writing can be expressed as

$$C_D = (H + W + n_l t_e E) \frac{N_W}{Y_D} = \frac{a_1 N_W}{Y_D} \tag{1.4}$$

where H represents the wafer handling and other costs, W the wafer material cost, n_l is the number of masking steps, t_e the exposure time, and E the machine cost per unit time. Similarly the cost of replicating N_W wafers from a mask can be written as the sum of the costs of fabricating masks by electron-beam lithography plus the replication costs:

$$C_R = n_l(t_e E + M)\left(1 + \frac{N_W}{\alpha Y_D}\right) + (H + W + n_l t_R R)\frac{N_W}{Y_R}$$

$$= a_2 + \left(\frac{a_2}{\alpha} + a_3\right)\frac{N_W}{Y_R} \tag{1.5}$$

where M represents the mask fabrication costs other than electron-beam exposure and R the cost per hour for the use of the replication system;

$a_2 = n_l(t_e E + M)$ and $a_3 = H + W + n_l t_R R$; t_R represents the exposure time; and α is the number of wafers processed per mask. The yield by replication is expressed as the product of yield of the direct electron-beam writing process Y_D and the replication yield (due to mask defects) $Y_R = Y_D(1 + AD)^{-n_l}$. The costs can then be expressed graphically as shown in Fig. 1.20. In order for replication to be cheaper, the mask cost must be low and the slope of the replication line (i.e., the cost per yielded wafer) must be lower than that for direct electron-beam lithography. Under these conditions there will be an intersection at the critical wafer quantity given by

$$(N_W/Y_D)_c = a_2/[a_1 - a_3(1 + AD)^{n_l}] \qquad (1.6)$$

The critical quantity $(N_W/Y_D)_c$ is obviously dependent on the resolution desired.

Because of the many variables and cost uncertainties involved, there is high risk in quantifying this analysis and representing it as typical. The calculated costs are strongly dependent on the projected mask defect density, resist sensitivity, intensity of exposing radiation source, and resolution (linewidth) desired. These quantities are still subject to evolutionary improvements, and therefore, difficult to estimate realistically at this time. Therefore, no numerical example will be given here.

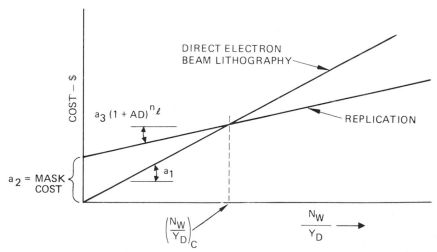

FIG. 1.20 Illustration of the cost of producing N_W wafers by direct electron-beam lithography and by replication from a mask made by the use of electron-beam lithography. In the latter curve it is assumed that α is large.

VII. STATUS AND FUTURE OF THE TECHNOLOGY

A graphical illustration of the development of advanced lithography, from the point of view of resolution, is shown in Fig. 1.21. The prior historical trends in linewidth obtainable in production and by the use of developmental methods are plotted together with some projections of future growth in this parameter.

Some of the first experiments that showed the high resolution pattern capabilities of electron-beam lithography were carried out in 1966–1970. Thus, at this writing (1979) this technology is only about 10 years old. However, electron-beam lithography has advanced rapidly. In the United States this progress has been largely under the support of private industry, from the laboratory stage to the present status where productive use in manufacturing has started. Masks for photolithographic replication, made by electron-beam lithography, are in use by several microelectronics manufacturers. Direct writing at 2 μm linewidth is now an established manufacturing process in at least one organization. Electron-beam lithography work is presently concentrated in less than a dozen industrial organizations throughout the world. These groups have carried out development programs on fabrication processes, devices, and machines, largely for their own use (although some licensing and sale of these machines has taken place). Of the five or six organizations in the United States presently active in electron-beam lithography, only one or two have as their principal business activity the manufacture of semiconductor devices; the others are system-oriented companies. Considering that one of the first applications of direct writing electron-beam lithography will be the fabrication of custom devices and integrated circuits, this initial location of activity in system-oriented companies is not surprising.

While the development of electron-beam–compatible fabrication processes, tailored for specific semiconductor devices, is an active ongoing effort, the basic processes for utilization of this technology are well developed. The important area of machine development has been emphasized by all active organizations, either by extensive modification of commercially available scanning electron microscopes or by building custom machines. Two classes of machine have reached the level of commercial scale. One type is designed for the fabrication of masks with 1–5 μm linewidth for photolithographic replication (either contact or projection). The second type is for use in direct writing at the laboratory level. A mask making machine that will make a 3 in. master chrome mask in about 45 min (see Chapter 5) is now commercially available on a complete "turn key" basis. Therefore, mask making by computer controlled electron-beam machine will be the first substantial application of this technology and is now beginning to be an important production step in many semi-conductor manufacturing companies. Several mask making organizations have purchased these machines, so that masks made by the use of electron-beam lithography are now available from commercial sources.

The second way of using electron-beam lithography involves the creation of higher resolution (<1 μm) structures by direct writing, for the fabrication of experimental or modest quantity production devices and of masks for high resolution replication. Electron-beam machines that exhibit ~ 0.1 μm ultimate resolution and ~ 0.5 μm routine fabrication capabilities are in use in laboratory environments. A wide range of developmental submicrometer devices are being fabricated by direct electron-beam lithography, including microwave field effect transistors, charge coupled devices, bubble memories, surface acoustic wave filters, and medium scale integrated circuits. Since large quantities of these types of devices will not be required for at least several years, prototype quantities of a thousand or so per year can be made by direct writing. At least one organization is using direct writing electron-beam lithography at 2.5 μm resolution for the production of integrated circuits.

There are at least four different techniques of high resolution replication under study. When the demand for production quantities of devices with $< \sim 1$ μm linewidth becomes a reality, there will be a need for an economically and technically viable batch lithography process. To be cost competitive such a process must exhibit the required resolution, alignment, and stability characteristics, but must also provide a substantial saving in unit cost of the lithographic steps over direct electron-beam writing. In general, this latter condition means that the process must exhibit considerably higher throughput than is possible by direct electron-beam writing, and the replication machine must be cheaper to purchase and operate than an electron-beam lithography machine. These factors were discussed in the previous section. It is too early to project which, if any, of the present replication techniques will offer these features.

All replication techniques will probably require step-and-repeat registration and exposure with exposure fields no larger than about 1 cm $\times$ 1 cm, unless the in-plane wafer distortion can be reduced to the level required for multilevel submicrometer pattern registration. Therefore, the concept of whole wafer replication of submicrometer patterns appears impractical at this time, thereby greatly reducing the theoretical exposure time advantage normally granted to a replication process.

While the fundamental feature offered by electron-beam lithography is the higher resolution patterns attainable, there are a number of other advantages that will also be of significant technical and economic value. The speed of making masks for photolithographic replication at 1–5 μm design rules, i.e., fast turnaround time from design change to completed mask, has been demonstrated. This turnaround time can be one or two days, vis-a-vis up to six weeks by contemporary rubylith, reduction, stepping, etc., methods. The ability to draw high resolution patterns, with step and repeat electron-beam lithography (including the ability to register on each scan field) provides a means to cope with in-plane wafer distortion. Linewidth control, feature placement accuracy, and overlay precision are superior; these are essential factors in the movement to higher density circuits. Many of these advantages result from the electric programability of the electron beam and from the computer control feature; they are, therefore, independent of resolution and are applicable to devices with design rules in the 1–5 μm range, as well as in the submicrometer regime. The ability to define the patterns in software, which can be modified relatively easily, could make the fabrication of low volume, custom, integrated circuits much more economical.

The future beneficial use of electron-beam lithography will depend principally on two factors, viz., first, the economic viability, i.e., the need for devices that only high resolution lithography can provide and the ability to manufacture them at an affordable cost, and second, the commercial availability to the semiconductor industry of machines that are reliable and easy to operate, again at an affordable cost. There is little doubt that these conditions are now being satisfied for photolithographic mask making; it will be several years before the large scale utilization of higher resolution lithography becomes clear.

A projection of the future growth in resolution capabilities of electron-beam lithography is shown by the lower two dashed lines in Fig. 1.21. By evolutionary improvements in machine technology, e.g., the use of field emitter sources, linewidths of ~100 Å are projected. The lowest curve, marked New Exposure Technique, undefined, is an expression of faith in the innovative ability of scientists; some new lithography technology will come along if adequate research support is provided. It is possible that one of these new exposure techniques could involve the use of a tiny focused ion beam (probably protons) to expose patterns in resist in the same programmed manner as now used with electron beams (Seliger *et al.*, 1979). Ions are not backscattered as much by the atoms of the substrate as are electrons; therefore, the line broadening limit due to this effect would be greatly reduced. The primary machine limitations in this process are the generation of a high brightness ion beam, and the focusing of that beam with electrostatic lenses.

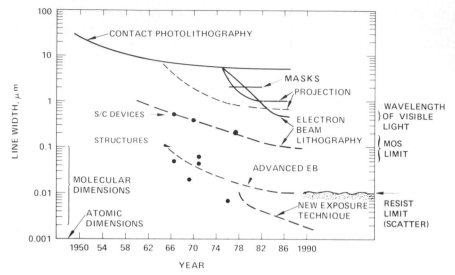

FIG. 1.21　History and projection of the resolution trends in lithography. ———, Production, ———, R&D.

Finally, three important points should be emphasized. Two considerations that are critical to the future use of high resolution lithography are of necessity not covered in this book. One of these issues is the means for testing high resolution LSI circuits; such testing may be done best by using electron beams in one of the several ways presently under study. Second, as circuits are designed with 10^5–10^7 elements the optimal architecture or organization may be fundamentally different from that used today in order to obtain the greatest memory capacity or computational power per unit cost. The optimization of design of complex circuits will certainly require use of more sophisticated computer-aided design techniques. In fact, the ability to design circuits with very high levels of integration, and the knowledge of how to use these circuits in systems, may form a temporary limitation on applicability of VLSI that is not related to the fabrication process. These issues can only be resolved as this technology is applied to increasingly larger circuits.

Second, the utilization of this relatively complex technology will require professional people who have been trained in this field; such people are presently scarce. Third, the development by an intended industrial user of high resolution lithography to the point of practical value in device fabrication requires far more than the purchase of machines and the employment of trained people. The user must be prepared to invest heavily, far more than the capital cost of the machines, in the development of the process sequences and methods of fabrication compatible with his own existing manufacturing style.

VIII. THE CONTENTS OF THIS BOOK

The rest of this book is organized into five additional chapters, each treating a major segment of the technology of high resolution lithography. Even though the chapters were written by different authors, the content of each has been structured to be complementary to the others, so as to cover all important aspects of this technology.

The fundamental processes by which patterns are created in resist masks are described in detail in Chapter 2. This work includes the electron–substrate and electron–resist interactions, resist character-istics, the principles of the proximity effect and the generation of registra-tion signals. Other high resolution fabrication processes, such as plasma etching, are discussed.

Electron-beam lithography machines are described in Chapter 3, in-cluding some details of each of the major elements in the electron-optical column and their effect on the focused electron beam. The limitations on beam and scan field size are brought out, together with the factors af-fecting economics of use of electron-beam machines. Several writing and machine design strategies are discussed. Three example machines are described as indicators of the state-of-the-art in machine development. A brief projection of the trend in design of higher throughput machines is presented.

The purpose of any lithography is to fabricate devices; therefore, the use of electron-beam lithography to make discrete devices and integrated circuits is treated in Chapter 4. This chapter includes discussion of the fabrication processes unique to electron-beam lithography and describes some of the design limitations in devices with small features.

The first commercial or production use of electron-beam lithography has been in the fabrication of modest resolution (1–5 μm) masks for pho-tolithographic reproduction. The techniques and economics of mask fab-rication by the use of electron beams is described in detail in Chapter 5.

Finally, Chapter 6 presents a comprehensive description and evalua-tion of the several high resolution replication processes currently under development. This chapter brings out clearly the reasons for considering replication as a production technique and shows the state-of-the-art of machines in the more advanced replication methods.

56   GEORGE R. BREWER

REFERENCES

Amboss, K. (1975). *J. Vac. Sci. Technol.* **12**, 1152–1155.
Baechtold, W. (1971). *Electron. Lett.* **7**, 275–276.
Baechtold, W., Walter, W., and Wolf, P. (1972). *Electron. Lett.* **8**, 35–37.
Baechtold, W., Walter, W., and Wolf, P. (1973). *Electron. Lett.* **9**, 232–234.
Brewer, G. R. (1971). *IEEE Spectrum* **8**, 23–37.
Brewer, G. R. (1972a). *Solid State Technol.* **15**, 43–47.
Brewer, G. R. (1972b). *Solid State Technol.* **15**, 36–39.
Broers, A. N. (1972). *Symp. Electron Ion Beam Sci. Technol. 5th* Electochemical Society, Princeton, New Jersey.
Broers, A. N. (1976). *Symp. Electron Ion Beam Sci. Technol., 7th* pp. 587–605. Electrochemical Society, Washington, D.C.
Broers, A. N. (1978). Technical Digest—IEDM, Washington, D.C., pp. 1–5.
Broers, A. N., and Hatzakis, M. (1972). *Sci. Am.* **227** (No. 5), 33–34.
Broers, A. N., Molzen, W. W., Cuamo, J. J., and Wittels, N. D. (1976). *Appl. Phys. Lett.* **29-1**, 596–598.
Butlin, R. S., Parker, D., Crossley, I., and Turner, J. (1977). *Inst. Phys. Conf. Serial No. 33a* Chapter 5, pp. 237–245.
Chang, T. H. P., and Viswanathan, R. (1978). *J. Vac. Sci. Technol.* **15**, 878–882.
Chang, T. H. P., Wilson, A. D., Speth, A. J., and Ting, C. H., (1976). *Proc. Symp. Electron and Ion Beam Science Technol.* Electrochemical Society, pp. 392–410.
Crewe, A. V., Wall, J., and Walter, L. M. (1968). *J. Appl. Phys.* **39**, 5861–5868.
Darley, H. M., Houston, T. W., and Taylor, G. W. (1978). Technical Digest—IEDM, Washington, D. C., pp. 62–65.
Dennard, H. D., Gaensslen, H. Y., Rideout, V. L., Bassous, E., and LeBlanc, A. R. (1974). *J. Solid State Circuits* **SC-9**, 256–267.
Elliott, D. J., and Hockey, M. A. (1978). *Proc. SPIE* **135**, 130–146.
Evans, S. A., Bartelt, J. L., Sloan, B. J., and Varnell, G. L. (1978). *J. Vac. Sci. Technol.* **15**, 969–972.
Everhart, T. E. (1960). *J. Appl. Phys.* **31**, 1483–1490.
Everhart, T. E. (1968). *Private communication.*
Fang, F. Hatzakis, M., and Ting, C. H. (1973). *J. Vac. Sci. Technol.* **10**, 1082–1085.
Feder, R., Spiller, E., Topalian, J., and Hatzakis, M. (1976). *Proc. Symp. Electron Ion Beam Sci. Technol., 7th* pp. 198–203.
Finnila, R. M., Su, S. C., and Braunstein, A. I. (1974). *Proc. Soc. Photo-Opt. Instrum. Eng.* **55**.
Fuller, C. E., Gould, P. A., and Vinton, D. J. (1978). *Proc. Symp. Electron Ion Beam Sci. Technol., 8th* pp. 108–116. Electrochemical Society.
Greiling, P. T., Ozdemir, F. S., Krumm, C. F., Sein, B. L., and Lohr, R. F. (1979). Technical Digest—IEDM, Washington, D.C., pp. 670–673.
Grivet, P. (1965). "Electron Optics." Pergamon, Oxford.
Hatzakis, M. (1979). Paper presented at the *Symp. Electron, Ion, Photon Beam Technol., 15th Boston, Massachusetts.*
Heim, R. C. (1977). *Proc. SPIE* **100**, 104–114.
Henderson, R. C. (1976). *Proc. Symp. Electron Ion Beam Sci. Technol.* pp. 204–217.
Hoeneisen, B., and Mead, C. A. (1972a). *Solid State Electron.* **15**, 819–829.
Hoeneisen, B., and Mead, C. A. (1972b). *Solid State Electron.* **15**, 891, 897.
Hooper, W. W., Fairman, R. D., and Bechtel, N. G. (1971). *IEEE Electron Devices Meeting, Washington, D. C.*

Ipri, A. C. (1978). Technical Digest—IEDM, Washington, D.C., pp. 46–49.

Keyes, R. W. (1977). *Science* **195**, 1230–1235.

Keyes, R. W. (1969). *IEEE Spectrum* **6**, 36–45.

Keyes, R. W. (1972). *Proc. IEEE* **60**, 1055–1062.

Keyes, R. W. (1975). *Proc. IEEE* **63**, 740–767.

Klaassen, F. M. (1978). *Solid State Electron.* **21**, 565–571.

Langmuir, D. B. (1937). *Proc. IRE* **25**, 977–991.

Lean, E. G., and Broers, A. N. (1970). *Microwave J.* **13**, 97–101.

Liechti, C. A., Gowan, E., and Cohen, J. (1972). *IEEE Int. Solid State Circuits Conf., Phila-delphia, Pennsylvania.*

Lin, Burn Jeng (1975). *J. Vac. Sci. Technol.* **12**, 1317–1320.

Livesay, W. R. (1978). *J. Vac. Sci. Technol.* **15**, 1022–1027.

Mayer, D. C., and Perkins, W. O. (1979). *IEEE Conf. Gigabit Logic, Orlando, Florida* May 3–4.

Moore, G. E. (1975). *Technical Digest—Int. Electron Devices Meeting,* December 1–3, pp. 11–13.

Moss, H. (1968). "Narrow Angle Electron Guns and Cathode Ray Tubes," p. 88. Academic Press, New York.

Pasiecznik, J. (1977). *Symp. Electron, Ion, Photon Beam Technol. 14th, Palo Alto, California* May.

Picquendar, J. E. (1972). *Proc. Conf. Electron Ion Beam Sci. Technol., 5th Houston, Texas, May, pp. 31–48.*

Picquendar, J. E. (1973). *J. Vac. Sci. Technol.* **10**, 1132.

Pucel, R. A., Haus, H. A., and Statz, H. (1975). *Adv. Electron. Electron Phys.* **38.**

Rensch, D. B., Seliger, R. L., and Csanky, G. (1979). Paper presented at the *Symp. Electron, Ion, Photon Beam Technol., Boston, Massachusetts* May 29 to June 1, 1979.

Schief, R. (1969). *Optik (Stuttgart)* **29**, 416–436.

Seliger, R. L., Kubena, R. L., Olney, R. D., Ward, J. W., and Wang, V. (1979). Paper presented at the *Symp. Electron, Ion, Photon Beam Technol. Boston, Massachusetts* May 29 to June 1, 1979.

Spiller, E., Feder, R., Topalian, J., Gudat, W., and Eastman, D. (1976). *Proc. Conf. Electron Ion Beam Sci. Tehcnol., 7th* pp. 233–239.

Stover, H. L., Hause, F. L., and McGreivy, D., (1979). Paper presented at the *Electron, Ion, Photon Beam Symp., Boston, Massachusetts* May.

Sullivan, P. A., and Hause, F. L. (1976). *J. Appl. Photo. Eng.* **2**, 82–85.

Swanson, R. M. (1974). *Stanford Electronics Laboratory Rep. 4963-1.*

Sze, S. M. (1969). *"Physics of Semiconductor Devices,"* p. 536. Wiley, New York.

Thomson, M. G. R. (1975). *J. Vac. Sci. Technol.* **12**, 1156–1159.

Thornton, P. R. (1979). *Adv. Electron. Electron Phys.* **48**, 271–380.

Tibbets, R. E., and Wilczynski, J. S. (1969). *IBM J. Res. Dev.* **13**, 192–196.

Vadasz, L. L., Chau, H. T., and Grove, A. S. (1971). *IEEE Spectrum* **8**, 40–48.

Wallmark, J. T. (1979). *IEEE Trans. Electron Devices* **E2-26**, 135–142.

Weber, E. V., and Moore, R. D. (1979). Paper presented at the *Symp. Electron, Ion, and Photon Beam Technol., 15th, Boston, Massachusetts* May.

Weglein, R. D., Wauk, M. T., and Nudd, R. G. (1973). *IEEE Ultrason. Symp. Monterey, California* November.

Wells, O. C. (1974a). "Scanning Electron Microscopy," Chapter 3. McGraw-Hill, New York.

Wells, O. C. (1974b). "Scanning Electron Microscopy," Chapter 4. McGraw-Hill, New York.

Wolf, E. D. (1972). *Nat. Conf. Electron Probe Anal., 7th San Francisco, California.* July 17–21.
Wolf, E. D., Ozdemir, F. S., and Weglein, R. D. (1973). *IEEE Ultrason. Symp., Monterey, California* November.
Wolf, E. D., Ozdemir, F. S., Perkins, W. E., and Coane, P. J. (1971). *Symp. Electron, Ion, Laser Beam Tech., 11th,* pp. 331–336. San Francisco Press, California.
Yourke, H. S., and Weber, E. V. (1976). Tech. Digest, IEDM, Washington, D.C., pp. 431–436.
Zaharias, A. (1979). Paper presented at the *Symp. Electron, Ion, Photon Beam Technol., 15th, Boston, Massachusetts* May.

2

Electron-beam processes

JAMES S. GREENEICH

BURROUGHS CORPORATION
SAN DIEGO, CALIFORNIA

I. INTRODUCTION

Finely focused electron beams are used in lithographic processes to expose polymer resist layers. Very complex device patterns with high resolution (submicrometer) can be created. Such resolution is in general superior to presently available optical lithography techniques because the electron-probe size may be made much smaller than the corresponding diffraction limited image in optical lighography.

In any lithographic process, the resist image is the important item; the writing machine is the means to achieve that image. Therefore, it is very important to understand how that resist image is produced by the incident electron beam. Once the image is created, it may be used in a variety of techniques such as to fabricate optical, ion-beam and x-ray masks, and in the direct fabrication of devices.

In order to utilize electron beams successfully in high resolution lithography, the interaction and scattering of electrons within the resist layer and the underlying substrate must be well understood. For example, the effects of beam energy, type of resist, resist thickness, substrate type, and several other variables are critical in producing an optimal pattern in the resist. The resolution obtainable with electron beams is not limited by probe forming characteristics, but rather it is presently limited by electron scattering. It is important to understand the limits imposed by electron scattering as well as methods of minimizing scattering effects and thereby improving resolution. In Section II, the underlying physical foundations for electron scattering and energy loss are presented. Important concepts of electron range, substrate backscattering, and the number of elastic forward-scattering events are introduced. Various models for calculating the absorbed energy density in the resist are also described. In Section III, these models are used to calculate resist images. Tradeoffs between resolution as a function of dose, beam energy, probe size, and type of substrate are treated. An example is also given on how the parameters of machine design and writing strategy influence the resist image. Finally, the important concept of pattern dependent exposure (proximity) effects is treated extensively.

The resist is the material in which the desired pattern is created; its exposure and development characteristics exert a dominant influence on the quality of the written pattern. Therefore, these characteristics must be understood in detail in order to select and use resists effectively to create on the substrate a faithful reproduction of the intended pattern. Electron resists are similar in many ways to conventional photo-optical resists except in the mechanism of alteration of the resist material. In electron-beam lithography the energy for alteration of the polymer molecules comes from the electrons; in photo resists this energy is from the exposing photons. The early work in electron-beam lithography used optical resists, but it was soon discovered that simple non-light-sensitive polymer and copolymer materials were electron sensitive and the present electron resists have evolved from this discovery. Perhaps the best known example is poly(methyl methacrylate), PMMA, which is a common material known under the tradenames of Lucite[R] and Plexiglass[R].* In order to use a resist most effectively, it is important to understand the factors involved in the design of electron resists, as well as their lithographic characteristics such as sensitivity, resolution, contrast, and etch resistance. For example, by using appropriate combinations of exposure and development, resist profiles can be tailored to be undercut, vertical, or overcut. Consequently, their use as masks in subsequent etching or additive fabrication processes can be optimized. The physical processes in resist exposure and development are presented in Section IV. In addition, a fundamental limit to the tradeoff between resist sensitivity and resolution based on signal-to-noise theory is presented. Section V emphasizes available resist materials, their properties, and their utilization as masking media in image transfer methods. Both additive and subtractive processes are described.

Another electron-beam process important in electron-beam lithography concerns the interaction of the electron beam with alignment marks residing on the host substrate. The interaction of the beam with such marks gives rise to the signal used in automatic registration schemes which are capable of less than 0.10 μm alignment accuracy. Since the alignment marks are almost always covered by resist, back scattered electrons are detected in these registration schemes. The signal-to-noise ratio of this interaction process is of vital importance because it affects both the accuracy and speed of alignment. Section VI discusses electron-beam alignment; the kinds of marks used, the generation of backscattered electrons, and the signal-to-noise ratio.

II. ELECTRON SCATTERING IN SOLIDS

Electrons entering a solid material are scattered by interaction with the atoms comprising that material. This scattering can be divided roughly into two classes: forward and backscattering. Since most of the electrons are forward scattered through small angles (less than 90°) from their original direction, this effect merely broadens the incident beam. Some electrons experience large angle scattering (approaching 180°), causing these

* [R] registered trademarks, E. I. Dupont and Rohm & Haas, respectively.

electrons to return to the surface. Consider the specific situation of a resist-coated substrate as shown in Fig. 2.1. It is intended that the line pattern as indicated by the dashed lines is to be written by the incident beam scanned along the length of the three lines. As the incident electrons penetrate the resist film, the associated scattering will broaden the incident current distribution. Further, backscattered electrons from the silicon will return to the resist and also contribute to the exposure of the resist. As a consequence, the developed resist images will be wider than originally expected, as indicated in Fig. 2.1. Therefore, this scattering forms a limit on minimum linewidth obtainable. Since the backscattered electrons may travel relatively large distances, a fraction of them will contribute to resist exposure in patterns closely spaced to the one being written. Both forward and backscattered electrons result in non-optimal exposure of the intended pattern. This effect is fundamental and of serious concern. The scattering is dependent on electron energy, the resist and substrate material, and on pattern geometry. These scattering effects must be controlled and compensation techniques used in order to obtain the best pattern features of which electron-beam lithography is capable.

These scattering effects are amenable to limited analytical modeling. Such modeling is used, for example, to predict exposed resist profiles. These models also provide information that allows the pattern shape, or the exposure time or current density to be tailored in such a manner as to make the exposed patterns conform as closely as possible to the desired pattern. A summary is given below of the physical mechanisms of scattering and the available analytical tools for explaining and predicting the observed effects.

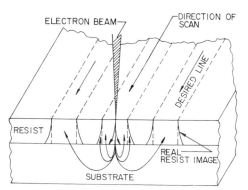

FIG. 2.1   A schematic illustration of electron penetration and scattering effects in exposing a resist-coated substrate.

A.   *Absorbed Energy Density*

A fundamental parameter in the exposure of electron resists is the absorbed energy density as a function of spatial position within the resist film. This energy density distribution is the result of cumulative energy loss of electrons scattered in the resist and electrons backscattered from the substrate into the resist. The geometry of the situation is shown in Fig. 2.2. For purposes of analysis consider the spatial current density profile of the beam entering the resist-coated substrate to be represented by a zero radius or delta function beam. Typically, the incident energy of the electrons is in the range of 5–30 keV, the resist film is 0.2–3.0-μm-thick, and the target material may consist of one or more thin layers on top of the host substrate. The energy loss at some observation point (r, z_0) can be divided into the primary or forward-scattered electrons and the backscattered electrons arising from within the resist, and those returning from the substrate to the resist. The absorbed energy density, $\epsilon_\delta(r, z_0)$ resulting from the incident delta function can be written as the sum of three components:

$$\epsilon_\delta(r, z_0) = \epsilon_{\delta p}(r, z_0) + \epsilon_{\delta r}(r, z_0) + \epsilon_{\delta s}(r, z_0) \qquad (2.1)$$

where $\epsilon_{\delta p}$ is the primary contribution, and $\epsilon_{\delta r}$ and $\epsilon_{\delta s}$ are the backscattered contributions from the resist and substrate, respectively. In general, the

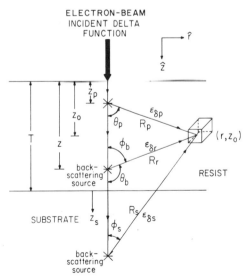

FIG. 2.2   Geometry for computing the delta function scattering response of the resist and substrate. The total contribution is divided into component parts $\epsilon_{\delta p}$, $\epsilon_{\delta r}$, and $\epsilon_{\delta s}$. [From Greeneich and Van Duzer (1974), and reproduced with permission of the IEEE.]

scattering sources form a continuum and a given component is found as an integral over the distribution of sources. Before examining several models for computing the absorbed energy density, the mechanisms of electron energy loss in the solid are reviewed. The concept of electron range is also introduced.

B. Electron-Scattering, Energy Loss, and Range–Energy Relationships

As an incident electron beam penetrates a solid, it is scattered both elastically and inelastically. Elastic scattering results only in a change of direction of the electrons, while inelastic collisions result in energy loss. Consequently, the incident electrons will spread out as they penetrate until all of their energy is lost or until they exit the solid as a result of backscattered deflections. Figure 2.3 illustrates this kind of scattering history for 100 electrons at 10 and 20 keV beam energies. These trajectories are the result of a Monte Carlo simulation of real electron trajectories for an assumed incident delta function beam exposing a 0.40 μm film coated on an Si substrate. Notice the relative portions of the trajectories in each of the two mediums; this is indicative of the relative energy dissipation and illustrates that most of the energy is deposited in the substrate. The forward-scattered electrons in the resist are difficult to identify because of their high density and small dimensional spread. On the other hand, the backscattered electrons are clearly evident. At 10 keV the backscattered electrons are spread out over distances on the order of 1 μm, while at 20 keV the distance is 3–4 μm.

As seen in Fig. 2.3, the electrons travel a zigzag path in the solid and the energy loss to the medium is a function of the total path length s traveled by the electron. The energy loss along an electron path fluctuates sta-

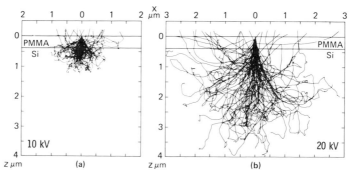

FIG. 2.3   Simulated trajectories (Monte Carlo calculations) for 100 electrons scattered in a PMMA film coated on a Si substrate. [From Kyser and Viswanathan (1975).]

tistically; however, because a large number of electrons are involved, it is adequate to know the mean rate of energy loss, rather than the details of each collision. For nonrelativistic energies, the Bethe rate-of-energy loss differential equation (Birkhoff, 1958) adequately describes the mean rate of energy loss $\mathcal{E}$ along the electron path. The Bethe equation can be written as

$$\mathcal{E} = \frac{-dE}{ds} = 2\pi N_0 q^4 \rho \frac{Z}{A} \frac{1}{E(s)} \ln \left[\frac{aE(s)}{I}\right] \tag{2.2}$$

where E is the electron energy, Z and A the atomic number and gram atomic weight of the solid, respectively, N_0 Avogadro's number, q the electron charge, I a mean excitation energy for energy loss in the solid, and the constant a has the value 1.1658 (Birkhoff, 1958). The value of I is difficult to evaluate theoretically so, in practice, tables or empirical formulas are used, such as (Berger and Seltzer, 1964)

$$I = (9.76 + 58.8Z^{-1.19})Z \tag{2.3}$$

which is valid for $Z \geq 13$. For compound solids the average atomic number and atomic weight may be used in Eqs. (2.2) and (2.3) or alternatively the weighted individual contributions of the atoms may be used.

It is convenient to treat the electrons as being continuously retarded according to Eq. (2.2) in what is called the "continuous slowing down approximation" (Berger and Seltzer, 1964). Hence the residual path length becomes a deterministic function of the energy and vice versa. In order to represent the electron energy as a function of path length in a general way, the length is usually normalized to the electron range. Electron range is that total path in the solid traveled by the average electron before it loses all of its energy.

The range is a function of the incident electron energy. Many different electron ranges have been defined depending on the particular experimental or theoretical treatment being considered. Generally, these range–energy relationships are proportional to each other. One of the most useful electron ranges is the Bethe range R_B, which is the path length for which the energy in the integral of Eq. (2.2) goes to zero. The Bethe range is plotted in Fig. 2.4 as a function of energy for several common materials and energies encountered in electron-beam lithography. The curves below 10 keV are shown dashed since Eq. (2.2) becomes inaccurate at low energies. For energies above 10 keV, approximate expressions of the form $R_B \propto E^n$ with $1.5 \leq n \leq 1.8$ are often used (Everhart and Hoff, 1971). From Fig. 2.4, R_B varies from 2.1 to 14.5 μm in the electron resist, PMMA, and from 1.5 to 10.0 μm in a Si substrate for a 10–30 keV variation in incident electron energy.

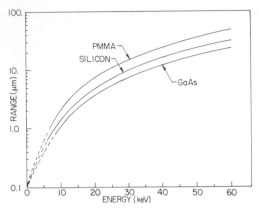

FIG. 2.4   The Bethe range as a function of incident beam energy for PMMA, silicon, and gallium arsenide materials.

If the energy as a function of path length $E(s)$ is normalized to the incident energy and the path length is normalized to the range, then the relation between E/E_0 and s/R_B is only weakly dependent on material properties. Figure 2.5 shows this relation for typical parametric values of $\xi_0 = aE_0/I$; for example, at 20 keV, ξ_0 is 135 and 355 for silicon and PMMA, respectively.

Elastic scattering results in a change in the direction of an incident electron. Elastic scattering results in spreading of the incident beam (small net angular changes) and also to large angular changes, which result in backscattered electrons. Such backscattered electrons can be spread over distances equal to the electron range. If device pattern features are separated by a distance apart which is less than the range, they can experience exposures that are dependent on the neighboring patterns.

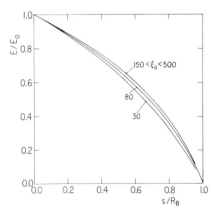

FIG. 2.5   The energy path length function for various values of the parameter $\xi_0 = aE_0/I$. [From Greeneich and Van Duzer (1973a) and reproduced with permission of the IEEE.]

To model elastic scattering, the screened Rutherford formula is used:

$$\frac{d\sigma}{d\Omega} = \frac{Z^2 q^4}{16E^2} \left[\sin^2 \frac{\theta}{2} + \frac{\theta_0^2}{4} \right] \tag{2.4}$$

where $d\sigma/d\Omega$ is the differential cross section per unit solid angle and θ_0 is the screening parameter

$$\theta_0 = 3.7 Z^{1/3} E^{-1/2} \tag{2.5}$$

Equations (2.4) and (2.5) are fundamental in energy loss models used to calculate spatial dependence of energy loss in resist-coated substrates.

C. Energy Loss Models

Models for predicting the energy absorbed in a resist-coated substrate are very useful in understanding the effects of beam energy, incident dose, resist thickness, substrate materials, and pattern dependent exposure effects (proximity effects). Fundamental understanding of the manner in which electron energy is absorbed is analogous to understanding the manner in which photon radiation is absorbed in the photoresist conventionally used in the majority of semiconductor lithographic operations. Using models, contours of constant absorbed energy density can be studied and the influence of design and exposure parameters optimized. Under certain developer conditions such contours accurately simulate real images. The use of developer simulation models combined with calculations of absorbed energy density improves accuracy in simulating actual resist images. In this section, a brief description of both analytic and Monte Carlo models will be described with the aim of illustrating the manner in which important parameters influence the absorbed energy density. The reader is referred to the literature for more extensive treatments.* In Section III these models will be applied to calculate energy density contours and to describe proximity effects. Such models may also be used to evaluate the effectiveness of proximity correcting algorithms. Consider first the forward-scattered or primary electrons. When resist is exposed it is very desirable to have the exposure dominated by the flux of the primary electrons. Backscattered electrons can be thought of as producing a "fogging" exposure, which usually leads to detrimental results such as linewidth broadening and proximity effects (see Section III). Consequently if the exposure from primary electrons dominates, then the fogging effect of backscattered electrons is minimized. It is very important to

* Nosker (1969), Hawryluk and Smith (1972), Greeneich and Van Duzer (1973b), Greeneich (1973), Greeneich and Van Duzer (1974), Sintou (1973), Kyser and Murata (1974), Hawryluk et al. (1974), Kyser and Viswanathan (1975), and Murata et al. (1978).

understand the parameters affecting the forward-scattering electrons, particularly the dependence on beam voltage and resist thickness which strongly influence the broadening of the forward-scattered electrons.

Common to all models for the primary electron contribution is the separation of energy density into the product of the flux of electrons passing through an elemental volume surrounding the observation point and the rate of energy loss in that elemental volume;

$$\epsilon_{\delta p}(r, z_0) = F(E_0, r, z_0)\mathscr{E}(s, E_0) \qquad (2.6)$$

where F is the flux and $\mathscr{E}$ is the rate of energy loss. Two analytic models, the plural scattering model and the multiple scattering model, have been used extensively to calculate the energy density for primary scattering $\epsilon_{\delta p}$. Both models calculate the flux of electrons as if the resist above the plane of observation is a thin film of polymer material which can be replaced by an "effective scattering source" located at the top of the resist. The path length is assumed to be the distance between the effective source and the observation point (see Fig. 2.2). This assumption somewhat underestimates the path length but the error introduced is not significant except for very low energy electrons (≤ 5 keV). The two models described below, as their names suggest, differ in their interpretation of how many scattering events are encountered by the incident beam in arriving at the plane of observation. In general, the plural scattering model more accurately predicts results for typical writing conditions of energy and resist thickness encountered in electron-beam lithography; it is, however, computationally more difficult than the multiple scattering model.

It is convenient to characterize scattering in thin films by the average number of elastic events P_e which an energetic electron suffers in passing through the film. When energy loss is neglected, the parameter P_e is obtained by multiplying the single atom elastic-scattering cross section, which is the integral of Eq. (2.4), by the number of scattering centers. Thus

$$P_e = \pi Z^2 q^4 z_0 N_0 / A E_0^2 \theta_0^2 \qquad (2.7)$$

where z_0 is the film depth at which the flux is being determined. For typical electron resists Eq. (2.7) becomes

$$P_e = 400 z_0(\mu m)/E_0(keV) \qquad (2.8)$$

Hence at 20 keV and $z_0 = 0.5$ μm, $P_e = 10$ events. The number of events is very important since the amount of scattering increases exponentially with P_e and minimizing P_e is very desirable. Equation (2.8) also illustrates that equivalent scattering effects result for different combinations of resist

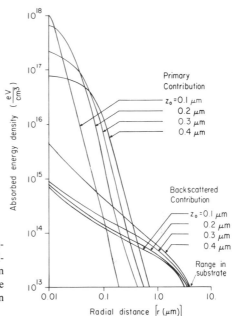

FIG. 2.6 Calculated absorbed energy density for primary and backscattered contributions at selected depths in a 0.4 μm PMMA film coated on an Al substrate (E_0 = 20 KeV. [From Greeneich and Van Duzer (1973b).]

depth and incident electron energy. Under conditions where resist exposures are dominated by the forward-scattered electrons, equivalent results can be obtained for two different resist thicknesses by scaling the incident beam energy. The distinction between plural and multiple scattering is determined by the value of P_e. For $P_e \leq 20–25$ events, scattering is plural and for larger values it is multiple, until a diffuse condition is reached at $\simeq 50$ events (Cosslett and Thomas, 1964a,b). As noted above, a typical resist exposure involves $\simeq 10$ events and hence this is in the plural-scattering regime. Since for both the plural and multiple-scattering theories the amount of scattering increases exponentially with P_e, it is very desirable to reduce P_e by increasing beam energy and reducing film thickness.

The details of the plural and multiple-scattering theories will not be included here but rather a typical result is presented. For the interested reader, the cited references contain details of the calculations.* Results from the plural-scattering model are shown in Fig. 2.6 which is a log–log plot of the absorbed energy density as a function of radial distance from the origin of an incident delta function beam. The simulated exposure conditions are for a 20 keV beam exposing 0.4 μm of PMMA resist coated

* Nosker (1969), Hawryluk and Smith (1972), Greeneich and Van Duzer (1973, 1974), and Greeneich (1973).

on an Al substrate. Although the substrate does not influence the forward-scattered electrons, it is included in the simulation for later reference in our discussion of backscattered electrons. Results are shown at various depths in the resist film; notice how the amplitude decreases and the distribution spreads out spatially as the electron beam penetrates deeper into the resist film. The significance of the number of elastic events is also apparent by comparing the results at a depth of 0.1 μm (2 events) to the results at a depth of 0.4 μm (8 events). It is also important to note that at small radial distances the absorbed energy density of the forward-scattered electrons in several orders of magnitude greater than the backscattered contribution. Although the multiple scattering theory gives *qualitatively* similar results as the plural model, it is not as accurate when less than 20 scattering events are involved. This is particularly significant when constant energy density contours are calculated throughout the depth of the resist, since a small number of events are always encountered near the surface of the resist.

Electrons backscattered from the substrate which return to the resist film can deposit substantial energy at large distances (several micrometers) from the beam center. This is an important contribution to the total energy absorbed by the resist because the resist integrates all of the contributing energies from all neighboring sources. Consequently, within a simple pattern element, the amount of exposure varies spatially and small pattern elements such as narrow lines require more incident electrons to reach the same dose as larger pattern elements such as large rectangles; this is called the intraproximity effect. Backscattered electrons are also responsible for exposure effects between closely spaced pattern elements. This is the interproximity effect. Proximity effects are described in more detail in Section III.

The details of simulation models for backscattered electrons will not be presented, but rather emphasis will be on the important parameters and their implications. Everhart (1960) has presented a simple method for computing the backscattering coefficient η, which is the ratio of the number of backscattered electrons to incident electrons. This analysis has been extended to form the basis of analytical backscattered electron simulations (Greeneich and Van Duzer, 1974; Hawryluk *et al.*, 1974). In this approach backscattered electrons are considered to be the result of *single* large angle scattering events. It is assumed that electrons deflected by less than 90° are not deflected at all and once an electron has suffered a large angle collision ($>90°$) it is not subsequently scattered. Picture the creation of backscattered electrons as an incident beam penetrates a resist-coated substrate. Two sources of backscattered electrons are present (see Fig. 2.2). One source is backscatter from within the resist. At some observation plane z_0 which lies above the resist–substrate interface there will be a contribution from backscattered electrons generated between z_0 and the interface. This contribution is usually small for typical resist materials. A much more important contribution comes from the substrate. Backscattered electrons are created within the substrate and some of these enter the resist to expose it at all planes within the resist (Fig. 2.2).

The total number of backscattered electrons is characterized by the backscattering coefficient η, which varies strongly with the type of substrate, moderately with the incident direction, and weakly with incident energy (Thornton, 1968). For a Si substrate at 20 keV, η is approximately 0.17, and for a Au substrate it is approximately 0.5. According to Everhart's theory (1960) for a normally incident beam on an uncoated substrate,

$$\eta = \frac{0.045Z - 1 + (0.5)^{0.045Z}}{1 + 0.045Z} \tag{2.9}$$

which is valid for $Z \le 60$. The backscattering coefficient is useful in assessing the relative effect of using different substrate and resist materials. The question arises, how much effect does an overlaying resist film have on η? It is expected that the actual ratio of backscattered electrons to incident electrons which return from the substrate to expose the resist is somewhat different from the value of η for an uncoated substrate. The difference arises because (a) the incident beam spreads and not all of the electrons enter the substrate along the normal direction, and (b) the energy of electrons entering the substrate is somewhat less than the incident beam energy. Table 2.1 illustrates this effect; Monte Carlo data for η for resist-coated substrates (Hawyrluk *et al.*, 1974) is compared with the

TABLE 2.1

Back Scattering Coefficients for Selected Materials

Substrate	Incident energy (keV)	Substrate range (μm)	η(uncoated) experimental	η(uncoated) calculated Eq. (2.9)	PMMA coating thickness	η(coated)
Silicon $Z = 14$	20	4.8	0.17	0.17	4000 Å	0.182
Silicon $Z = 14$	10	2.1	0.186	0.17	4000 Å	0.242
Silicon $Z = 14$	20	4.8	0.17	0.17	10000 Å	0.213
Permalloy $Z = 27.6$	20	1.6	—	0.30	—	—
Copper $Z = 29$	20	1.6	0.319	0.31	4000 Å	0.332
GaAs $Z = 33$	20	3.7	—	0.34	—	—
Silver $Z = 47$	20	1.7	0.42	0.43	—	—
Gold $Z = 79$	20	1.1	0.51	0.58	4000 Å	0.538

experimental data (Thornton, 1968) and the results of Eq. (2.9) for uncoated substrates. It is apparent that the backscattered contribution is well characterized by calculated values of η. It is clear that use of a low atomic number substrate reduces the backscattered contribution and consequently proximity effects are minimized and resolution is improved. The second important parameter in the backscattered contribution is the distance over which the contribution is significant; this distance is characterized by the Bethe range in the substrate. This is indeed the characteristic distance because a backscattered electron is often the result of a single large angle event and once created it could travel in a nearly straight line until its energy approaches zero. Bethe ranges for silicon and other substrates are presented in Fig. 2.4 and Table 2.1. Backscattered contributions over several micrometers are possible.

The results for the backscattered contribution at various depths z_0 in a 0.4 μm PMMA resist film coated on an aluminum substrate are shown in Fig. 2.6. Aluminum ($Z = 13$) was chosen as being representative of materials encountered in IC fabrication, such as Si ($Z = 14$), SiO_2 ($Z = 10$), Si_3N_4 ($Z = 10$), Al itself, and their multilayer combinations. For example, the atomic number, density, and substrate range of Si is very similar to that of Al. Figure 2.6 shows that the backscattered contribution has a much smaller amplitude at small radial distances compared to the forward scattered contribution, but the backscattered contribution remains significant over larger spatial distances on the order of the range in the substrate. The backscattered contribution from within the resist is spread out over an even larger range; however, its amplitude is small at distances larger than the substrate range. The effect of higher atomic number substrate materials is important. The results for Al, Cu, and Ag substrates are compared in Fig. 2.7 where the delta function response is plotted as a function of radial distance normalized to the substrate range. Results for permalloy substrates such as used in bubble memory device fabrication would be similar to those for copper since they have similar atomic number and density. Gallium arsenide substrates would give similar results except for a somewhat different density and hence electron range. When results are normalized to the range as in Fig. 2.7, the difference in range is not important. The increased backscattered contribution to the absorbed energy density for materials having higher atomic numbers is not, as one might expect, due solely to the increased number of backscattered electrons for the higher Z materials. The dominant effect is the range in the substrate, which is considerably smaller for Cu and Ag, and hence the backscattered electrons come out in a smaller area around the incident beam. The ranges for Cu and Ag are nearly the same, and hence the difference in their backscattered contribution is due to the increased number of backscattered electrons for Ag compared to Cu.

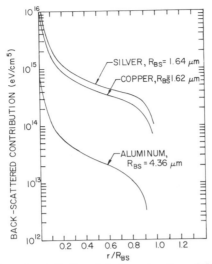

FIG. 2.7   The backscattered contribution plotted as a function of radial distance normalized to the range in the substrate for Al, Cu, and Ag. (PMMA $T = 0.4$ μm, $E_0 - 20$ KeV, $Z_0 = 0.4$ μm.)

Monte Carlo methods have been used extensively to calculate the absorbed energy density in resist coated substrates, to study backscattered electrons, secondary electron emission, and x-ray production.* The Monte Carlo technique is simple in concept and offers somewhat better accuracy than the analytic techniques described above; however, large expenditures of computer time are required (several tens of CPU minutes on a high speed computer). If one of the parameters such as polymer thickness, substrate composition, or beam energy is changed, another complete computation is required.

In the Monte Carlo technique an individual electron is followed as it penetrates the solid and undergoes angular deflection and energy loss. The direction of scattering is chosen by a random number which is weighted by the screened Rutherford expression [Eq. (2.4)] for the scattering cross section. The Bethe expression [Eq. (2.2)] is used to calculate the energy loss between distinct scattering events. The distance between scattering events is taken as the mean free path, which is a function of the energy after the last scattering event. When the target is multilayered, care must be taken to follow the electrons across the discontinuities in materials. If the target materials comprise more than one atomic species, the probability for scattering by a particular atom is weighted by its frac-

* Sintou (1973), Kyser and Murata (1974), Hawryluk *et al.* (1974), Kyser and Viswanathan (1975), and Murata *et al.* (1978).

tional cross section. This technique simulates the actual penetration and scattering of a real electron beam.

The accuracy of this calculation is heavily dependent on the chosen model for the differential cross section and the method of computing energy loss, as well as on the use of a large number of trajectories. The statistical accuracy increases as $(n)^{1/2}$ where n is the number of trajectories. Typical results for 100 trajectories for 10 and 20 keV electrons incident on 0.4 μm of PMMA on Si were shown in Fig. 2.3a,b. Notice the trajectories of backscattered electrons that are generated in the substrate and reenter the resist. Such plots of electron trajectories show qualitatively the effect of beam voltage on the extent of both forward and backscattered electrons. For example, the lateral extent and volume of scattering depends on the electron range and varies as $E_0^{1.7}$. At 10 keV the lateral extent is 1 μm while at 20 keV it is 3.2 μm. When the Monte Carlo technique is applied to a calculation of the absorbed energy density in a resist-coated substrate, the results are very similar to those shown in Fig. 2.6 for the analytic model. Compared to Monte Carlo results, the plural model gives good results while the multiple-scattering model is less accurate, particularly at small depths (low number of elastic events), where it underestimates the absorbed energy density at small radial distances. The multiple-scattering model also has a failure at the resist–substrate interface where the energy density falls rapidly to zero at small radial distances compared to the results obtained with either the Monte Carlo or plural scattering models. The results of the large angle backscattered analytic model compares reasonably well with Monte Carlo results for low atomic number materials ($Z \le 30$), although the former method overestimates the contribution at large radial distances (near the substrate range). These deficiencies are expected in light of the many simplifying assumptions involved, particularly the assumption of only one scattering event to characterize backscatter. It is well known that backscattered electrons are generally the result of several medium angle collisions and many small angle collisions for high atomic number materials. Nevertheless, these calculations provide a very useful insight into the electron–substrate interaction.

D. Approximate Analytic Functions and Convolutions

The use of complex analytic or Monte Carlo calculations is expensive in that large computer programs and computing times are required. A change in exposure conditions requires additional calculations. Consequently approximate analytic functions are useful for giving first-order information when a variety of exposure conditions and/or pattern geometries are involved. For example, the study of proximity effects can be facilitated by suitable approximate analytic expressions.

The use of Gaussian functions to approximate the absorbed energy density has been proposed for both the forward and backscattered responses (Chang, 1975; Parikh and Kyser, 1978). There are two reasons for utilizing such approximate functions. They are (1) to reduce computation time when calculating total energy deposition for proximity effects for large high density patterns, and (2) to facilitate convolution of calculated delta function responses with real incident beam shapes. Chang's work was motivated by the desire to correct proximity effects for closely spaced geometries; the Gaussian functions which he used were based on the limited available experimental data. Using results from Monte Carlo calculations, Parikh and Kyser have proposed the following formulation:

$$\epsilon(r) = k[\exp(-r^2/\beta_f^2) + \eta_e(\beta_f^2/\beta_b^2)\exp(-r^2/\beta_b^2)] \tag{2.10}$$

where β_f and β_h are the characteristic half-widths of the forward and backscattered distributions. If we define the integrals of the forward and backscattered distributions as I_f and I_b, respectively, then

$$\eta_e = I_b/I_f \tag{2.11}$$

where

$$I_i = 2\pi \int_0^\infty r\,dr\,\exp(-r^2/\beta_i^2) \tag{2.12}$$

The reason Eq. (2.10) is written in the form shown is to define the parameter η_e, which has some physical interpretation, namely, the ratio of the contribution to the total energy disposition due to backscattered electrons compared to forward-scattered electrons. The parameter η_e should not be confused with the backscattering coefficient [Eq. (2.9)], but rather it contains information on the relative amount of energy absorbed in the resist due to backscattering.

Equation (2.10) must be used with caution; it is an approximation which does not apply in some situations. Figures 2.8a–2.8c illustrate three situations where actual Monte Carlo data is compared with Gaussian functions. In each of these figures the logarithm of the absorbed energy density at a depth z_0 in the resist film is plotted against the square of the radial distance from beam center. Figure 2.8a shows the results for the forward-scattered electrons. The solid curve represents the Gaussian fit. A closer fit to the forward distribution is realized by use of a double Gaussian fit to the forward distribution as indicated by the dashed lines in Figure 2.8a. Figures 2.8b and 2.8c compare the backscattered results for Si and Cu substrates. It is apparent that a single Gaussian fit is very good for low

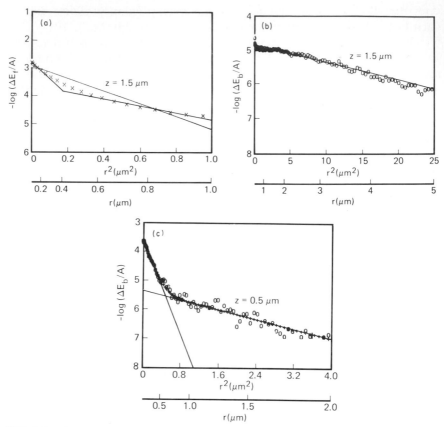

FIG. 2.8 Plot of radial distribution of absorbed energy density in (a) forward scattered (1.5 μm PMMA on Si, 25 keV), (b) backward scattered electrons from Si (1.5 μm PMMA on Si, 25 keV), and (c) backscattered electrons from Cu (0.5-μm PMMA on Cu, 15 keV). The symbols represent actual Monte Carlo data while the solid lines indicate the fit of single and double gaussian approximation functions. [From Parikh and Kyser, 1978.]

atomic number materials (e.g., Si), but a double Gaussian fit is better for higher Z materials. Mathematically for high Z materials the backscattered energy density $\epsilon_{\delta s}$ is

$$\epsilon_{\delta s} = \frac{\eta_e}{1 + \eta_{ds}} \frac{\beta_f^2}{\beta_{bs}^2} \exp\left(\frac{-r^2}{\beta_{bs}^2}\right) + \eta_{ds} \frac{\beta_{bs}^2}{\beta_{bd}^2} \exp\left(\frac{-r^2}{\beta_{bd}^2}\right) \qquad (2.13)$$

where β_{ds} and β_{bd} are the half-widths of the sharp and diffuse distributions, respectively, and

$$\eta_{ds} = I_{bd}/I_{bs} \qquad (2.14)$$

where the integrals are found from Eq. (2.12). In spite of the limitations involved with Eqs. (2.10) and (2.13), such formulations are useful in *qualitatively* predicting energy distributions and in estimating proximity effects.

What are values of the parameters β_f, β_b, and η_e? While some experimental data are known, much of this data is not necessarily unique and the techniques used to determine the parameters are open to interpretation. Parikh and Kyser (1978) have used Monte Carlo calculations to tabulate values of β_f, β_b, and η_e. They also discuss the available experimental data. Since the forward-scattered distribution is independent of substrate, values of β_f can be plotted, as in Fig. 2.9, as a function of the number of elastic events P_e; this result can be used for any substrate. The curve is a smooth fit to the Monte Carlo data extracted from the work of Parikh and Kyser (1978). The data illustrate once again the usefulness of representing the forward-scattered electrons by the number of elastic events. The backscattered distributions differ depending on the atomic number of the substrate. Results for Si, Cu, and Au substrates are tabulated in Table 2.2; single Gaussian data are used for the Si substrate while double Gaussian data are used for Cu and Au substrates. Values of the parameters η_e and η_{ds} are also recorded in Table 2.2 Note the near constancy of η_e for a given substrate and its increase with increasing atomic number. Recent experimental (Grobman and Speth (1978); Jones and Hatzakis (1978)) and theoretical work (Greeneich, 1979) indicate that the value of η_e for a Si substrate is ~0.9 rather than ≈0.5 value calculated by Parikh and Kyser (1978).

Thus far the simulations of resist scattering have only been concerned with an incident delta function beam of electrons. While this is an

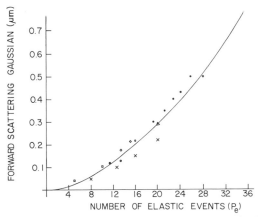

FIG. 2.9 Characteristic half-width for forward scattered electrons is shown as a function of the number of elastic events. × = 10 kV, ○ = 15 kV, △ = 20 kV, ● = 25 kV, ◇ = 30 kV, ■ = 35 kV, □ = 40 kV. [Data is from the work of Parikh and Kyser (1978).]

TABLE 2.2

Coefficients Used in the Gaussian Approximations for Absorbed Energy Density

Substrate	Energy	Resist thickness	β_b or β_{bs}	β_{bd}	η_e	η_{ds}
Si	10	0.5	0.65	—	0.51	—
Si	15	0.5	1.14	—	0.51	—
Si	15	1.0	1.41	—	0.52	—
Si	25	0.5	2.6	—	0.51	—
Si	25	1.0	2.9	—	0.49	—
Si	25	1.5	2.9	—	0.52	—
Si	40	0.5	6.0	—	0.42	—
Si	40	1.0	6.0	—	0.45	—
Si	40	1.5	6.2	—	0.44	—
Cu	10	0.5	0.23	0.8	0.60	0.66
Cu	15	0.5	0.33	1.0	0.60	0.19
Cu	25	1.0	0.77	3.0	0.65	0.19
Cu	40	1.0	1.43	3.6	0.63	0.16
Au	10	0.5	0.16	0.5	0.65	0.9
Au	15	0.5	0.16	0.8	0.76	0.24
Au	25	1.0	0.37	1.4	0.79	0.28
Au	40	1.0	0.64	4.0	0.82	0.15

extremely useful approach from conceptual and computational aspects, real beam shapes need to be considered. Using the delta function response, the effects of many different real beam shapes can be analyzed by convolution. The convolution technique is similar to the use of an impulse response in circuit theory to analyze many different source waveforms. Actual electron beams are usually taken to be Gaussian, or in the case of a rectangular beam with real edges, the shape can be synthesized out of multiple Gaussian spots with characteristic half-widths corresponding to the real edge slope. Consequently the convolved response ϵ, is found to be

$$\epsilon(r, z_0) = \int_0^{2\pi} d\theta' \int_0^{\infty} r' \, dr' \, \epsilon_\delta(r', z_0) \exp(-|r - r'|^2/\beta_g^2) \quad (2.15)$$

where β_g is the incident Gaussian half-width. If the Gaussian functions are used to approximate the delta function response, then Eq. (2.15) can be evaluated analytically, and Eq. (2.10) can be used with the modification

$$\beta_i \rightarrow (\beta_i^2 + \beta_g^2)^{1/2}$$

Thus the effects of electron scattering are added in the rms sense to the incident Gaussian beam. This treatment is much like that used with electron-optical aberrations. Indeed it is very useful to characterize the effects of electron scattering in terms of an electron-scattering aberration. Under conditions where forward scattering dominates, the value of β_f

taken from Fig. 2.7 may be convolved with the writing beam width and an optimization can be performed. In this way, the choice of resist thickness, beam energy, and developer strategy affects the resolution and reflects on the design of the electron-beam machine. In the next section the influence of electron scattering on electron-beam writing strategies, choice of beam energy, resist resolution, and proximity effects will be examined.

III.   RESIST IMAGES

In the previous section, the physical foundation and modeling of electron scattering in resist-coated substrates was presented. Various key parameters, such as the number of elastic events, the backscattering coefficient, and the substrate range were introduced and their variations with beam energies and materials discussed. The remaining issues are the way in which electron scattering affects resist images and the tradeoffs in writing strategies, resolution, beam energy, and proximity effects. This section is concerned with these issues.

A.   Energy Density Profiles

One of the most illustrative methods for presenting the results of simulated electron scattering and energy absorption is to view a cross section of the resist and plot contours of constant energy absorption. Results for a single line scan are shown in Fig. 2.10 for three different beam energies. Contours of constant energy density are shown; the outer contours in each case represent 3.3 times the dose of the inner contours. The contours

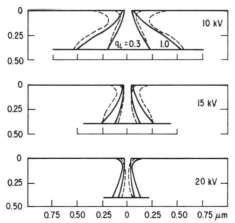

FIG. 2.10   A comparison of developed profiles (dashed lines) and theoretical profile (solid lines) for 0.4 μm PMMA on Si substrate. The incident dose is expressed as the charge per unit length q_1, in units of 10^{-8} C/cm. [From Greeneich and Van Duzer (1973b).]

in Fig. 2.10 represent the latent resist image—that is, the image independent of developer effects. Using the information contained in the constant energy density contours as an input into a developer simulation model, actual resist images can be predicted [see, for example, Van Duzer *et al.* (1976), Neurether (1978) and Greeneich (1979)]. For electron-beam exposures, such modeling shows that, for example, resist images evolve with time. For present purposes, it is very instructive to assume, as a *first-order approximation,* that for a constant developer time the developer removes resist out to a constant energy density contour and no further. As a consequence, the curves in Fig. 2.10 represent developed contours. The dotted lines in Fig. 2.10 show a comparison with experimental data of Wolf *et al.* (1971). Except for the rounding near the top of the resist, which is due to developer effects, the modeling of the resist image is rather good. Note how strongly and nonlinearily the shapes depend on beam energy and dose. The useful resolution of the developed image depends on its application; the way regist images are used influences the way they should be shaped. (See Section V.B and Chapter 4.) Under any definition of linewidth, it can be concluded from Fig. 2.10 that under identical conditions of resist thickness, dose, and substrate, the resolution is improved at higher energies. This is hardly surprising, since the effect of electron scattering decreases at higher energies. The next section considers this subject in more detail.

B.   Resolution and Linewidth Control

When discussing linewidth and resolution in electron-beam generated resist images, a distinction must be made between the smallest linewidth (resolution) obtainable under a given set of exposure conditions by a single pass of the beam and the capability to obtain a desired linewidth. In the former, the linewidth represents the obtainable resolution and is a fundamental property of the exposure conditions and resist properties. The capability of obtaining the linewidth specified by a circuit design is usually accomplished by the use of several passes of the beam in closely spaced proximity; typically four passes of the beam spaced at the Gaussian half-width of the beam are used to generate the minimum feature size in the circuit designer's pattern. Such a writing strategy improves linewidth control. In this section, the fundamental resolution is examined as a function of dose and energy, and the influence of different writing strategies on the ability to obtain a designed linewidth is described.

Consider a single line scan made with a small diameter electron beam. Very small linewidths are possible (≤ 0.05 μm) as evidenced by the profiles shown in Fig. 2.10. Narrow lines made by a single pass of the beam are of importance both from a fundamental viewpoint and in the fabrica-

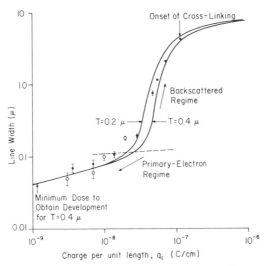

FIG. 2.11 The linewidth as a function of incident charge per unit length for PMMA resist. The data is from Wolf *et al.* (1971); open circles (SiO$_2$ − Si, T = 0.4 μm) and Greeneich and Van Duzer (1974), solid circles (glass, $T = 0.3\mu$m). $E_0 = 20$ keV; PMM on Al; $\epsilon_c = 6.8 \times 10^{21}$ eV/cm^3. [From of Greeneich and Van Duzer (1974) and reproduced with permission of the IEEE.]

tion of specialty devices, such as acoustic surface wave transducers (Ozdemir *et al.*, 1973). In many process situations, such as the metal lift-off technique (see Section V), the linewidth is determined by the smallest region or neck in the developed resist profile, such as illustrated in Fig. 2.10. Defining linewidth in this manner, the linewidth as a function of the incident line dose, coulombs per centimeter may be plotted as shown in Figs. 2.11 and 2.12. In Fig. 2.11 experimental data are compared with theoretical predictions for a single pass of a 200 Å, 20 kV beam on 0.2–0.4 μm of PMMA coated on a low atomic number substrate. The theoretical predictions were based on a developer model that assumed development out to a critical energy level; this assumption is reasonably accurate for the weak developers used in the actual experiments. The critical energy density for development was taken as 6.8 × 10^{21} eV/cm^3. Two interesting features are observed in Fig. 2.11. The dotted line represents the linewidth at which half the energy density is contributed by primary electrons and half by backscattered electrons. Consequently, at low doses the linewidth is dominated by the primary electrons and the slope of the curve is low.

At higher doses the backscattered electrons dominate; the slope is large. The response begins to flatten as the linewidth approaches twice the range in the substrate. Figure 2.12 illustrates the expected linewidth variation for a finely focused beam for 10, 15, and 20 keV beam energies. Note

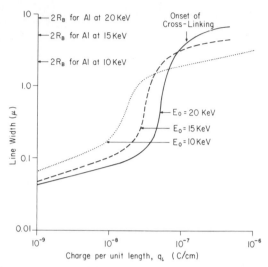

FIG. 2.12   The linewidth as a function of dose for 10, 15, and 20 keV beam energies (PMM, $T = 0.4 \mu$, Al substrate). [From Greeneich and Van Duzer (1974) and reproduced with permission of the IEEE.]

that the linewidth is smaller at low incident doses for the higher beam energies; this is a consequence of less scattering at high energies. At large doses the linewidths approach twice the substrate range, and lower beam energies result in smaller linewidths. Experimental data illustrating this behavior has been reported by Hawryluk et al. (1975). From a practical view, it is desirable to expose the resist in the region dominated by the primary (forward) scattered electrons, and hence conditions favoring a small number of elastic events should be utilized. This condition implies high beam energies and thin resist films. Furthermore, identical results can be obtained for a variety of resist thicknesses if the beam energy is scaled to keep the number of events identical. It would appear then that increasing beam voltage is very desirable; however, two other considerations are also important. The first of these is a required increase in resist exposure; according to the Bethe relationship [Eq. (2.2)] the rate of energy loss per electron decreases as beam energy is increased and consequently more electrons are required to reach a required critical energy density. The second limiting aspect in using very high voltage beams is the proximity effect; as energy increases the substrate range increases and consequently there is more interaction between closely spaced features. This subject is discussed in more depth later (Section III.C).

Consider the influence of electron scattering on the capability of obtaining the designed linewidth specified by a given circuit design (Greeneich, 1979). It is worthwhile to examine how various choices of writing strategy, as exemplified by beam energy, spot size, and the number of beam address points per linewidth influence that linewidth. Calculations of absorbed energy density are presented which utilize the double Gaussian approximation presented in Section II.D. Furthermore, the linewidth will be defined by the width in the pattern at the resist–substrate interface; such a definition is particularly useful when the resist image is used as mask against an etching environment.

In comparing the effects of various exposure conditions, interest is focused on obtaining a predetermined linewidth and knowledge of the sensitivity of that linewidth to the parameters under consideration. The situation is shown in Fig. 2.13a, where linewidth L is specified in the topographic layout of the circuit design. It is assumed that the line is made by several scans each with an incident Gaussian current distribution. The interscan distance is the pixel dimension P_x. The beam center is at the center of the pixel stripe, as indicated in Fig. 2.13a. In Fig. 2.13b the absorbed energy density ϵ at the resist–substrate interface is shown as a function of spatial position x across the desired linewidth. The critical energy density for development is shown by the dashed line labeled ϵ_{dev} as shown in Fig. 2.13b, and consequently the linewidth extends from $-X_0$ to $+X_0$. If, for example, the incident dose is increased by a small amount, the energy density will be given by the dotted line in Fig. 2.13b, and the developed linewidth will be L'. Alternatively, if the developer conditions

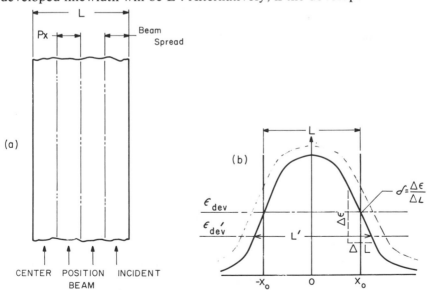

FIG. 2.13 Schematic representation of (a) topographical description of line of width L made by four passes of a Gaussian beam and (b) energy density at resist–substrate interface illustrating the concept of edge slope.

were changed to a level ϵ'_{dev} (Fig. 2.13b), then the linewidth would also be L'. It is useful to introduce the concept of edge slope δ, which is defined by

$$\delta \equiv \Delta\epsilon/\Delta L = |\epsilon(X_0 + 0.05L) - \epsilon(X_0 - 0.05L)|/(0.1L) \qquad (2.16)$$

where L is the desired linewidth and X_0 represents the absorbed energy density at the edge of the line (see Fig. 2.13b). This definition corresponds to a $\pm 5\%$ variation in linewidth. The edge slope is a measure of how sensitive the linewidth is to changes in dose, developer conditions, beam shape, and pixel dimension. To minimize linewidth changes, it is desirable to maximize the edge slope.

Figure 2.14 is a plot of the edge slope as a function of the incident Gaussian half-width for 25, 15, and 7.5 kV beam energies. It is assumed that four passes of the beam are used in writing each line and the spacing between passes equals the half-width. Data for a minimum desired linewidth of 2.0 μm, which is typical for fabricating optical masks by electron beam, is shown in Fig. 2.14a, while data for a minimum designed linewidth of 0.5 μm, which is typical of direct wafer writing, is shown in Fig. 2.14b. For convenience, the edge slope has been normalized to the value δ_0, which is the value corresponding to $\beta_g = 0.5$ μm, $L = 2.0$ μm, and 25 keV beam energy. The absolute value of δ_0 is not really important; what is

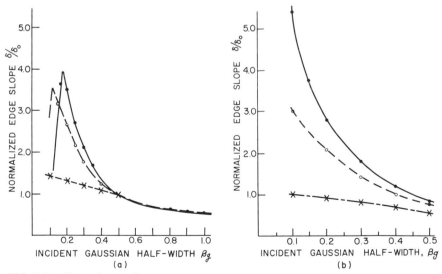

FIG. 2.14 Plots of normalized edge slope as a function of the incident gaussian half-width ($\bullet$ = 25 keV, $\bigcirc$ = 15 keV $\times$ = 7.5 keV) for (a) 2.0 μm linewidth (0.50 μm resist, Si substrate) and (b) 0.5 μm linewidths (0.50 μm resist, Si substrate assuming 4 pixels per linewidth.

important is the change in δ under different exposure conditions. It is evident from Figs. 2.14a and 2.14b that increasing beam energy and decreasing the beam half-width increases the edge slope, and hence linewidth control is improved. For the 2.0 μm linewidth, notice that for sufficiently small beam half-widths and at high energies, the edge slope decreases. At high energy and when the beam width is reduced, the energy deposited in the exposure oscillates with position, and for sufficiently small beam half-widths, the troughs in the oscillation become very deep. The resulting edge slope is small. In essence the 2.0 μm line is trying to be created by four passes of a very narrow beam spaced at 0.5 μm intervals, and the individual scan lines are resolved in the resist.

In the design and application of scanning Gaussian electron-beam machines, the number of address structures or pixels per linewidth is typically taken as four and the beam half-width is matched to the pixel element. This combination is designed to give a flat-top shaped exposure, as illustrated by the solid curve in Fig. 2.15a. The desired linewidth is taken as 0.50 μm. It has already been demonstrated that the edge slope improves as the Gaussian half-width is reduced. The solid curve in Fig. 2.15b illustrates the absorbed energy density for a half-width equal to half the address structure, while the solid curve in Fig. 2.15c illustrates the exposure at the resist–substrate interface after the 25 keV beam has passed through 0.5 μm of resist. By the time the beam reaches the interface, the ripples have been smoothed by electron scattering.

Consider the effect of the number of pixels per minimum linewidth. The dashed curves in Figs. 2.15a–2.15c illustrate the identical exposure conditions made by (a) two pixels, 0.25 μm half-width, (b) two pixels, 0.125 μm half-width, and (c) same as (b) but with the response plotted at the interface. It is known from experiment that acceptable 0.5 μm images can be made with four pixels of 0.125 μm half-width. Furthermore, it appears from Fig. 2.15 that two pixels of 0.125 μm half-width on 0.25 μm address structure also yields acceptable exposures. Since machine throughput is strongly related to the number of address points per minimum geometry (Chapter 3), the exposure speed might be increased by a factor of four in this second strategy provided the exposure is not limited by resist sensitivity or beam current.

The effect of electron scattering on relative edge slope can be treated as an aberration in much the same way as spherical and chromatic aberrations are used in designing the electron probe of the writing machine. Using the Gaussian approximation to model the electron scattering, the effective Gaussian half-width β_{eff} becomes

$$\beta_{\mathrm{eff}} = (\beta_{\mathrm{f}}^2 + \beta_{\mathrm{g}}^2)^{1/2} \tag{2.17}$$

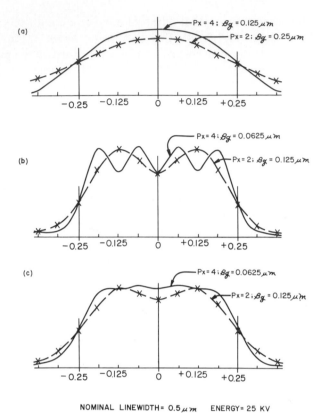

NOMINAL LINEWIDTH= $0.5\,\mu m$ ENERGY= 25 KV

FIG. 2.15   The absorbed energy density as a function of position perpendicular to a line scan for a nominal 0.5 μm width illustrating the effects of beam half-width and the number of pixels per linewidth on edge slope. (a) Resist surface: $\beta_g = 0.125$ μm, four pixels, and $\beta_g = 0.25$ μm, two pixels; (b) resist surface: $\beta_g = 0.0625$ μm, four pixels, and $\beta_g = 0.125$ μm, two pixels; and (c) same as (b) except at resist–substrate interface.

where β_f is the half-width for the forward scattered Gaussian and β_g is the incident beam half-width. A universal plot of relative slope δ/δ_0 versus β_{eff}, shown in Fig. 2.16, verifies the merit of this approach. The data are taken from the various exposure conditions tabulated in the insert to Fig. 2.16.

The use of electron-scattering simulation to calculate edge slopes for a desired linewidth has been illustrated in Figs. 2.14–2.16. Several important conclusions may be summarized as follows. (1) Electron scattering can be treated as an aberration in predicting the effect of various exposure conditions on edge slope. (2) High beam energies (typically 25 keV) are effective in reducing the forward-scattered half-width and thereby improving edge slope. (3) Reducing the incident beam half-width to approxi-

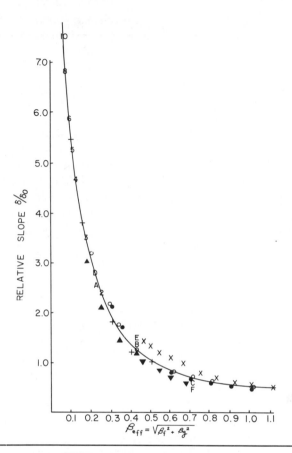

Symbol	Energy	Resist Thk.	Line width	# Pixels	β_g
●	25	0.5	2.0	4	
○	15	0.5	2.0	4	
×	7.5	0.5	2.0	4	
+	25	0.5	0.5	4	
▲	15	0.5	0.5	4	
▼	7.5	0.5	0.5	4	
1–10	25	0.5	0.5	1–10	
A, B, C	25	1.0, 1.5, 2.0	0.5	4	0.125
D, E, F	25	1.0, 1.5, 2.0	0.5	4	0.625

FIG. 2.16 A universal plot of relative edge slope as a function of effective beam half-width.

mately one-half the address distance improves edge slope. (4) The use of two pixels per linewidth can give acceptable resist images and result in faster writing.

C. Proximity Effects

Perhaps the most serious aspect of electron scattering in the resist and substrate is the proximity effect.* Electron scattering over large distances, i.e., up to several micrometers, contributes to the total energy deposited at any given point in the resist. This means that the energy absorbed at a given point in the resist depends upon the "proximity" of adjacent exposures. In the center of a large area of exposure, such as at point A in Fig. 2.17, there are many contributions from the surrounding incident electrons. Unfortunately, corners and edges of exposed patterns do not receive the same total dose. For example, the edge, point B, receives half the dose of point A, and the corner, point C, receives one-fourth the dose of A. The resist is usually developed out to a level represented by the best fit to the desired pattern—this corresponds to development out to the absorbed energy density at the edge of the pattern. The shaded area in Fig. 2.17 shows schematically the developed image. The result is that the corners are not developed out to their desired position. This is termed the intraproximity effect—that is, the positional nonuniform absorbed energy density *within* an exposed area. This effect reduces pattern fidelity. Another example of the intraproximity effect is illustrated by the long narrow line shown at the left in Fig. 2.17. If because the optimal incident dose and developer conditions are chosen to produce the proper edge at point B, there will not be enough exposure in narrow lines, and when developed, the images will be too narrow. Since backscattered electrons extend over large distances, there can be cooperative

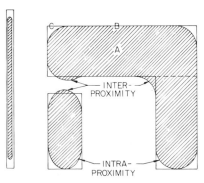

FIG. 2.17   A schematic illustration of inter- and intraproximity effects.

* Greeneich and Van Duzer (1973), Hawryluk *et al.* (1974), Chang (1975), Parikh (1978a,b), Sewell (1978), and Youngman and Wittels (1978).

exposure effects between adjacent patterns when they are closely spaced together. This effect results in bulging of patterns toward each other, and under extreme conditions actual bridging may occur; refer again to Fig. 2.17. This is the *inter*proximity effect. Fortunately, proximity effects can be corrected.

The distance over which proximity effects appear is a function of the electron energy. In particular, high energy exposures have large exposure tails, on the order of the range in the substrate. Consequently, patterns separated by distances less than that range will experience cooperative effects. Using the range–energy relationship, e.g., Fig. 2.4, the maximum distance over which interproximity effects are important may be estimated. For example, in Si the maximum distances are 1.4 and 7.0 μm for 10 and 25 keV beam energies, respectively. The magnitude of the cooperative exposure is a strong function of the distance between exposures.

How close exposures may be spaced is determined by the individual requirements on pattern fidelity. It is clear, however, that for submicron gaps between exposures, interproximity effects are very important and compensation methods are needed. Early efforts in proximity effect correction techniques utilized empirical methods to alter locally the dose so that critically exposed areas were properly exposed. This is in fact still a powerful method for experimental work and can lead to some very useful rules in developing more sophisticated correction methodology. Chang (1975) has successfully used experimentally measured promimity functions for correction of large area bubble memory patterns; however, more general methods for correction are required for arbitrary patterns.

Parikh (1978a,b) has analyzed various alternative methods of solving the proximity effect, developed an implementation procedure for large area, high density patterns, and experimentally verified its usefulness. This technique requires experimentally determined scattering parameters and an iterative procedure to arrive at satisfactory results. In this technique, the desired pattern is divided into primitive shapes, such as trapezoids and rectangles, much like the information used in vector scan machines (Chapter 3). Parikh utilizes a self-consistent technique which alters the incident dose in each primitive shape so that the average dose in each shape is equal. In the vector-scan machine used by Parikh, the dose in each primitive shape was altered by changing the beam dwell time in each shape as needed. This approach is mathematically attractive since a unique solution results—that is, only one parameter, the incident dose, for each shape is altered to give satisfactory experimental results. For N total shapes, correction requires the solution of N simultaneous equations. For large area high density patterns, the practical implementation of the correction algorithm requires clever partitioning of the patterns. Figure 2.18 shows a before-and-after correction of a pattern written in

PMMA resist. In Fig. 2.18a both inter- and intraproximity effects may be observed.

Note in Fig. 2.18a the incomplete development of the narrow lines (intraproximity effect) and the bulging between closely spaced patterns (interproximity effect). Since only the average dose per shape is altered with this technique, adequate pattern fidelity may require subdividing the primitive shape into many smaller shapes and adjusting the dose in each shape. This approach increases computer computation and the machine overhead times during pattern writing.

Sewell (1978) has reported a successful pattern correction technique based on altering the shapes of the patterns to correct not only for proper resist exposure, but for etch bias effects. In essence this technique recognizes that under a given set of exposure, develop, and etch conditions, only a single shape will conform exactly to the design dimension; this is called a control pattern. All other patterns will deviate in their dimensions. By experimentally measuring the change in dimensions compared to a control pattern, a set of tables can be generated. This technique allows the input shapes to the electron-beam system to be altered in such a manner that the desired dimensions for all patterns is achieved after development. This technique has not only been applied to a scanning electron-beam system, but in addition to an electron-image projector. Although this latter system is not quite as flexible as altering the dose for each pattern shape, adequate pattern definition has been shown. Sewell reports that a ± 0.10 μm linewidth tolerance can be maintained on all pattern features down to 0.5 μm.

A technique which combines dose control and alteration of pattern shapes is a very flexible method of correcting proximity effects to obtain developed contours matching desired design dimensions. Youngman and Wittels (1978) have described such a technique. In their computer program, they allow not only the incident dose, but the pattern dimensions to vary in order to contour fit the resulting pattern to the design dimension. With this technique, the most sensitive region of the desired pattern may be tailored to achieve excellent pattern fidelity. Figures 2.19a and 2.19b illustrate a pattern with and without proximity effect correction. In Fig. 2.19b the various stages of pattern description are shown; notice the various rectangle sizes and gaps shown in the box description of the desired pattern. One disadvantage of the contour fitting technique is that large amounts of computer time are required compared with the equal average dose technique.

It is apparent that, although proximity effects can seriously degrade pattern fidelity, there are several compensation methods that can be used to achieve adequate pattern fidelity. Further work to simplify computer algorithms would be useful. Also, it should be noted that the use of multilayer resist techniques (Section V) can be used to reduce electron backscattering and associated proximity effects (Grobman et al., 1978).

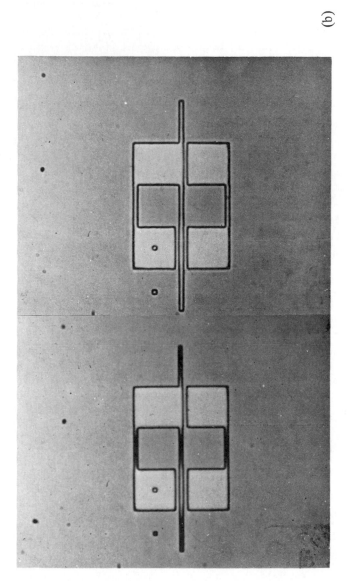

(b)

(a)

FIG. 2.18 Proximity effect pattern: (a) optical micrograph showing an uncorrected pattern which shows both inter- and intraproximity effects. The smallest dimension is 1 μm; (b) optical micrograph showing a corrected pattern. [From of Parikh (1978a&b)]

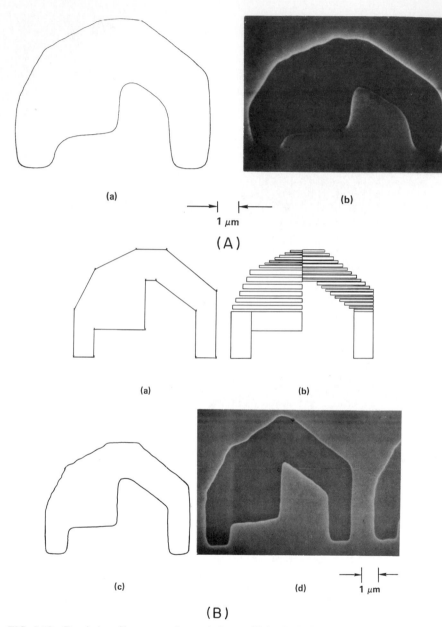

(a)

1 μm

(A)

(a)   (b)

(c)   (d)   1 μm

(B)

FIG. 2.19 Proximity effect correction technique utilizing both dose control and pattern altering techniques: (A) predicted and actual patterns which are uncorrected; (B) pattern correction techniques showing predicted and actual pattern. [From Youngman and Wittels, (1978) and reproduced with permission of SPIE.]

IV. ELECTRON–RESIST CHARACTERISTICS

A. *Positive–Negative Resists*

The capability of an electron-beam machine to create high resolution patterns can only be realized if suitable electron-sensitive materials are available to record the desired pattern information. Furthermore, these materials must be resistant to subsequent processing steps, such as chemical etching, which transfers this image into the metallic or dielectric layers required in device fabrication. Such materials are termed electron resists by analogy to photo-resist materials used in pattern definition by photon exposure. Electron resists are almost exclusively organic polymers of high molecular weight.

When an organic polymer is subjected to electron radiation, the absorbed energy induces chemical changes in the polymer that affect both its physical and chemical properties. Since the energy of penetrating electrons is much larger than that associated with chemical bonds, the electron-induced effects are not directed at altering any specific bond and hence the interaction is termed nonspecific. The approach most commonly used is to characterize the electron–polymer interaction is by the overall chemical effects (Chapiro, 1962). There are two generic types of interactions. One is polymer cross-linking, in which adjacent chains cross-connect to form a complex three-dimensional structure that has a higher average molecular weight than the original. If enough cross-linking occurs, then the irradiated material cannot be dissolved in solvents which are designed to remove the nonirradiated material. This process constitutes a method of image formation; irradiated areas remain after solvent development while nonirradiated areas are removed. Such cross-linking materials, e.g., polystyrene, are termed negative resists. The second polymer–electron interaction is chemical bond breaking or chain scission in which the molecular weight is reduced in the irradiated area. If enough chain scission occurs, then the irradiated material can be dissolved in a solvent which does not remove the nonirradiated areas. Materials which undergo chain scission, such as poly (methyl methacrylate), are termed positive resists. In general, both cross-linking and scission events occur to different degrees in the same polymer. When both occur in relatively equal amounts, the resist has very poor characteristics.

The following are *general* requirements for electron–resist materials: (1) high resolution and contrast resulting in 0.1–1.0 μm images; (2) sensitivity, as measured by incident charge per unit area, between 10^{-4} and 10^{-7} C/cm²; (3) ease of application giving pinhole free films with good adhesion on desired materials; (4) resistance to etching, particularly dry etching methods used in high resolution patterning; (5) good thermal stability for withstanding material deposition and other processes in which heat is dissipated; (6) good shelf life (≈ 1 yr); and (7) preferably insensitive to light for ease in handling. A wide variety of materials have been investigated as electron- resists [see reviews by Thompson (1974) and Roberts (1977)]. However, only a few have been found to be lithographically useful and even fewer are commercially available. In Section V, the characteristics of several typical resists are tabulated. However, before discussing them, the important properties of electron resists are described, including concepts of sensitivity, resolution, contrast, and developer effects and their relationship to molecular parameters and absorbed energy density.

B. Resist Properties

The sensitivity S of a resist as defined by the required incident dose (charge per unit area) is strongly influenced by many parameters, including beam energy, resist thickness, substrate material, proximity effects, polymer molecular weight and its distribution, susceptibility to radiation, strength of developer, developer temperature, and agitation. Sensitivity comparison between various materials is difficult at best. Contrast, which is defined in terms of the rate at which a resist undergoes chain scission or cross-linking as a function of dose, is also very difficult to define uniquely. Nevertheless, in this section some fundamental considerations are put forth from which the sensitivity and contrast of resists can be understood and judged. Typically the sensitivity of a resist is measured by an area exposure. In the case of a resist exposure on a low atomic number substrate, such as silicon, the absorbed energy density ϵ_{area} is given in terms of a depth dose function (Everhart and Hoff, 1971). The depth dose function gives the absorbed energy as a function of penetration depth z in the material. For an incident energy E_0,

$$\epsilon_{area} = \frac{Q}{q} \frac{E_0}{R_G} \lambda(f) \tag{2.18}$$

where

$$\lambda(f) = 0.74 + 4.7f - 8.9f^2 + 3.5f^3 \tag{2.19}$$

is the normalized depth dose function. In (2.18), Q is the incident charge per unit area, $f = z/R_G$, where R_G (cm) is the Grün range, given by

$$R_G = \frac{4.6 \times 10^{-6}}{\rho} E_0^{1.75} \tag{2.20}$$

when E_0 is units of keV and ρ is the density. The Grün range is proportional to the Bethe range, described in Section II; however, it relates to electron-penetration depth rather than electron path.

In measuring and comparing resist sensitivity in terms of Q, one must be aware of the effects of various beam energies, resist thicknesses, and substrate types.

Consider first a negative or cross-linking resist. Negative electron resists are in general more sensitive than positive resists because radiation groups with high sensitivity, such as vinyls, episulphides, and epoxies, may be easily incorporated in resist formulations (Thompson, 1974; Thompson et al., 1975). Some of these groups possess an enhanced susceptibility or amplification effect because a single initial cross-linking event can result in many additional cross-linking events. However, as a general rule, negative resists exhibit poorer contrast than positive resists, and as a result, lower resolution is obtained. Presently available negative resists are also more susceptible to swelling during development; this effect can degrade resolution.

For a polymer to cross link into an insoluable gel, a certain absorbed energy per unit volume of resist ϵ_x is required so that on the average, one cross link per chain is formed. This energy can be related to the molecular properties of the polymer as

$$\epsilon_x = \rho N_0/(g_x \overline{M}_w) \tag{2.21}$$

where $\overline{M}_w$ is the original average molecular weight and g_x is the number of cross links per electron volt of absorbed energy. When a cross-linking resist is exposed, an insoluable gel will begin to form at the resist–substrate interface because the absorbed energy density in the resist is a maximum at the interface. The minimum required dose (C/cm²) is denoted Q_x^i. If a resist were exposed to a level Q_x^i and developed, only a thin "scum" of resist would remain; however, if a resist is exposed with more dose, the volume of remaining resist increases. Finally, all of the initial resist film remains at a dose Q_x^0. If the volume of remaining resist for an area exposure, as measured by remaining resist thickness after development, is plotted as a function of incident dose, then a curve such as curve A in Fig. 2.20 is obtained; this curve is for the copolymer resist COP (Thompson et al., 1975). The sensitivity S of the resist depends on how much remaining gel is lithographically useful. A convenient definition is one that results in dimensional equality of clear and opaque features which are nominally equal in pattern design (Ballantyne, 1975). In the case of COP, this definition corresponds to a 50% remaining resist thickness as shown in Fig. 2.20.

Resist contrast γ is defined as the slope of the linear portion of the

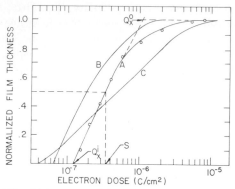

FIG. 2.20 Fractional film thickness remaining after development (normalized to final resist thickness) as a function of electron dose for COP resist = 10 kV [$\gamma = |\log(Q_x^0|Q_x^i)|^{-1}$]. Curve A shows a typical response curve and illustrates the definitions of Q^i and Q^0. Curve B shows the improved sensitivity by use of a higher molecular weight while curve C shows the degraded contrast from a high dispersivity in the molecular weight distribution. [Data from Thompson *et al.* (1975).]

curve of remaining resist versus dose. Mathematically,

$$\gamma \equiv |\log(Q^0/Q^i)|^{-1} \qquad (2.22)$$

where Q^0 is the extrapolated dose for full thickness, as shown in Fig. 2.20. The contrast of a material is very important since it gives a measure of the susceptibility of the material to a change in dose. High contrast resists are very desirable for obtaining better edge definition and higher resolution. Ideally a binary resist is desired, in which case the resist image corresponds to a "black-and-white" pattern. Such a resist would then be very tolerant to low doses of exposure, such as caused by backscattered electrons as long as their contribution is below the threshold value of the resist. As a result, proximity effects would be much less severe in a high contrast resist. Negative resists in general have lower contrasts than positive resists. A typical contrast for the negative COP resist is 0.9–1.0, while the positive PMMA resist typically has a contrast of 2. As a rule of thumb, $\gamma > 1$ is required for submicron imaging. The molecular properties of a negative resist affect both its sensitivity and contrast. From Eq. (2.21) it is evident that increasing the average molecular weight $\overline{M}_w$ reduces the required value of energy density ϵ_x to cross link the material. This fact has been experimentally verified, and a typical example is shown in Fig. 2.20, curve B for COP resist (Thompson *et al.* 1975; Feit *et al.* 1978). The molecular weight of sample B is ≈ 1.5 times that of sample A. However, limits on increasing $\overline{M}_w$ result from practical considerations of resist filtering and spin coating. The molecular weight distribution also affects the contrast of a negative resist. Consider a single molecular weight polymer; such a polymer requires a single value of energy to produce a required volume of gel. On the other hand, in a polymer with a wide distribution of molecular weights, the high molecular weight chains will require a small electron dose while the low molecular weight chains will require a larger dose. Thus gel formation occurs over a large range of doses and the contrast is low. This effect is illustrated schematically as curve C in Fig. 2.20 for another sample of COP resist. Consequently, negative resists should have a narrow distribution of molecular weights.

The chemical yield g_x is important to both sensitivity and contrast in negative resists. Cross-linking resists are usually chosen which have a higher resistance to undesirable scission events, since for each fractured chain an additional cross-linking event is required to maintain gelation. Susceptibility of a cross-linking resist to chain scission results in a lower sensitivity and contrast. The absolute value of g_x in negative resists is important. Certain highly sensitive resists such as the "epoxy" groups have been shown to have a large value of g_x as a result of a sequential process. Energy is absorbed and an initial reactive species is formed. Prior to generating a cross link, this species induces additional reactive species; the result is more cross links per electron volt of absorbed energy than is typically associated with cross-linking materials (Feit *et al.*, 1978). Such highly reactive groups are desirable for increasing resist sensitivity. Another aspect of *certain* negative resists is worth noting, namely, the vacuum curing effect. If a wafer or mask takes several tens of minutes to completely expose and is immediately removed from vacuum, the resist exposed at the beginning of the cycle will have cured to a greater thickness than the resist exposed near the end of the writing sequence. Experimental evidence for COP resist shows that the amount of remaining resist thickness for a constant dose is an increasing function of amount of time in vacuum until a saturation level is approached. It is believed that once the cross-linking reaction is initiated, it proceeds in vacuum, but it is quenched by exposure to atmosphere. Oxygen is considered to be the quenching agent; similar oxygen effects are known to exist in photo-resist exposure. The effect is minimized by allowing the resist to cure in vacuum for approximately 30 min, so that the most recently exposed resist catches up to the area first exposed. Exposed resist samples can be allowed to cure in the load lock of a modern electron-beam writing instrument.

Consider a positive resist—that is, one that is dominated by chain scission in the irradiated area. A useful resist results if the rate of dissolution in the developer is much higher in the irradiated region compared to the nonirradiated regions. Increased solubility in the developer is the result of significantly lower molecular weight in the irradiated region. Schematically illustrated in Fig. 2.21 are the initial (nonirradiated) and final (irradiated) molecular weight distributions of a positive resist. The distribution or dispersivity is characterized by the ratio of the weight average molecular weight $\overline{M}_w$ to the number average molecular weight $\overline{M}_n$. Of fundamental interest is the degraded or fragmented number average molecular weight $\overline{M}_f$. Greeneich (1973) has shown that

$$\overline{M}_f = \overline{M}_n/(1 + N_s) \qquad (2.23)$$

where $\overline{M}_n$ is the initial number average molecular weight and N_s the number of scission events per molecule given by

$$N_s = g_s \epsilon \overline{M}_n/(\rho N_0) \qquad (2.24)$$

where ϵ is the absorbed energy density (electron volts per cubic centimeter) and g_s is the radiation chemical yield for scission events (events per electron volt). Combining Eqs. (2.23) and (2.24),

$$\overline{M}_f = \overline{M}_n/(1 + K\overline{M}_n) \qquad (2.25)$$

with $K = g_s \epsilon/(\rho N_0)$. The influence of original molecular weight on $\overline{M}_f$ is shown in Fig. 2.22 for various values of K (Herzog et al., 1972). To maximize resist sensitivity, it is desirable for the final molecular weight distribution to be centered much lower in molecular weight than the original distribution. This corresponds to a large ratio in $\overline{M}_n/\overline{M}_f$, and according to Fig. 2.22 implies that either K be large or $\overline{M}_n$ be large or both. In practice, $\overline{M}_n$ is typically in the range 10^5–10^6, in which case the value of $\overline{M}_f$ is independent of $\overline{M}_n$ for typical valves of K and $\overline{M}_f$ only depends upon the absorbed energy density.

Although the dependence of $\overline{M}_n$ on $\overline{M}_f$ can be eliminated, the original

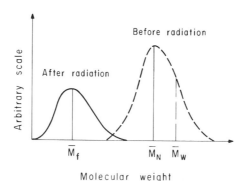

FIG. 2.21   A typical distribution of molecular weights for a positive resist showing how electron radiation reduces the molecular weights in the irradiated region. $\overline{M}_n$ and $\overline{M}_w$ are the number and weight average molecular weights, respectively. [From Herzog et al. (1972) and reproduced with permission of the IEEE.]

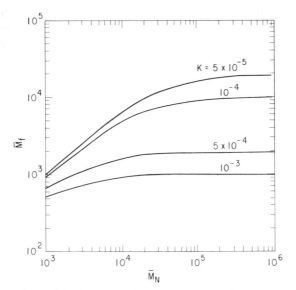

FIG. 2.22 Plots of $\overline{M}_f$ vs. $\overline{M}_n$ with $K = g\epsilon/\rho N_0$ as a parameter. [From Herzog *et al.* (1972) and reproduced with permission of the IEEE.]

molecular weight and its distribution affect the measured sensitivity of positive resists because of developer effects. As noted earlier, an acceptable image results when the irradiated areas have a much higher solubility rate in the developer than nonirradiated areas. Generally the solubility rate R of a polymer in a solvent follows a power law dependence:

$$R \propto (\overline{M}_f)^{-\alpha} \qquad (2.26)$$

Values of α are typically $\gtrsim 1.5$. If R_u is the solubility rate of the unirradiated polymer in the developer, then the ratio of solubilities of the exposed to nonexposed regions is found to be

$$R/R_u = (1 + K\overline{M}_n)^\alpha \qquad (2.27)$$

Large values of R/R_u are desired. Clearly for a suitable solvent and a desired solubility ratio, a resist with higher values of $\overline{M}_n$ requires less absorbed energy density (hence less dose); it exhibits higher sensitivity. Limits on sensitivity improvements by increasing $\overline{M}_n$ result from practical considerations, such as resist filtering and coating characteristics. The molecular weight distribution can also be important in a positive resist since the final molecular weight distribution should be well separated from the initial distribution. Clearly, low dispersivities will increase the sensitivity of the resist since less electron dose is required to separate narrow distributions compared to wide distributions.

TABLE 2.3

Values of Scission Events and Sensitivities for Selected Positive Results

Material	g_s (events/eV)	Resist sensitivity (C/cm^2)
Poly (methyl methacrylate)	0.019	5×10^{-5}
Poly (α-methyl styrene)	0.003	1×10^{-4}
Poly (isobutylene)	.04	$2-5 \times 10^{-5}$
Olefin–sulfones	.11	$0.8-2 \times 10^{-6}$
e.g., Poly (butene-1-sulfone)		
Copolymer, methyl,	0.031	6×10^{-6}
methacrylate, methyl-α-		
chloracrylate		

A fundamentally important parameter to positive resist sensitivity is the efficiency of chemical events g_s. If some cross-linking events also occur in the positive resist material, then it is the net yield $g_s - g_x$ that determines resist sensitivity. Values of g_s and resist sensitivity are tabulated in Table 2.3 for a number of polymer materials investigated as positive resists. Of these the poly (olefin–sulfones) have the highest g_s value. They have been successfully utilized in electron-beam mask making; however, in general, they show poor resistance to dry etching, so that use in direct wafer writing is limited.

Under a fixed set of conditions of beam energy, resist thickness, substrate type, and developer conditions, positive resists are characterized by a plot of the amount of resist removed as a function of log dose. A typical example is shown in Fig. 2.23 for PMMA resist. Note that by definition of a positive resist, all of the resist material must be removed to be useful, and hence sensitivity is measured at the complete removal point. Increased developer time can improve sensitivity at the expense of re-

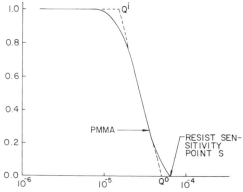

FIG. 2.23   Typical thickness remaining vs incident dose curve for PMMA positive resist.

duced resist thickness in nonirradiated areas. As with negative resists, the contrast is defined by the slope of the linear portion of the dose curve; Eq. (2.22) is valid when Q^0 and Q^1 are found as shown in Fig. 2.23. As typified by PMMA, contrasts are generally much higher in positive resists compared to negative resists.

C. Resist Development

Positive resists are developed in a solution chosen as a good solvent for the irradiated area and a poor solvent for the nonirradiated area. Often a developer is obtained by combining a good and poor solvent for the unirradiated polymer. Experimentally, a series of test exposures are conducted and a good solvent–poor solvent combination is chosen which provides the highest solubility ratio between exposed and nonexposed regions. Alternatively, a predetermined solubility ratio is defined, and a matrix of experiments is carried out to minimize the required dose as a function of relative developer strength. The effects on resolution, contrast, and linewidth control must also be determined. A more fundamental approach to positive resist development is to measure the removal of resist as a function of developer time for various fragmented molecular weights since the fragmented molecular weight relates the absorbed energy density to the molecular and radiation sensitive parameters of the resist. Under most developer conditions, the solubility of a uniformly irradiated polymer is linear with time; this is a rate limited process. The temperature dependence is given in terms of an activation energy E_a; hence

$$R = A \exp(-E_a/kT) \tag{2.28}$$

where k is Boltzman's constant and T is absolute temperature. Equation (2.28) for developer action has been experimentally verified by Greeneich (1975) for PMMA resist for a series of solvent–nonsolvent combinations of methyl isobutyl ketone (MIBK) and isopropyl alcohol (IPA). Typical values of E_a are 1.04 eV for MIBK and 2.43 eV for 1 : 3 MIBK : IPA developers.

Typical data is shown in Fig. 2.24 for PMMA resist. The empirical relationship described by the solid lines fits the expression

$$R = R_0 + \beta/\overline{M}_f^\alpha \tag{2.29}$$

Table 2.4 gives the measured parameters R_0, β, and α; data compiled from other investigators are also shown. The most significant parameters in Eq. (2.29) are α and R_0. The parameter R_0 characterizes the removal of very high molecular weight materials such as the nonirradiated regions, and hence R_0 should be minimized to increase the solubility ratio. Under

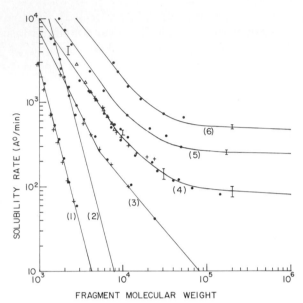

FIG. 2.24   The solubility rate vs. fragmented molecular weight for three different developers and for various temperatures. Data is for original molecular weights between 10^4 and
2×10^5. Developer Conditions: (1) 1:3 MIBK:IPA at 22.8°C.; (2) 1:3 MIBK:IPA at
32.8°C.; (3) 1:1 MIBK:IPA at 22.8°C; (4) MIBK at 22.8°C; (5) MIBK at 34.1°C; and (6)
MIBK at 35.6°C. ($\bullet$, $M_n = 1.7 \times 2 \times 10^5$; +, $M_n = 3.1 \times 10^4$; $\triangle$, $M_n = 1 \times 10^4$; I, no dose
data). [From Greeneich (1975) and reproduced with permission of the Electrochemical
Society.]

certain conditions the parameter α equals the contrast γ of the resist previously defined. Consider an area exposed to a dose Q. From Eqs. (2.18),
(2.25), and (2.29),

$$R \propto Q^a \tag{2.30}$$

where it is assumed that $R_0 = 0$, and $\bar{K}\bar{M}_n > 1$, which is typical because
$\bar{M}_n$ is large. For a fixed development time the amount of removed resist
may be plotted as a function of Q; this plot will have the slope α. This
slope is the contrast and hence $\alpha = \gamma$. PMMA has been used extensively
as a high resolution resist because of its high contrast, as evidenced by the
tabulated values of α in Table 2.4. From the values in Table 2.4, note the
tradeoff in sensitivity and contrast (resolution). When there is more good
solvent (MIBK) in the developer, then less dose is required to achieve a
given solubility rate, but the lower the contrast and ultimately resolution.
Even when PMMA is developed in pure MIBK the contrast (1.5) is larger
than the typical contrast values ($\gamma \simeq 1$) found with negative resists.
     The total volume of irradiated positive resist removed by the developer

TABLE 2.4

Values of Parameters R_0, β, and α for PMMA Resist

Developer	Temperature	Range of frag. mol. wt.	R_0 (Å/min)	β	α	Reference
1 : 3 MIBK : IPA	22.8°C	$\leq 2 \times 10^5$	0.0	9.332×10^{14}	3.86	Greeneich (1975)
1 : 3 MIBK : IPA	32.8°C	$\leq 2 \times 10^5$	0.0	1.046×10^{16}	3.86	Greeneich (1975)
1 : 1 MIBK : IPA	22.8°C	$\leq 5 \times 10^3$	0.0	6.700×10^9	2.00	Greeneich (1975)
1 : 1 MIBK : IPA	22.8°C	5×10^3– $\leq 2.10^5$	0.0	6.645×10^6	1.19	Greeneich (1975)
MIBK	22.8°C	$\leq 2 \times 10^5$	84	3.140×10^8	1.50	Greeneich (1975)
MIBK	34.1°C	$\leq 2 \times 10^5$	242	5.669×10^8	1.50	Greeneich (1975)
MIBK	35.6°C	$\leq 2 \times 10^6$	464	1.435×10^9	1.50	Greeneich (1975)
MIBK	20.5°C	Unknown	0	1.25×10^9	1.40	Hatzakis et al. (1974)
2 : 3 MIBK : IPA	≈Rm. temp.	Unknown	—	9.37×10^{12}	2.75	Hawryluk et al. (1974)
MIBK	≈Rm. temp.	6×10^3– 3.2×10^4	0	2.31×10^8	1.45	Hawryluk et al. (1974)
MIBK	≈Rm. temp.	$<6 \times 10^3$	0	1.82×10^{11}	2.5	Hawryluk et al. (1974)

increases with time. Since there is considerable fragmentation of molecular chains at large lateral distances from the beam center, the resist profile and resulting linewidth evolve with time. Developer simulation can be combined with calculations of absorbed energy density to predict actual resist images (Kyser and Viswanathan, 1975; Van Duzer et al. 1976; Neureuther, 1978). Such modeling is useful in understanding the shape of developed profiles and changes in linewidth as a function of development and dose. Experimentally, cross sections of developed resist profiles are studied as a function of dose and/or developer conditions. It is possible with suitable combinations of dose and developer conditions to generate vertical, undercut, or overcut profiles as the actual micrographs of developed PMMA resist shown in Fig. 2.25 (Hatzakis, 1975). Pure MIBK was used as the developer to obtain these profiles. Note in Fig. 2.25c a considerable amount of the original resist thickness has been removed; this is caused by prolonged soaking in the developer, which has a finite removal rate for unexposed resist.

Developer action in negative resists is also very important. To first

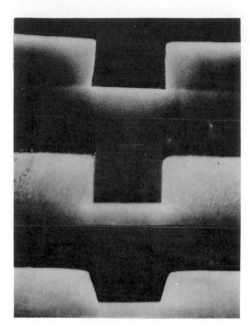

PMMA EXPOSED AT 20 kV

FIG. 2.25   Actual cross-sectional views of PMMA resist profiles at (a) $Q = 10^{-4}$ C/cm²; (b) $Q = 8 \times 10^{-5}$ C/cm², and (c) $Q = 5 \times 10^{-5}$ C/cm² illustrating the undercut, vertical, and overcut profiles. Exposure was at 20 kV and the developer was pure MIBK. [From Hatzakis (1975).]

order, negative resist development appears easy since what is required is the choice of a good solvent for the unexposed resist because the cross-linked areas are not usually soluble in solvents. That indeed negative resist development is not easy has been shown by Feit *et al.* (1978) for COP and related resists. Fundamentally the problem is one of swelling of the resist during development; Fig. 2.26 shows the kind of catastrophic failures that can occur in negative resists that are improperly developed (Thompson *et al.*, 1978). The strength of the developer also plays an important role in determining the useful resolution of a given negative resist. The series of micrographs shown in Fig. 2.27 shows this effect for poly (glycidyl methacrylate) resist. The developer consisted of a solvent–nonsolvent mixture of a ketone and an alcohol. The 3:1 developer is sufficiently strong to develop the unexposed resist, but yet it cannot remove the tails associated with the lines as illustrated in Fig. 2.27. The line broadening or tails shown in Fig. 2.27a are lightly cross-linked regions which result from electron scattering. The use of the 4:1 developer gives a prop-

FIG. 2.26   SEM micrographs of developed COP resist, 0.4 μm final thickness exposed at 20 kV at 6 × 10^{-7} C/cm^2: (a) bridging as a result of polymer swelling during development; (b) severe swelling resulting in gross pattern distortion. [From Thompson *et al.* (1978).]

erly developed image; such a developer is just strong enough to remove the lightly cross-linked region. If a stronger developer is used, such as 5: 1 or 7: 1 (Figs. 2.27c and 2.27d), then the swelling in the resist is great enough to strain the resist beyond the elastic limit and line broadening results. Such swelling of the resist can result in distorted shapes, loss of resolution, and bridging of closely adjacent features in negative resists. Con-

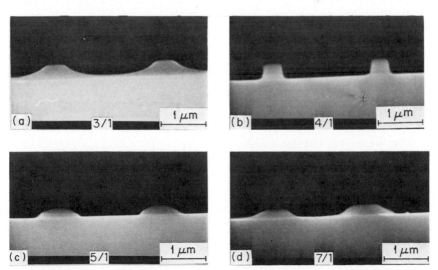

FIG. 2.27   Effect of developer strength on cross line sections and resulting resolution; PGMA resist and various proportions of ketone–alcohol developers. [From Feit *et al.* (1978).]

sequently, great care must be taken to choose a proper developer, one that is strong enough to force develop lightly cross-linked material, but not so strong as to overswell the resist image. Development time must also be controlled to minimize swelling in negative resists.

D. Fundamental Limit to Resist Sensitivity–Resolution

It is a general rule that on a comparative basis slow resists are required to obtain high resolution. This rule is analogous to that in photography according to which slow film is used for high resolution. In order to use resists effectively, it is important to understand the limits on sensitivity–resolution for electron resists; this analysis is based on the signal-to-noise theory presented by Everhart (1978).

Consider a resist that has an experimentally measured sensitivity, S (coulombs per squared centimeter). Further, consider that the area to be exposed consists of a grid of addressable locations under control of the writing instrument. Each element in this grid is called a pixel; a pixel represents the minimum resolution element which can be defined by the absence or presence of charge striking that element. Pixels are combined to form the desired pattern shapes, e.g., lines and spaces. If it is assumed that the resist can be exposed in a binary manner, that is, the resist in each pixel is either completely exposed or unexposed, then the minimum discernible pattern is one pixel exposed and one pixel not exposed. If the pixel dimension is defined as l_p, then the minimum total number of electrons N_{min} that must strike each exposed pixel element for a given sensitivity S is

$$N_{min} = Sl_p^2/q \qquad (2.31)$$

This equation shows the basic sensitivity–resolution tradeoff because the product of sensitivity and pixel size is fixed by N_{min} and, as shown below, signal-to-noise theory prohibits N_{min} from being made arbitrarily small. Thus, for example, PMMA ($S = 5 \times 10^{-5}$ C/cm²) requires 32,250 electrons to expose a 0.1 μm square pixel element, while COP ($S = 4 \times 10^{-7}$ C/cm²) requires only 250 electrons for the same pixel element. If it could be guaranteed that each exposed element received exactly N_{min} electrons, then exposure of resist would not pose a limit on the smallest pixel element (resolution). However, electron emission is a random process and the number of electrons striking a given element in a time T varies statistically. For the large number of electrons N involved in resist exposure, the mean square deviation is $\sqrt{N}$. As indicated in Chapter 1, Everhart defined a signal-to-noise ratio for resists as

$$(S/N)_{resist} = N/\sqrt{N} = \sqrt{N} \qquad (2.32)$$

Adopting the signal-to-noise analysis found in Schwartz (1959) to the binary exposure of resist, it can then be shown that the probability of properly exposing a given pixel element for a large mean number of electrons $\bar{N}$ is

$$P = \left(\frac{\pi}{2}\,\bar{N}\right)^{1/2} \exp\left(-\frac{\bar{N}}{8}\right) = \left(\frac{\pi}{2}\,\frac{S}{q}\right) \exp\left(\frac{-Sl_p^2}{8q}\right) \qquad (2.33)$$

where the last equality is obtained by letting $\bar{N} = N_{\min}$ and using Eq. (2.31). Evidently the probability of an error decreases very rapidly as l_p and S are increased. Using Eq. (2.33) Everhart examined probabilities of an error for various values of $\bar{N}$ and concluded that for $\bar{N} = 200$, the probability of an error in one pixel is 7.8×10^{-13}; this is sufficiently small so that 10^{10} pixels can be properly exposed. This number of pixels corresponds for example, to a 25 mm $\times$ 25 mm area comprised of 0.25 μm pixel elements. This area is considerably larger than that allowed by deflection distortion and other machine errors. Therefore, the pixel size per unit area is limited by technology rather than by fundamental considerations. With $N_{\min} = 200$, Eq. (2.31) becomes

$$l_\rho = [200q/Q]^{1/2} \qquad (2.34)$$

which is plotted in Fig. 2.28. The shaded area represents combinations of pixel size and resist sensitivity that produce an unacceptable probability of error in the exposure. The 200 electron limit corresponds to the signal-to-noise value of 14.1.

Data on sensitivity–resolution for several typical electron resists are compared in Fig. 2.28 with the theoretical limit. The data shown in Fig. 2.28 is representative of the best combination of resolution and sensitivity for the indicated resists and typically is the result of a single scan line. Better resolution can be obtained, for example, in PMMA by increasing the incident dose, using a weaker developer, and eliminating back scat-

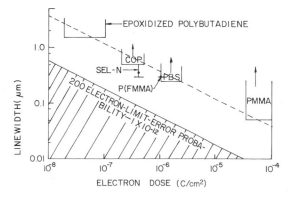

FIG. 2.28   Minimum pixel size (resolution) as a function of resist sensitivity illustrating the limit based on probabilities of successful exposure which requires a minimum of 200 electrons. Actual resist sensitivity–resolution data are also shown. The region between the solid and dashed line represents possible future growth in electron resist sensitivity or resolution.

tered electrons by use of a thin substrate. The properties of the resist materials shown in Fig. 2.28 under typical exposure conditions are presented in Section V with the exception of the epoxidized poly butadiene which is discussed by Nonogaki *et al.* (1974) and Feit *et al.* (1974). Interestingly, all of the resists shown in Fig. 2.28 lie along a single sensitivity–resolution line as indicated by the dotted line. This line represents the present state-of-the-art in electron resists. Using Eq. (2.31) the number of electrons per pixel element corresponding to this line is 8125 and the S/N ratio is 90:1. The probability of an error is extremely small and ongoing research on resists can safely be directed toward improving resolution and sensitivity in order to approach the 200-electron theoretical limit.

The treatment by Everhart considered a binary exposure, but in fact resists are not binary; they have a finite contrast; e.g., refer to Fig. 2.23, which illustrates the response curve for a positive resist. For this resist it is necessary to deposit a charge Q^0 to fully expose it, while the charge must be less than Q^i in the unexposed region. The total error probability is the product of the individual probabilities for obtaining a properly exposed pixel and properly unexposed pixel;

$$I_T = \frac{\pi}{2} \frac{l_p^2}{q} (Q^0 Q^i)^{1/2} \left[\exp\left(\frac{-l_p^2}{8q}\right) (Q^0 + Q^i) \right] \qquad (2.35)$$

If Q^i is increased, resist contrast is increased; it is also apparent from Eq. (2.35) that increasing Q^i reduces the total probability of error. Negative resists are seldom developed to their full thickness; some intermediate dose denoted by Q_1 is taken as proper exposure. Since $Q_1 < Q^0$, the probability of error is larger for a negative resist not exposed to the maximum value Q^0; as a consequence, resolution will suffer.

In this section the treatment of resist exposure in terms of probability of error shows that there is a sensitivity–resolution tradeoff [Eq. (2.31)] and that slow resists are required to obtain high resolution. Available resists do not even approach the limit based on the probability of a pixel error of $\simeq 1 \times 10^{-12}$. Furthermore, it has also been shown that resist contrast and the signal-to-noise concept are interrelated; high contrast lowers the probability of an error and hence higher resolution is obtained.

V.   PROCESSING WITH ELECTRON RESISTS

The primary purpose in exposing high resolution patterns in resist with electron beams and x rays (Chapter 6) is to use the resulting image as a mask in the fabrication of devices, circuits, and masks for pattern replication. Many different processes exist for the fabrication of devices and circuits and in the production of masks for replication. Some of the applications include the fabrication of silicon and GaAs integrated circuits, bubble memory circuits, surface acoustic wave devices, and superconducting devices. The resist mask can be used in several ways to define patterns and regions for subsequent processing. These ways can be grouped generically under additive processes, subtractive processes, and as ion implantation masks. These processes are described in Section V.B. The choice of resist material is important since the intended use of the image plays a role in the choice of that resist. For flexibility, it is desirable to have both positive and negative resists available. The properties of several electron-beam and x-ray resist materials are presented in Section V.A.

A. Electron–Resist Materials

Many different polymer materials have been evaluated for electron-beam sensitivity. No attempt will be made here to describe all of these materials nor their synthesis; the reader is referred to the literature for more complete details (see Table 2.6 for reference list). It is, in general, very difficult to directly compare resists since the intended use of the resist image in the subsequent processing plays a significant role. Often a distinction is made between mask making (particularly photo-optical masks) and direct wafer writing or x-ray mask making. The requirements for photo-optical mask making differ significantly compared with direct wafer writing; several pertinent parameters are compared in Table 2.5. In general, resists used for direct write and x-ray mask making are thicker, have higher contrast, better resolution, are exposed at higher energies, and are more resistant to dry etching than electron resists used in making photo-optical masks.

TABLE 2.5

Comparison of Resist Requirements for Optical Mask Making and Direct Write Applications

Parameter	Optical mask making	x-ray masks and direct write
Resolution	1.0–2.0 μm	<0.5 μm
Sensitivity	1. $\times$ 10^{-6} C/cm^2	2–10 $\times$ 10^{-6} C/cm^2
Contrast	>0.9	>1.5
Beam voltage	Low, 10 KV	High ≳ 20 KV
Etching	Wet chemical	Dry etch
Resist thickness (typical)	thin, 0.3–0.6 μm	Thick, 0.5–1.5 μm

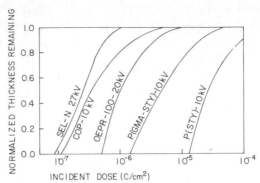

FIG. 2.29 Response curves for selected negative electron resists showing normalized thickness remaining vs. incident dose.

Figures 2.29 and 2.30 show normalized thickness versus dose curves for selected negative and positive resists. These curves give information on the resist sensitivity and contrast at the indicated beam voltages. Sensitivities covering approximately three orders of magnitude for both positive and negative resists are available. In general, the negative resists are more sensitive than positive resists, while positive resists have higher contrast and hence better resolution. A direct comparison between published data on resists is somewhat difficult because of differences in accelerating voltage, initial resist thickness, and developer optimization.

Table 2.6 summarizes published information concerning seven negative and eight positive materials; eight of these are commercially available, one is under commercial development, and six others are not presently available. The data tabulated in Table 2.6 is *representative* of each material. For example, sensitivities have all been normalized to 20 kV

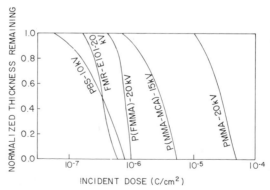

FIG. 2.30 Response curves for selected positive electron resists showing normalized thickness remaining vs. incident dose.

Properties of Selected Electron Resists

Material	Tone	Sensitivity at 20 kV ($\mu C/cm^2$)	Contrast	Resolution (μm)	Typical developed film thickness	Etching wet	Etching dry	Commercially available	References
PMMA	Pos	40–80	2–3	0.1	>1.0	Good	Fair	Yes	Hatzakis (1969); Wolf et al. (1971); Herzog et al. (1972); Greeneich (1975); Hatzakis (1975); Gipstein et al. (1977)
COP	Neg	0.4	0.9–1.2	1.0	0.3	Exc	Fair	Yes	Thompson (1974); Thompson et al. (1975); Feit et al. (1978)
PBS	Pos	1.6	1.3–2	0.5	0.4	Good	Poor	Yes	Thompson (1974); Thompson and Bowden (1973); Bowden et al. (1975)
OEBR-100	Neg	1.0	1.6	<0.5	0.3	Good	Fair	Yes	Information Bulletin, Tokyo-Ohra Kogyo Co. Ltd.
FMR-E101	Pos	0.6	2–3	0.5	0.4	Good	—	Yes	Matsuda et al. (1977b)
SEL-N	Neg	0.4	1	0.3–0.5	—	Good	—	Yes	Information Bulletin, Somar Manufacturing Co., Ltd.
P(GA-STY)	Neg	0.25	1.5–1.8	1.0	0.6–1.0	Exc	Exc	Under development	Thompson et al. (1978); Lai and Sheppard (1975)
P(STY)	Neg	40	1.8	0.5	0.4	Exc	Exc	Yes-not mixed	Thompson (1974); Ku and Scala (1969)
Cross-linked PMMA	Pos	20–40	2–3	<0.5	0.5–1.0	Good	Good	No	Roberts (1974)
P(MMA-MACN)	Pos	5	—	0.5	0.8	Good	Exc	No	Hatano et al. (1975)
P(GMA-STY)	Neg	10	1.4	1.0	0.8	Exc	Exc	No	Thompson et al. (1978); Lai and Sheppard (1975)
P(FMMA)	Pos	1.0	4.5	0.3	0.3	Good	Fair	No	Kakuchi et al. (1977)
P(MMA-MCA)	Pos	8	1.7	0.4	—	Good	—	No	Li et al. (1977)
KMER	Neg	12	0.9	2	—	Good	Fair	Yes	Thornley and Sun (1965)
P(MMA-MAA)	Pos	20	—	<0.4	1.0	Good except for base etch		No	Haller et al. (1979)

beam energy and the sensitivities for positive resists are defined at total resist removal. Development affects sensitivity and contrast, particularly for positive resists; therefore Table 2.6 gives representative numbers. Resolution is very difficult to tabulate based on the limited data available in the printed literature, particularly for some resists for which little information has been published. Similarly dry etching characteristics can only be qualitatively evaluated. From Table 2.6 the following can be concluded concerning presently available resists:

(1)   Positive resists have high resolution, are only moderately sensitive, and have fair to poor dry etching characteristics.
(2)   Negative resists have high sensitivity, have only moderate resolution, and have fair to excellent dry etching characteristics.

In selecting resist materials, the user can choose several different materials which appear suitable for the planned process and carry out detailed evaluation to select the one most effective.

Electron and x-ray resists are also required in pattern replication techniques (see Chapter 6). When electrons are used in a pattern replication technique, the same resist considerations discussed for scanning systems generally apply with the possible exception that somewhat less sensitivity may be acceptable. X-ray resists are themselves electron sensitive. X rays are absorbed by generation of a photoelectron; this electron exposes the resist in much the same way as an incident electron beam. Energetically, the photoelectron has energy equal to that of the absorbed x ray, typically 0.3–3 keV. This value is considerably smaller than the electron energies used in electron-beam systems. Since the penetrating x-ray flux is not scattered, and the range of the low energy photoelectrons is small, there is minimal broadening of the x-ray resist image. The photoelectron range does, however, limit the minimum linewidth in the x-ray process. Consequently, proximity effects are negligible in x-ray lithography and very high resolution patterns may be replicated.

Many electron-beam resists such as PMMA have been used as x-ray resists (Bernacki and Smith, 1974; Lenzo and Spencer, 1974). In addition, several materials have been synthesized primarily for x-ray lithography.* Figure 2.31 shows normalized thickness versus dose curves for selected negative and positive resists used in x-ray lithography. In x-ray lithography the exposure dose is characterized by the incident energy per unit area, usually given in millijoules per squared centimeter, as used in Fig. 2.31. In the case of positive resists, the sensitivity is characterized by complete removal of the resist, while for negative resists some fractional

* Kakuchi *et al.* (1977), Imamura *et al.* (1977), and Taylor *et al.* (1976).

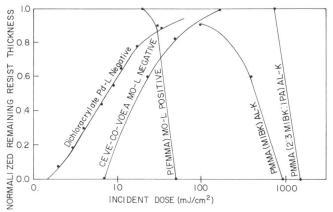

FIG. 2.31 Response curves for selected positive and negative resists utilized in x-ray lithography.

remaining resist thickness (typically 50%) is lithographically useful. Note that different sources of x-ray radiation were used to expose the resists shown in Fig. 2.31. Since resist energy absorption is a function of the radiation, a direct comparison of sensitivities between various resists based on incident energy flux cannot be absolute. Table 2.7 summarizes information on various materials used as x-ray resists at selected wavelengths. The tabulated data is representative of the material under the given exposure conditions, but is not necessarily unique. For example, development procedures can affect the measured sensitivities of positive resists because strong developers may be used if reduced resist thickness and contrast can be tolerated.

For a conventional x-ray source, the flux incident on a resist coated wafer is at most about one-fifth of a millijoule per squared centimeter per second. Consequently, high sensitivity materials are required to reduce exposure times and thereby increase machine throughput. In addition to the usual electron–resist sensitivity factors of radiation susceptibility, molecular weight, dispersivity, and development techniques, the efficiency of x-ray absorption is important in x-ray resists. X-ray absorption in a material follows an exponential law:

$$\phi = \phi_0 \exp(-\mu_m \rho T) \qquad (2.36)$$

For an incident flux ϕ_0, the flux ϕ remains after penetrating a film of thickness T, density ρ, and mass absorption coefficient μ_m. Mass absorption is a function of the x-ray wavelength λ; between absorption edges it follows a power law:

$$\mu_m \propto \lambda^n \qquad (2.37)$$

TABLE 2.7
Properties of Selected x-Ray Resists

| Material | Radiation | | | μ_m (cm²/g) | Calculated sensitivity | | Resolution (μ_m) | Reference |
	Tone	Source	Wavelength		(mJ/cm²)	(J/cm³)		
PMMA	Pos	Al-k·α	8.34	8.63	500–1500	500–1500	<0.25	Bernacki and Smith (1974)
								Lenzo and Spencer (1974)
		MO-L-α	5.4	255	2400	735	<0.25	Kakuchi et al. (1977)
COP	Neg	Al-k-α	8.34	825	6	5	0.5–1.0	Lenzo and Spencer (1974)
		Pd-L-α	4.37	135	159	21		Taylor et al. (1976)
PBS	Pos	Al-k-α	8.34	981	14	14	0.5	Lenzo and Spencer (1974)
		Pd-L-α	4.37	553	94	52	0.5	Taylor et al. (1976)
P(FMMA)	Pos	Mo-L	5.4	235	50–80	12–19	<0.5	Kakuchi et al. (1977)
CEVE-co-VOEA	Neg	Mo-L	5.4	250	18	4.5	1.0	Imamura et al. (1977)
Dichloroacrylates	Neg	Pd-L	4.37	859	5–15	4.3–13	0.5–1.0	Taylor et al. (1976)
Copolymer methylmethacrylate methacrylic acid	Pos			~1000	100–200	100–200		Spiller & Feder (1977)
T1 doped copolymer	Pos	Al-k-α	8.34	~3000	25–50	75–150	<0.5	Haller et al. (1979)

where $2.5 < n < 3.0$ typically. Consequently, increasing the mass absorption of the resist at a selected wavelength improves sensitivity. In Table 2.7 values of μ_m for the indicated resists have been included; for certain materials the data at two different wavelengths is reported. Notice the use of chlorine containing resists such as the dichloracrylates, which have high absorption coefficients for the indicated radiation. Haller et al. (1979), have reported the use of Tl and Cs doping of the methylmethacrylate–methacrylic acid copolymer resist to improve x-ray sensitivity as shown in Table 2.7. In addition to the measured sensitivities in terms of millijoules per squared centimeter, the required absorbed energy density using the calculated mass absorption coefficients and densities of the resist materials is tabulated. This measure of sensitivity allows a direct comparison between materials and allows the user to predict sensitivities at wavelengths other than those given in Table 2.7. The field of x-ray resists is new, and improved materials are being investigated in a number of research laboratories.

B. Electron Resist as Masks

There are many ways of utilizing electron–resist images as a masking medium in semiconductor fabrication, bubble memory fabrication, mask making, and other devices requiring high resolution patterning. In fact, because under certain exposure and development procedures it is possible to control the shape of electron–resist profiles, more optimized and elegant masking techniques are possible; for example, PMMA may be exposed to give undercut, vertical, or overcut profiles as shown in Fig. 2.25. The expression "resist mask" is intended to describe the use of the resist image in a one-time only application for the fabrication of devices as opposed to the use of masks in photolithography or electron-beam or x-ray pattern replication techniques. In this section the use of electron resists as masks is reviewed. The treatment is not intended to be exhaustive, but rather to describe the varied uses of electron resists, particularly in relationship to advanced processing techniques required for high resolution device–mask fabrication. The actual fabrication of devices and mask making for image replication are covered in Chapters 4 and 5, respectively.

Consider first additive processing. Additive processes refer to the deposition of material, e.g., metal, on to an already defined resist image. Additive techniques are appealing since they avoid the necessity of wet or dry etching and are capable of very high resolution. Figures 2.32 and 2.33 show the two common additive techniques of "liftoff" (Hatzakis, 1969) and electroplating (Spiller et al., 1976). Positive resists are almost univer-

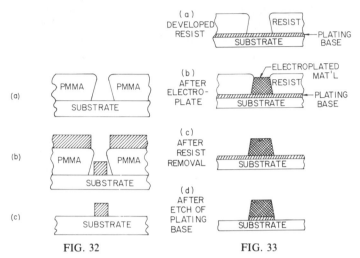

FIG. 32   FIG. 33

FIG. 2.32   The liftoff technique used in defining metal patterns: (a) the PMMA resist after development; (b) the structure after metal deposition; (c) the desired metal pattern left on the substrate after resist removal.

FIG. 2.33   The electroplating technique showing (a) the developed resist image on a plating base, (b) subsequent plating of desired material, (c) after resist stripping, and (d) after etching plating base.

sally used in such additive processes because of the ability to obtain vertical or undercut profiles such as shown in Fig. 2.25.

The lift-off technique is often used in the delineation of very high resolution metal patterns. In this technique, metal is deposited over the entire substrate by, for example, electron-gun evaporation. If the resist is exposed and developed to produce an undercut profile in the resist (Fig. 2.32a), there will be no connecting material between the desired metal pattern and unwanted metal (Fig. 2.32b). Stripping of the resist leaves the desired metal pattern (Fig. 2.32c). There are two processing difficulties that may be encountered in utilizing the liftoff technique. The first of these is to avoid heating the substrate during metal deposition. If the temperature increases beyond the glass transition temperature of the resist, then the resist will flow and ruin the vertical or undercut profile needed in the lift-off technique. One elegant approach used by Roberts (1974) to reduce this problem is to begin with a positive resist material which already is cross linked and hence has a high stability to increased temperature. Upon radiation, the cross links are broken and the resist is developed in a good solvent for the non-cross linked material. The resist developed by Roberts is a cross-linked methyl methacrylate and can stand processing temperatures between 165 and 175°C, which is about 60–70°C higher than

PMMA. The other potential problem with liftoff techniques is incomplete liftoff of the undesired material, particularly for thick metal conductor patterns. Sometimes there is bridging between the top layer and the defined line when wide lines and/or thin resists are used. In addition, poor metal adhesion to the substrate sometimes occurs due to residual organics. The lift-off technique is improved by the use of multilayer polymer materials. The use of polysulfone material under the resist has been reported (Carr, 1976). After normal resist development the polysulfone may be easily dissolved (etched). As a consequence, relatively thick layers with undercut edges are produced which facilitates the lift-off technique. The lower polymer in a bilayer system may itself be a radiation sensitive resist. Spiller *et al.* (1976) have reported the use of a bilayer resist in x-ray pattern replications, while Grobman *et al.* (1978) have reported a two-layer resist system for fabrication of high density circuits by electron-beam writing. In the latter, typically 0.4 μm of the copolymer resist, methyl metharylate–methacrylic acid, is used on top of 0.7 μm of PMMA (see Fig. 2.34). The image is formed in the top resist layer, and subsequently the PMMA layer is developed to achieve a profile very favorable to the lift-off technique. In the irradiated regions, the PMMA is

FIG. 2.34 SEM micrographs of a two-layer resist system. The top 400 nm layer is the image defining layer while the 1 μm PMMA bottom layer acts like a spacer. Notice the desirable undercut profile needed for metal liftoff [From Hatzakis.]

partially exposed by the penetrating beam and accordingly has a higher solubility rate than the unexposed region. Owing to electron scattering, this region of higher solubility extends slightly under the top layer resist image. Consequently after development of the PMMA resist, the undercut profile is achieved. Further, this built-in lift-off profile is not very sensitive to dose. Therefore, proximity effects are minimized because shapes receiving differing doses do not suffer significant variations in resist profile during development. Another advantage of the dual resist system is that the image producing layer is on top of the PMMA layer which has flowed over the device topography, and hence, better control of top layer patterning is achieved.

Electroplating of conductor patterns gives the most perfect replica of resist walls and hence allows the thickest remaining metal film for a given thickness of developed resist. Highly vertical or shaped conductor cross sections can be obtained by suitable control of the developed resist profile. The electroplate method requires the deposition of a thin metal conductor film prior to resist coating (Fig. 2.33): this metal carries the necessary electroplating current and should be as uniform as possible. Since resists are nonconductive, the metal will only plate up from the bottom of the developed hole—it will faithfully follow the resist profile (Fig. 2.33b). After plating, the resist is simply stripped and a light etch is used, if necessary, to remove the thin underlying metal layer (Fig. 2.33c and 2.33d). Two potential problems can occur in electroplating technology. Organic residue in the developed image will produce nonuniform deposition and poor adhesion of the electroplated material. As little as 20–50 Å will cause problems, and thicker layers will actually prohibit plating (Spiller et al., 1976). Residue problems are easily overcome by using a slight flash strip of the resist in a plasma reactor. Care must be taken to remove only 500–1000 Å of resist. Good uniformity in plating thickness over varying pattern geometries and over the diameter of the wafer is another potential problem in electroplating technology. Since the volume of electroplate is a function of the local current density, great care must be taken to insure proper plating thickness. The use of bath addivities, bath agitation, and "thief" rings improves uniformity to an acceptable level. Examples of electroplated metal patterns are shown in Fig. 2.35 (Spiller et al., 1976).

Subtractive processes involve the removal of material using the resist image to protect the desired pattern—this is the most common type of pattern delineation technique. In extending resolution to the submicron level, delineation of the desired materials required in device fabrication becomes a very difficult task. As a result of undercutting, wet chemical etching is not satisfactory for submicron patterning except for the thinnest of films (≈ 0.1 μm) such as found in optical mask making. Consequently

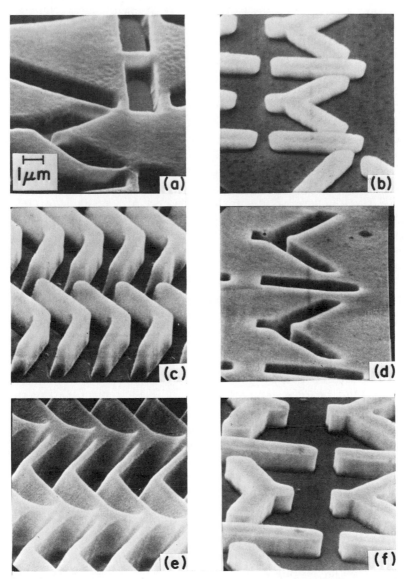

FIG. 2.35   Electron-beam and x-ray resist images in PMMA before (left) and after (right) electroplating. Electron-beam fabricated mask (top), negative x-ray copy (middle), and positive x-ray copy of the negative (bottom) are shown. Linewidth is 1 μm in all patterns. [From Spiller *et al.* (1976).]

the use of dry etching techniques is important, and the stability of the resist to dry etch is vital. There are a variety of dry etching techniques, including plasma etch, with both barrel and planar type reactors, reactive ion etching, sputter etching, and ion milling. The key requirements in dry etching are (1) to avoid or control undercutting in the etched material, and (2) provide selectivity between the etched material and any underlying materials. The profile of the resist image is important. Most often resist profiles should be vertical, although shaped resist profiles are useful in certain processes when the etched material should be sloped to facilitiate coverage of topological features. Dry etching technology is an increasingly important process in device fabrication; many different types of equipment, etching techniques, and process conditions have been successfully used. Dry etching technology continues to be in a state of very active development. No attempt is made here to describe all of the techniques or processes, but rather emphasis is placed on several generic methods and on the general resist requirements demanded by those methods. The reader is referred to several review articles for more complete descriptions.*

Plasma etching utilizes an rf excited plasma of a chemically reactive species to etch the exposed material revealed through the developed resist image. Three types of reactors are commonly used and are known as barrel, planar, and reactive ion; these are schematically illustrated in Figs. 2.36a–2.36c. In the typical barrel reactor a low pressure flow (0.3–1 Torr) of a specific reactant gas is established and an rf discharge is generated by use of external electrodes or coils. Active radicals are generated in the plasma near the chamber walls, and if the radical lifetime is sufficiently long, chemical reaction at the substrate can occur. Etching occurs if the chemical reactions form volatile compounds which are removed by the vacuum pump. Often the substrates are shielded from ionizing radiation by use of a faraday cage as shown in Fig. 2.36a. Barrel reactors are not suitable for etching certain materials, notably Al, because suitable etching radicals have too short a lifetime to reach the substrate in a barrel reactor. The planar plasma reactor (Fig. 2.36b) operates in a pressure range 0.1–1 Torr and by immersing the wafer in the plasma itself, materials can be etched by short-lived radicals. Additional advantages ascribed to planar reactors are better etch uniformity, reproducibility, and substrate temperature stability, which produces a fixed etched rate with time (Somekh, 1976). To reduce resist undercutting it is desirable to have the incident radicals normal to the substrate. One method to accomplish this is to use reduced pressure (≤0.1 Torr) and a bias between anode and

* Somekh (1976), Melliar-Smith (1976), Bondur (1976), and Reinberg (1978).

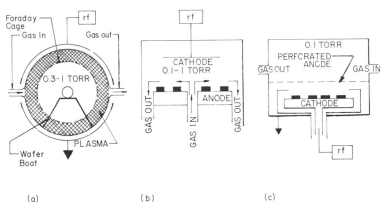

(a)   (b)   (c)

FIG. 2.36   Schematic drawings of several different plasma type reactors utilized in dry etching technology: (a) barrel reactor; (b) planar reactor; and (c) reactive ion etching reactor.

cathode. This procedure results in the process of reactive ion etching (Fig. 2.36c). Because of bias between the electrodes, ions are accelerated toward the substrate and some sputtering of the substrate material can occur. The directionality of this process is very desirable in reproducing in the etched material the very high resolution images obtainable with electron-beam exposed resist. The utilization of any given reactor depends on the material being etched and the actual performance of the equipment in the intended application. Detailed comparisons among methods and materials to be etched and resist performance are required in order to specify a desired process sequence.

The important processing considerations in plasma etching are the rate at which the material is removed, the etch rate of the resist, the degree of undercutting, which is usually characterized by the degree of isotropic etch, and the etch selectivity or etch ratio between the material being etched and the underlying layers. This last consideration is particularly important if it is nonselective and device performance permits very little or no erosion of the underlying material. In general, all of the plasma reactors etch Si, SiO_2, and $Si_3 N_4$ to a sufficient degree that very close control of the etching must be employed to avoid undesirable etching of underlying materials. Considerable effort has been expended to find favorable etch ratios for specific applications; the reader is referred to the previously referenced literature for more details. Relative etching characteristics of materials common to silicon integrated circuits are compared in Table 2.8 for some typical gas systems and reactor configurations. No attempt to quantify etch rate has been attempted since details of processing conditions such as power, gas flow rates, and temperature greatly affect

TABLE 2.8

Etching Characteristics of Selected Materials in Plasma Reactors

Material etched	Typical gas system(s)	Reactor(s)	Etching characteristics[a]
Silicon	CF_4/O_2	Barrel, planar	$Si > Si_3N_4 > SiO_2$—high rate isotropic
	CF_4	RIE	$Si_3N_4 \gtrsim SiO_2 \gtrsim Si$— Both possible
	CCl_2F_2	RIE	$Si > SiO_2$
	CCl_4	Planar	$Si > Si_3N_4 > SiO_2$— Anisotropic
Silicon oxide	C_3F_8, C_4F_8 C_2F_6, CF_4H, CF_3H	Planar, RIE	$SiO_2 > Si$—Anisotropic
Silicon nitride	CF_4/A_R	Planar	Si_3N_4 (plasma) $> Si > SiO_2$—Isotropic
Aluminum	CCl_4/A_R	Planar, RIE	Not quite completely anisotropic
Cr	CCl_4	Planar	Anisotropic
	$Cl_2 + O_2$	Barrel	Suitable for Cr photomasks
Resists	O_2	All	Complete removal
	CF_4/O_2	Barrel, RIE	$AZ1350J^b \simeq SiO_2$
	CHF_4/H_2	RIE	$SiO_2 > PMMA > AZ1350B^b \simeq Si$
	C_3F_8	Planar	$Si_3N_4 > SiO_2 > PMMA > Si$

[a] Data from Reinberg (1978), Bondur (1976), Bersin (1976), and Ephrath (1976).
[b] Registered trademark, Shipley Co.

absolute rates. The information in Table 2.8 illustrates the relative etch rates of various materials in various systems. For example, Si is etched more rapidly in CF_4/O_2 than SiO_2, while the reverse is true in C_3F_8 plasmas. The degree of isotropic etch is very important. If it is desired to replicate accurately the resist image in a relatively thick material ($\geqslant 0.2$ μm), then undercutting must be avoided, and an aniosotropic etch is desired. As shown in Table 2.8, several gas etching systems provide anisotropic etching, which promotes good profile control. In addition, the use of reactive ion etching favors anisotropic etching because of the long mean free path and directionality of the etching species. Bondur (1976) reports for CF_4 etching of Si in a reactive ion etching system that by varying system pressure, the etched profile can be made vertical or tapered as desired.

Two important aspects of plasma processing are the etch rate of the resist and the substrate temperature. Although the published data on resist removal is rather sparse, the data indicates that electron resists are removed at rates comparable to SiO_2 removal. Such a rate is large enough that care must be taken to ensure that the thickness of the developed image is sufficient to provide adequate etch protection for the desired process. Temperature is another important parameter. Since high temperatures cause resist flow, pattern fidelity and linewidth control can be ruined. The planar and reactive ion etching techniques allow convenient cooling of the substrate by the use of water cooled susceptors. In the barrel plasma reactor the wafers are free standing and temperature control is more difficult; in fact, preheating of the chamber and substrates with an inert gas is common practice in barrel reactors to insure constant etch rates from batch to batch.

Ion milling and similarly sputter etching utilize momentum transfer to etch nonselectively the target material (Somekh, 1976; Melliar-Smith, 1976). Surface erosion or sputtering occurs when the energy of the incident ions transfer $\geqslant 10$ eV of energy to the surface layers. The sputtering yield defined as the number of sputtered atoms per incident ion is a very important property which depends upon the incident ion, ion energy, the angle of incidence, and the target material. The relative sputtering rate of various materials is important. For example, by comparing the relative sputtering rates of a resist and the desired material to be etched, the requirements on resist thickness can be determined.

Two types of commonly used ion etching equipment are schematically illustrated in Fig. 2.37; they are sputter etching and ion milling equipment. In the sputter etching equipment, the applied rf power causes a dark space to occur between anode and cathode across which ions are accelerated towards the cathode. Under typical conditions of bias (500–1000 V) and pressures (10^{-2} Torr), the incident atoms arive normal to the surface. As a

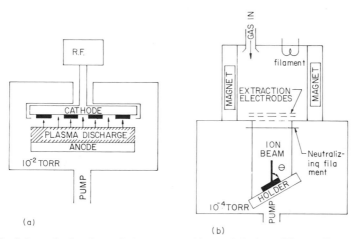

FIG. 2.37   Schematic drawings of (a) sputter etching and (b) ion milling equipment.

consequence, the etching is anisotropic and very steep etched profiles can be obtained. As discussed below, it is important to be able to control the angle of the incident ions. Ion-beam milling equipment allows the incident angle to be varied because the ion source is designed to give a directional beam of ions and the substrate can be inclined at a chosen angle with respect to that beam—this equipment is schematically illustrated in Fig. 2.37b. A variety of ions may be used as the bombarding species in ion etching equipment. Most often an inert gas, typically Ar, is used because of high sputtering yields and the lack of chemical reactions. On the other hand, chemically reactive species present in the chamber can be desirable. For example, activated fluorine and chlorine compounds may be used; this is in essence the reactive ion etching approach. Another common reactive gas is oxygen. A small amount of oxygen present in an ion milling apparatus drastically affects etch rates for certain materials like Ti, Ta, Si, and Al, which form oxides with low etch rates. This fact is often used to improve the etch rate difference between oxygen and non-oxygen reactive materials. The ion etching rate $V(\theta)$ is a function of the incident angle θ between the ion beam and the substrate. Mathematically the rate in angstroms per minute per milliampere per squared centimeter of incident ion flux is

$$V(\theta) = 9.6 \times 10^{25}(S(\theta)/N_T) \cos \theta \ (\text{Å/min})/(\text{ma/cm}^2) \qquad (2.38)$$

where $S(\theta)$ is the sputtering yield, N_T the density of the target material, and the term $\cos \theta$ accounts for reduced incident current at angles away from the normal (Somekh, 1976). The sputtering yield $S(\theta)$ initially increases with θ ($\theta = 0°$ for normal incident) since the incident ions travel a longer distance along the surface of the target and the resulting increased interaction causes a higher removal rate. Above a critical angle θ_c, the sputtering yield decreases owing to ion reflection from the surface. Data for several materials commonly ion etched and two resists, COP and AZ−1350,* are given in Fig. 2.38 as a function of incident angle. Note also in Fig. 2.38 the reduction in etch rate of Ti etched in O_2 compared to pure Ar etching of Ti. Since sputtering is a nonselective process, care must be taken to choose, if possible, a high etch rate difference between the material to be etched and underlying layers or more typically, some etching of the underlying layers must be tolerated.

There are several important characteristics of ion etching which are important in designing a suitable etch process. These are (1) resist faceting, (2) material redeposition, and (3) substrate temperature. Because a developed resist image is usually somewhat rounded near the top edge, the

* Registered trademark, Shipley Co.

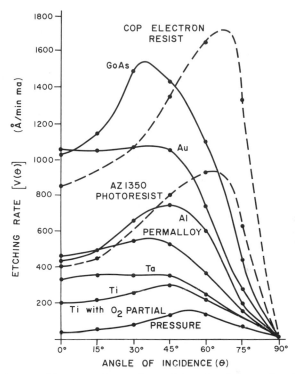

FIG. 2.38 Ion-beam etching rates of several materials and resists as a function of incident angle θ. The rates are normalized to milliampere per squared centimeter; acceleration voltage was 500 V. Air pressure 1×10^{-4} Torr and current was 0.6 mA/cm.

angle between a normally incident beam and the resist will be greater than zero, and according to Fig. 2.38 the milling rate is larger than for the beam striking the top of the resist (0° incident angle). As a consequence a facet will begin to form at the corner of the resist. As ion milling continues, the facet will propogate until it intersects the resist–substrate interface. Continued ion milling will erode the desired linewidth and create a new facet in the thin film being etched. To avoid this problem, much thicker resist films are required than would be expected based on sputtering rate data (Melliar-Smith, 1976). Since the sputter etched material is ejected in a cosine distribution from within the resist opening, some of this material may redeposit along the walls of the resist image. Upon resist removal undesirable thin walls of material may remain. By varying the incident ion angle and/or use of a suitable resist profile, the rate of redeposition can be made equal to the rate of sputtering and material redeposition can be avoided. The third consideration in ion etching is substrate temperature. By the very nature of the momentum transfer process, large amounts of kinetic energy must be dissipated as heat. Such heat can be very detrimental to resist profiles. Even though water cooled susceptors are used, care in maintaining good thermal contact with the substrate must be maintained in ion-etching applications using resist masks.

In summary, ion milling can produce very sharp features with very high resolution because of the aniosotropic nature of the etching action, but care must be taken in understanding and controlling possible deleterious effects such as resist faceting. The applicability of a given ion-etching application must be determined by empirical work with the intended material to be etched and resist material used as the mask. This experimentation is particularly important with electron and x-ray resists where little published information on sputtering yield exists.

Electron resists are used in much the same manner as photoresists to mask against ion implantation. There are two areas of interest concerning the use of resists as implant masks. They are (1) the stopping power as a function of ion energy and (2) any deleterious effects such as cracking or conversion into an insoluble material. The stopping power of a resist is important because few ions should be allowed to penetrate through the resist. Ion stopping power is characterized by the projected range R_p of the impinging ion in the resist material. This range represents the average penetration depth z into the substrate. Limited data exist on ion penetration in resists. The experimental data of Barraconi and Piker (1972) are shown in Fig. 2.38 for boron in KTFR*. Based upon a large amount of experimental data on many ion–substrate combinations, Wilson (1979) has developed an empirical formula for ion range. Calculations for B, P, and As in PMMA resist are shown in Fig. 2.39. Wilson's analytical expression is

$$R_p \text{ (Å)} = \frac{5300 A_{\text{sub}} \, E_{\text{ion}}}{\rho N_0 Z_{\text{sub}}^{2/3} \, Z_{\text{ion}}} \qquad (2.39)$$

Equation (2.39) is accurate to ± 10% when compared with experimental data on many ion–substrate combinations. In Eq. (2.39) E_{ion} is the ion energy in kilo-electron-volts, Z_{ion} the atomic number of the ion, and Z_{sub} and A_{sub} the average atomic number and weight of the substrate. Since $A_{\text{sub}}/Z_{\text{ion}}^{2/3}$ is nearly constant for all materials, the primary material dependent quantity is the substrate density ρ. Since all organic resists have very similar densities, the range is nearly identical. Because high resolution patterning of electron resists is usually restricted to thin resists, the use of electron resists as ion-implantation masks is restricted to combinations of heavy ions and low ion energies.

* Registered trademark, Kodak, Co.

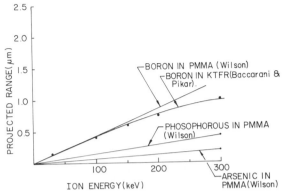

FIG. 2.39 Projected ion range vs. ion energy for typical resist materials. Results from Wilson's formula (1979) are shown for PMMA for B, Ph, and As ions. Experimental data for B in KTFR (Baccarani and Pikar, 1972).

Another problem in using resist for ion implantation masks is conversion to an insoluble material at high implant doses. Okuyama *et al.* (1978) have studied the behavior of photoresist under high dose implant conditions. It was observed at high doses ($> 1 \times 10^{15}$ ions/cm^2) of argon, phosphorous, or boron that the optical transmission of the film was greatly reduced and that the resist becomes more mechanically, thermally, and chemically resistant. Further experimental evidence suggests that the resist implanted at high doses could be changed into graphite. Consequently, the use of resists at high implant doses must be done with caution to avoid problems in removing the resist after implantation.

VI. ELECTRON-BEAM ALIGNMENT

A. *Introduction*

Many solid state devices and all integrated circuits require several levels of lithography, and each succeeding pattern must very accurately overlay the preceding ones. In a typical photolithographic system, an operator adjusts the relative position of mask and wafer while viewing alignment marks through an optical microscope. Alignment accuracies from 0.25 to 0.5 μm can be achieved by this method. However, as the linewidths are reduced to micron and submicron levels, alignment accuracies of 0.05–0.20 μm are required. Fortunately, electron-beam writing systems used for submicron pattern writing are capable of such alignment accuracies (Chapter 3). In essence, the electron-beam system can be used in a scanning electron-microscope mode to detect topographic or material changes; this process is capable of very high resolution. In fact, early electron-beam registration systems used the instrument in a SEM mode to detect alignment marks, and operator initiated adjustments were made to achieve a high degree of alignment accuracy. Low contrast video signals with poor signal-to-noise ratio were acceptable because the operator could interpret the pictures. In modern electron-beam writing instruments, the registration of successive layers is done automatically with high precision and at high speed. The implementation of sophisticated alignment methods is described in the next chapter; it includes discussion of both laser interferometric alignment and chip-by-chip electron-beam alignment schemes. Automatic alignment methods operate at high speed and require high contrast marks with high signal-to-noise ratio; it is the purpose of this section to describe the interaction of the incident electrons with the marks used in chip-by-chip alignment systems. Of interest are the types of signals available, their signal-to-noise ratio, and the contrast available from various kinds of marks used. Several different types of scan techniques are also mentioned as they affect the signal-to-noise ratio.

B. Back Scattered Electrons

When an electron beam penetrates a target material, various kinds of signals are available for detection, including secondary electrons, backscattered electrons, x rays, and Auger electrons. Of these the secondary and backscattered electrons are most often used to generate an image of the surface topography. The distinction between secondary and backscattered electrons is somewhat arbitrarily chosen in terms of their energy. Secondaries are considered to have energies less than 50 eV although the peak of their distribution is between 0 and 10 eV. Backscattered electrons generally have very high energies, with their peak close to that of the primary electron energy. In a typical alignment operation, the alignment signal must come from a multilayered target. For example, an alignment mark might consist of a raised pedestal or etched hole in the target material; it may be overcoated with a layer of oxide and in all cases a layer of resist is present. Figure 2.40 schematically illustrates this layered structure. Because of the overlayed resist, the low energy secondary electrons do not give useful signal information from the mark; however, backscattered electrons have sufficient energy to pass through the overlaying materials and can be detected and used for alignment. Consequently, it is of interest to examine the nature of the backscattered electron signal, the influence of mark composition and overlayed resist thickness on contrast and signal-to-noise ratio.

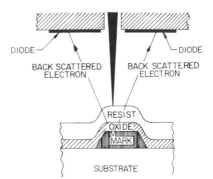

FIG. 2.40 The geometry of the incident electron beam, backscattered electrons, and diode detector encountered in electron-beam alignment systems. Typically the alignment marks are overcoated with oxide and a resist coating.

Several types of detectors can be used to detect backscattered electrons, including (1) back-biased diodes,* (2) grounded scintillators (Wilson et al., 1975), and (3) channel electron multipliers (Varnell et al., 1973). These detectors are energy sensitive in that the current gain is dependent on the energy of the backscattered electrons. Above the "dead layer" or threshold voltage (2–5 kV) of the diode detector, the gain is linear. The dead layer acts as a high energy pass filter by excluding all secondaries and low energy backscattered electrons. The response of the scintillator detector as a function of energy is somewhere between quadratic and cubic (Wilson et al., 1975). The most frequently used detector appears to be the back-biased Si diode. Figure 2.40 also shows a typical geometrical arrangement of detectors, substrate, and incident beam. To increase the total number of electrons, the geometrical arrangement should allow a large solid angle of electron collection between detector and substrate. Typically, a single annular detector or four small area quadrant detectors are used. A benefit of using multiple detectors is the use of basic analog arithmetic operations of the signals prior to digital conversion (Stickel, 1978).

Consider the interaction and generation of backscattered electrons as the primary beam is scanned across the registration mark depicted in Fig. 2.41. The composition or geometry of the mark must differ from that of the substrate in order to be detected. As discussed in Section II.C, the spatial dependence for the generation and escape of backscattered electrons from a target material is very complex and statistical. To study the mechanism of the backscattered electron signal from scanning a beam across a mark, Monte Carlo calculations could be performed; however, a simple geometrical view of the problem is sufficient for understanding the fundamental signal source and contrast mechanisms. The distribution of backscattered electrons for a beam normally incident on a target obeys

* Wolf et al. (1975), Stickel (1978), and Davis et al. (1977)

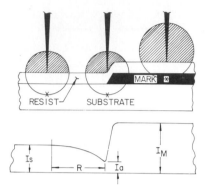

FIG. 2.41 Schematic illustration of the way backscattered electrons generated near the alignment mark give rise to the detector signal such as that shown in (b).

the cosine law. For simplicity consider a single "effective" source of backscattered electrons located at the points labeled by the ×'s in Fig. 2.41a. The number of generated backscattered electrons is schematically denoted by the diameter of the circle. Since in this example the mark is of different composition, both the effective source and number of generated backscattered electrons is different (indicated in Fig. 2.41a by the circles of differing diameter). Recall the discussion in Section II.C concerning the large angle backscattering model; once a backscattered electron has been generated by a large angle collision, it travels in a relatively straight line. The more material a backscattered electron travels through, the more likely it will be deflected again; hence a certain fraction will not escape the material. Thus the number of backscattered electrons escaping from a target depends on how much material they must pass through prior to escape into vacuum. Further, the energy of the escaping backscattered electrons decreases as the amount of material they pass through increases. The shaded areas of the circles in Fig. 2.41a schematically illustrate these effects. With this understanding, it is possible to predict qualitatively the number and energy of the backscattered electrons arriving at the detector. At a large distance from the pedestal, a background level of electrons will be detected. As the beam approaches the edge of the mark, the number and energy of the backscattered electrons will decrease because of the increased distance the electrons must travel prior to escape. As the beam reaches the edge of the pedestal, the number and energy of electrons will increase substantially. The output of the detector will respond to the number of arriving electrons and to their increased energy because of the energy dependent gain of the detector. A typical response for a diode detector is shown in Fig. 2.41b for a line scan orthogonal to the alignment mark. If an etched hole is used as a mark, a complementary signal is obtained. Referring to Fig. 2.41b, two measures of contrast may be defined in a conventional manner as

$$C = (I_m - I_s)/I_s \quad \text{or} \quad C_m = (I_m - I_a)/I_a \qquad (2.40)$$

where I_m is the maximum current, I_s the background level, and I_a the value at the dip. The dip in the detector response is indicative of the large distance that backscattered electrons must travel to escape the mark. The distance R indicated in Fig. 2.41b from that dip to the beginning of dropoff in response from the background is representative of the electron range in the substrate. In this description of the signal source due to backscattered electrons, it was assumed that the background and pedestal were of somewhat different material. The marks may be of the same or widely differing atomic numbers than the substrate, and since the yield of backscattered electrons is very dependent on atomic numbers, the contrast can be changed appreciably by choice of material. As discussed in the next section, the use of a high atomic number material on a low atomic number substrate results in very high contrast.

C.   Registration Marks

Many different kinds of marks have been used in electron-beam registration schemes. Typical examples are Si holes, SiO_2 pedestals,* V grooves (Friedrick et al., 1977), and high atomic number pedestals (Wolf et al., 1975). The composition of the substrate, the incident beam energy, the composition of the marks, and their height all influence the backscattered signal and resulting contrast. The amount of overlaying resist reduces the quantity and energy of backscattered electrons and hence decreases contrast. An important feature in the selection of an alignment mark is its compatibility with the process under consideration. For example, in silicon integrated circuit processing the mark must be able to withstand the high temperatures associated with oxidation and diffusion; silicon holes and oxide pedestals are compatible and they can be created during the first level processing. High atomic number materials are very advantageous, but their use requires an extra step in the fabrication procedures and certain materials such as Au are not compatible with certain device performance and processing procedures. Certain oxides and silicides of high atomic number materials such as $TaSi_2$ are compatible, however. Wolf et al. (1975) have studied the contrast of various marks on Si and GaAs substrates as a function of the primary beam energy. For convenience, these authors used Au to illustrate the contrast obtainable from a high atomic number mark; the results should be applicable to other high

* Wilson et al. (1975), Varnell et al. (1973), Stickel et al. (1978), and Davis et al. (1977).

atomic number materials. Figure 2.42 shows the results for Au marks on Si, Si on Si, and SiO$_2$ holes on Si; the large improvement for high atomic number materials is very evident. The width of the marks has a relatively small effect on the measured contrast. Much more important is the height of the marks, as shown in Fig. 2.43. Notice that the contrast increases with beam energy and saturates for thick gold marks, but decreases some-what for shallow marks. This behavior is expected. For thick marks the energy dependence of the detector accounts for the increase in contrast because on the average the backscattered electrons possess higher energy. For thinner marks at high energy, only a portion of the possible bulk number of backscattered electrons are generated from within the Au marks—that is, the primary beam penetrates through the mark and the average backscattering coefficient is reduced compared to the bulk value for Au. The results for Au marks on GaAs substrates show the same saturation behavior illustrated by Fig. 2.43. Consequently, the maximum contrast is obtained for thicknesses above some minimum mark thickness; this minimum thickness depends on beam energy. According to Wolf *et al.* (1975), the minimum Au thickness is very nearly 25% of the Bethe range in Au for the energy of interest; at 30 keV this corresponds to a 0.56-μm-thick film while at 10 keV this corresponds to a 0.10-μm-thick film. The effect of resist and oxide layers on top of Au marks is to reduce the contrast as shown in Fig. 2.44. This behavior is expected because both the quantity and energy of the electrons reaching the detector is reduced.

Anisotropic etching of (100) oriented silicon to produce V grooves has also been used to generate alignment marks (Friedrich *et al.*, 1977). This technique is attractive from a processing standpoint since accurate control of the etching process is not required as it is self-limiting. The contrast

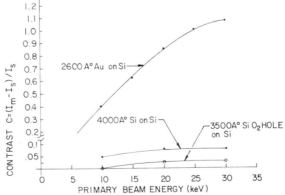

FIG. 2.42   Contrast as a function of primary beam energy for Au, Si, and SiO$_2$ alignment marks.

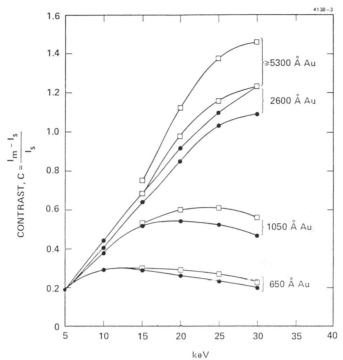

FIG. 2.43 Contrast as a function of primary beam energy for various thicknesses of Au marks on silicon ($W = 3$ μm, $0 \leq t \leq 10^4$ Å, $\Box C_m$). [From Wolf *et al.* (1975).]

for such a mark is good, and accurate alignment can be achieved. Since the common use of anisotropic etching is restricted to Si with a (100) orientation, the use of V groove marks is restricted to that material and hence it is useful principally for MOSFET fabrication.

In general it is somewhat difficult to compare the various types of alignment marks, detection, and methods of scan since each machine and device has unique requirements and registration techniques. Furthermore, processing considerations may strongly influence the choice of mark. The user must therefore decide on the choice of mark based on machine and process considerations. If possible, high atomic number marks are preferred.

D. Signal-to-Noise Ratio

In automated detection systems, the signal-to-noise ratio (SNR) is a fundamentally important quantity. The higher the SNR, the faster the detection can be accomplished and/or the more accurate the position of the

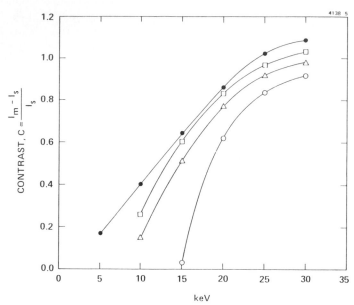

FIG. 2.44 Contrast for gold marks on silicon with PMMA and SiO_2 ($W = 3$ μm) over-coated layers ($\bullet$, 2600 Å Au/Si; $\square$, 5200 Å PMMA/2600 Å Au/Si; $\triangle$, 3500 Å SiO_2/2600 Å Au/Si; $\bigcirc$, 5200 Å PMMA/3500 Å SiO_2/2600 Å Au/Si).

mark determined. Both the signal and noise components must be optimized to increase the SNR. Noise is produced throughout the generation, detection, and amplification of the detected signal. Typically, the shot noise of the primary beam and the electronic circuit noise are considerably below the noise associated with the scattering of the beam and the detector gain mechanism (Wilson *et al.*, 1975). Since the backscattered electrons arrive at the detector in the form of random discrete quanta, the response is subject to statistical fluctuations. For such a situation the signal increases as the current, while the noise increases as the square root of the current, and hence the SNR increases as the square root of the current. Consequently, increasing the amount of backscattered electrons collected by the detector is important. This may be accomplished in several ways. Increasing the incident primary beam current is desirable, but this is not always possible given the constraints on the maximum beam current in the desired spot and the sensitivity of the resist; most beam writing instruments usually operate near maximum current in a given focused spot. As indicated in the last section, the use of high atomic number marks to improve the number of backscattered electrons is also desirable.

The above discussion concerned fundamental methods of increasing the amount of detected signal; there are in addition various different scan methods for enhancing the SNR. One method is to slow the scan rate, integrate the signal, and filter it from the broadband noise. However, the scanning speed must be fast enough to prevent the resist from "bubbling," which would distort the backscattered signal reaching the detector; this distorted signal appears as additional noise. Heavy exposure of a positive resist can lead to development of the scan lines used in registration. The mark is therefore subject to degradation in a subsequent etch step. To reduce exposure and bubbling, a high frequency "dither" of the beam perpendicular to the direction of scan is sometimes used (Davis et al., 1977). This effectively increases the area over which the beam energy is deposited. Any high frequency component added to the signal can be easily removed by a low pass filter. A very common scanning technique used to avoid resist bubbling and to enhance the SNR is the use of multiple scans at different locations along the mark.* Assuming random noise the SNR is improved by the square root of the number of scans summed. Another advantage of multiple scans is to average out errors in mark position which result from random defects in the marks. The penalty in using multiple scans and slow scanning techniques is in the added time of registration, which should be kept to a small fraction of the chip writing time. Accuracy improves as the square root of the time; hence some compromise between registration time and accuracy must be reached.

The use of multiple alignment marks to achieve constructive signal enhancement has been studied by Stickel (1978). The use of multiple marks separated by relatively long distances increases the number of signal transitions; and the larger the number of transitions, the more averaging of signals with a resulting improvement in SNR. The use of closely spaced multiple marks allows the possibility of constructive interference of the backscattered signals when appropriate scanning and differentiation of the signals is utilized. For example, Stickel reports a 100% signal enhancement for two SiO_2 marks separated by 2.5 μm compared to a single mark. The marks were 2.3 μm high and covered by 3.3 μm of resist, and scanning was done with a 2.5 μm square beam. Additional data is given in the reference (Stickel, 1978).

Davis, et al. (1977) have reported on theoretical alignment error as a function of the SNR; their results are shown in Fig. 2.45. These results are for marks of two or four edges and after 30 scans are averaged. From these data it is apparent that very high precision can be obtained using electron-beam writing systems. For a 2.5 μm square spot machine, Davis et al. (1977) report automatic registration with accuracies of better than 0.5 μm at a three sigma level. Other machines with smaller electron

---

* Wilson et al. (1975), Varnell et al. (1973), Stickel et al. (1978), and Davis et al. (1977).

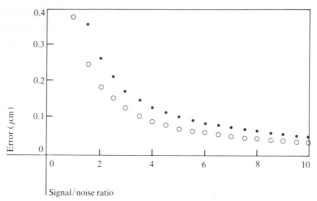

FIG. 2.45 Mark identification error vs. signal to noise ratio ($\cdots$, mark with two edges; $\infty\infty\infty$, mark with four edges.) [From Davis *et al.* (1977) and reproduced with permission of IBM J. Res. Dev.]

probes report overlay precision to 0.1–0.2 μm using automatic registration schemes.* Further improvements in overlay precision are possible, particularly if longer registration times are utilized. Electron-beam alignments are considerably better than the best optical alignment systems presently available.

VII. SUMMARY

The electron-beam processes discussed in this chapter are fundamental to the understanding and use of electron-beam lithography. Electron scattering is a very complex process and it is an important factor in determining resolution, linewidth control, and proximity effects. To minimize electron scattering, a high energy beam, thin resists, and low atomic number substrates are favored. In addition, pattern writing is improved by controlling proximity effects by means of dose control and/or pattern biasing. Electron resists are organic polymers which are susceptible to the incident electron radiation. In the irradiated areas, the resist changes molecular weight, and by use of a suitable developer which distinguishes between regions of differing molecular weights a resist image is formed. Electron resists do not yet approach the highest sensitivity–best resolution limit based on signal-to-noise theory. The resist image is used in a conventional manner in the processing steps required for integrated circuit and other device fabrication procedures; however, the availability of submicron resolution with electron-beam technology requires the use of advanced technologies (e.g., lift-off metalization) and dry etching tech-

* Wilson *et al.* (1975), Varnell *et al.* (1973), and Grobman *et al.* (1978)

niques (e.g., plasma and ion etching). Another important electron-beam process is the generation and detection of backscattered electrons used in high speed, high accuracy automatic alignment systems. A large signal-to-noise ratio is vital; this can be achieved in a variety of combined detection schemes, alignment marks, and scan techniques. The SNR is improved by the use of a diode detector, high atomic number marks, multiple scans, and constructive signal interference effects; it is degraded by overlaying oxide and resist layers.

Consider the future with regard to resolution in electron-beam exposure of resists. The results shown in Figs. 2.10 and 2.11 already indicate that 400 Å linewidths have been achieved in PMMA exposed on Si by a single pass of a 20 kV beam. Based on the discussion in Sections II and III, electron scattering may be reduced and resolution improved by using a higher energy beam, smaller probe sizes, thinner resists, and by reducing backscatter. This is exactly what Broers et al. (1976, 1978) did to achieve 250 Å linewidths with PMMA resist and 80 Å linewidths using electron-beam polymerized silicones as a masking resist. Metal lines were formed by ion milling. In the Broers experiments, a fine focused ($\simeq 10$ Å) probe, a high energy beam ($\simeq 50$ kV), and a thinned substrate (600 Å) of Si_3N_4 were used in order to minimize scattering effects. Although the resolution achieved in these experiments is very high, the PMMA resist required a large exposure (approximately 5×10^{-4} C/cm^2). This combination of resolution and sensitivity lies along the same state-of-the-art curve shown in Fig. 2.28. Consequently, much effort should be expended in improving this state-of-the-art in resists. New materials are probable, such as the organic electron resists described by Yoshikawa et al. (1977). In addition, new development techniques can be used. For example, wet or solvent development of the resist can be replaced by "dry" development (e.g., by plasma). In much the same manner that dry etching is an improvement compared with wet etching, dry resist development should allow higher resolution patterns to be developed with better linewidth control. It is apparent that the resist and etching technology exists to create structures below 500 Å; at present, this lithographic capability is outpacing the need to build such small devices because as yet our understanding of the physics of such small structures is limited. As the subject of very small devices receives additional research and discussion, the push for higher resolution and better sensitivity in resists will receive further impetus.

REFERENCES

Baccarani, G., and Pickar, K. A. (1972). *Solid State Electron.* **15**, 239.
Ballantyne, J. P. (1975). *J. Vac. Sci. Technol.* **12**, No. 6, 1257.

Berger, M. J., and Seltzer, S. M. (1964). Nat. Acad. Sci. Nat. Res. Council, Publ. No. 1133, p. 205.
Bernacki, S. E., and Smith, H. I. (1974). *In Int. Conf. Electron Ion Beam Sci.* Technol., *6th* (R. Bakish, ed.). Electrochemical Society, Princeton New Jersey.
Bersin, R. L. (1976). *Solid State Technol.* **19**, No. 5, 31.
Birkhoff, R. D. (1958). *In* "Handbuck der Physik" (E. Fluegge, ed.), p. 53, Springer, Berlin and New York.
Bondur, J. A. (1976). *J. Vac. Sci. Technol.* **13**, No. 5, 1023.
Bowden, M. J., Thompson, L. F., and Ballantyne, J. P. (1975). *J. Vac. Sci. Technol.* **12**, No. 6, 1294.
Broers, A. N., Molzen, W., Cuomo, J., and Wittels, N. (1976). *Appl. Phys. Lett.* **29**, 596.
Broers, A. N., Harper, J. M. E., and Molzen, W. W. (1978). *Appl. Phys. Lett.* **33**, No. 5, 392.
Carr, P., Havas, J., Paul, G., and Rompaia, L. J. (1976). *IBM Tech. Disclosure Bull.* **19**, No. 4.
Chang, T. H. P (1975). *J. Vac. Sci. Technol.* **12**, 1271.
Chapiro, A. (1962). *In* "Radiation Chemistry of Polymeric Systems," Vol. 15. Wiley, New York.
Cosslett, V. E., and Thomas, R. N. (1964a). *Brit. J. Appl. Phys.* **15**, 235.
Cosslett, V. E., and Thomas, R. N. (1964b). *Brit. J. Appl. Phys.* **15**, 883.
Davis, D. E., Moore, R. D., Williams, M. C., and Woodward, O. C. (1977). *IBM J. Res. Dev.* **21**, No. 6.
Ephrath, L. M. (1976). *In* "Extended Abstracts," Abstr. 135, p. 376. Electrochemical Society, Princeton, New Jersey.
Everhart, T. E. (1960). *J. Appl. Phys.* **31**, 1483.
Everhart, T. E. (1978). Private Communication; also *In* (1976). "Basic Limitations in Microcircuit Fabrication Technology" (I. E. Sutherland, C. A. Mead, and T. E. Everhart). Rand Rep. R-1956-ARPA.
Everhart, T. E., and Hoff, P. H. (1971). *J. Appl. Phys.* **42**, 5837.
Feit, E. D., Heidenreich, R. D., and Thompson, L. F. (1974). *In Appl. Polym. Symp.* No. 23, p. 117. Wiley, New York.
Feit, E. D., Wurtt, M. E., and Kammlott, G. W. (1978). *J. Vac. Sci. Technol.* **15**, No. 3.
Friedrick, H., Zeitler, H. V., and Bierhenke, H. (1977). *J. Electrochem. Soc.* **124**, No. 4, 627.
Gipstein, E., Ouano, A. C., Johnson, D. E., and Need III, O. U. (1977). *IBM J. Res. Dev.* **21** iv. (2), 143.
Greeneich, J. S. (1973). Ph.D. dissertation, Univ. of Calif., Berkeley, California, unpublished.
Greeneich, J. S. (1975). *J. Electrochem. Soc.* **122**, No. 7, 970.
Greeneich, J. S. (1979). *In* Proc. *Symp. Electron, Ion, Laser Beam Technol., 65th* (T. H. P. Chang, ed.). American Institute of Physics, New York.
Greeneich, J. S., and Van Duzer, T. (1973a). *IEEE Trans. Electron Devices* **ED-20**, No. 6, 598.
Greeneich, J. S., and Van Duzer, T. (1973b). *J. Vac. Sci., Technol.* **10**, 1056.
Greeneich, J. S., and Van Duzer, T. (1974). *IEEE Trans. Electron Devices* **ED-21**, 286.
Grobman, W. D. *et al.* (1978). IEDM, Washington, D.C., p. 58.
Grobman, W. D., and Speth A. J., (1978), *In Proc. Int'l. Conf. Electron and Ion Beam Sci. and Technol., 8th* (R. Bakish ed.). p.276, Electrochemical Society. Princeton, New Jersey.
Haller, I., Feder, R., Hatzakis, M., and Spiller, E. (1979). *J. Electrochem. Soc.* **126**, No. 1, 154.

Hatano, Y., Morishita, H., and Nonogaki, S. (1975). *Am. Chem. Meeting Coatings and Plast. Preprints* **35,** 258.

Hatzakis, M. (1969). *J. Electrochem. Soc.* **116,** 1033.

Hatzakis, M. (1975). *J. Vac. Sci. Technol.,* **12,** No. 6, 1276.

Hatzakis, M., Ting, C. H., and Viswanathan, N., (1974), *In Int. Conf. Electron Ion Beam Sci. Technol., 6th* (R. Bakish, ed.), p. 542. Electrochemical Society, Princeton, New Jersey.

Hawryluk, R. J., and Smith, H. I. (1972). *In Int. Conf. Electron Ion Beams Sci. Technol., 5th* (R. Bakish, ed.), p. 51. Electrochemical Society, Princeton, New Jersey.

Hawryluk, R. J., Hawryluk, A. M., and Smith, H. I. (1974). *J. Appl. Phys.* **45,** 2551.

Hawryluk, R. J., Smith, H. I., Soares, A., and Hawryluk, A. M. (1975). *J. Appl. Phys.* **46,** No. 6.

Herzog, R. F., Greeneich, J. S., Everhart, T. E. and Van Duzer, T., (1972). *IEEE Trans. Electron Devices* **ED-19,** 624.

Imamura, S., Sugawara, S., and Murose, K. (1977). *J. Electrochem. Soc.* **124,** No. 7, 1139.

Jones, F., and Hatzakis, M., (1978). *In Proc. Int. Conf. Electron Ion Beam Sci. Technol., 8th* (R. Bakish, ed.), p. 256. Electrochemical Society, Princeton, New Jersey.

Kakuchi, M., Sugawara, S., Murose, K., and Matsuyana, K. (1977). *J. Electrochem. Soc.* **124,** No. 10, 1648.

Ku, H. Y., and Scala, L. C. (1969). *J. Electrochem. Soc.* **116,** 980.

Kyser, D. F., and Murata, R. (1974). *Int. Conf. Electron Ion Beams Sci. Technol., 6th* (R. Bakish, ed.), p. 205. Electrochemical Society, Princeton, New Jersey.

Kyser, D. F., and Viswanathan, N. S. (1975). *J. Vac. Sci. Technol.* **12,** No. 6, 1305.

Lai, J. H., and Sheppard, L. T. (1975), American Chemical Meeting, Coatings and Plastics Preprints, Vol. *35,* p. 252.

Lai, J. H., Sheppard, L. T., Ulmer, R., and Griep, C. (1977). *Polym. Eng. Sci.* **17,** No. 6, 402.

Lenzo, P. V., and Spencer, E. G. (1974). *Appl. Phys. Lett.* **24,** No. 6, 289.

Matsuda, A., Tsuchiya, S., Honma, M., and Hasegawa, K. (1977a). *Polym. Eng. Sci.* **17.**

Matsuda, A., Tsuchiya, S., Honma, M., Hasegawa, K., Nagamatsu, G., and Asano, T. (1977b) *Int. Conf. Microlithogr.* p. 277.

Melliar-Smith, C. M. (1976). *J. Vac. Sci. Technol.* **13,** No. 5, 1008.

Murata, K., Nomura, E., Nagami, K., Kato, T., and Nakata, H. (1978). *Jpn. J. Appl. Phys.* **17,** No. 10, 1851.

Neureuther, A. R. (1978). *J. Vac. Sci. Technol.* **15,** No. 3.

Nonogaki, S., Morishita, H., and Saitou, N. (1974). *Appl. Polym. Symp.* No. 23, p. 117. Wiley, New York.

Nosker, R. W. (1969). *J. Appl. Phys.* **40,** 1872.

Okuyama, Y., Hashimoto, T., and Koguchi, T. (1978). *J. Electrochem. Soc.* **125,** No. 8, 1293.

Ozdemir, F. S., Perkins, W. E., Yim, R., and Wolf, E. D. (1973). *J. Vac. Sci. Technol.* **10,** No. 6, 1008.

Parikh, M. (1978a). *J. Vac. Sci. Technol.* **15,** No, 3, 931.

Parikh, M. (1978b). IBM Research Rep. RJ2252-RJ2254.

Parikh, M. and Kyser, D. F. (1978), IBM Research Rep. RJ2261.

Reinberg, A. R. (1978). IEDM, Washington, D.C., p. 441.

Roberts, E. D. (1974). *Appl. Polym. Symp.* No. 23, p. 87.

Roberts, E. D. (1977). *Vacuum* **26,** No. 10/11, 459.

Schwartz, M. (1959) *In* "Information Transmission, Modulation, and Noise," pp. 382–384. McGraw-Hill, New York.

Sewell, H. (1978). *J. Vac. Sci. Technol.* **15,** No. 3, p. 927.

Sintou, N. (1973), *Jpn. J. Appl. Phys.* **12**, 941.

Somekh, S. (1976). *J. Vac. Sci. Technol.* **13**, No. 5, 1003.

Spiller, E., and Feder, R. (1977). *In* "X-Ray Optics" (H. J. Queissel, ed.), p. 63.

Spiller, E., Feder, R., Topolian, J., Castelloni, E., Romankin, L., and Heritage, M. (1976). *Solid State Technol.* **19**, 64.

Stickel, W. (1978). *J. Vac. Sci. Technol.* **15**, No. 3.

Taylor, G. N., Coquin, G. A., and Somekh, S. (1976). *Soc. Plast. Eng. Regional Tech. Conf., Mid-Hudson Sect.* p. 130.

Thompson, L. F. (1974). *Solid State Technol.* **17**, No. 8, 41.

Thompson, L. F., and Bowden, M. J. (1973). *J. Electrochem. Soc.* **120**, 1722.

Thompson, L. F., Ballantyne, J. P., and Feit, E. D. (1975). *J. Vac. Sci. Technol.* **12**, No. 6.

Thompson, L. F., Stillwagon, L. E., and Doerries, E. M. (1978). *J. Vac. Sci. Technol.* **15**, No. 3.

Thornley, R. F. M., and Sun, T. J. (1965). *J. Electrochem. Soc.* **112**, No. 11, 1151.

Thornton, P. R. (1968). *In* "Scanning Electron Microscopy." Chapman and Hall, London.

Van Duzer, T., Jewett, R. J., Hagouel, P. I., and Neureuther, A. R. (1976). *Soc. Plast. Eng., Regional Tech. Conf., Mid-Hudson Sect.* p. 105.

Varnell, G. L., Spicer, D. F., and Roger, A. C. (1973). *J. Vac. Sci. Technol.* **10**, No. 6.

Wilson, R. G. (1979). Private communication.

Wilson, A. D., Chang, T. H. P., and Kern, A. (1975). *J. Vac. Sci. Technol.* **12**, No. 6, 1240.

Wolf, E. D., Ozdemir, F. S., Perkins, W. E., and Coane, P. (1971). *Rec. Symp. Electron. Ion Laser Beam Tech., 11th.* San Francisco Press, San Francisco, California.

Wolf, E. D., Coane, P. J., and Ozdemir, F. S. (1975). *J. Vac. Sci. Technol.* **12**, No, 6, 1266.

Yoshikawa, Ochi, O., Nagai, H., and Mizushima, Y. (1977). *Appl. Phys. Lett.* **31**, No. 3, 161.

Youngman, C. I., and Wittels, N. D. (1978). *In* "SPIE: Developments in Microlithography III," p. 54. SPIE, Bellingham, Washington.

3

Electron-beam lithography machines

DONALD R. HERRIOTT

BELL LABORATORIES
MURRAY HILL, NEW JERSEY

GEORGE R. BREWER

HUGHES RESEARCH LABORATORIES
MALIBU, CALIFORNIA

141

I. GENERAL DESCRIPTION

The process of electron-beam lithography was shown in Chapters 1 and 2 to be based on the drawing of patterns in a resist material by the use of a fine electron beam. The characteristics of the machine that generates, focuses, and deflects the electron beam in a controlled manner over the area to be written are of first-order importance in determining the technical and economic utility of electron-beam lithography. The material in this chapter provides a detailed description of the characteristics of the several key components that make up the total machine, the various forms of machines in use for electron-beam lithography, a discussion of machine design and writing strategies, and performance characteristics of representative machines. The intent of this chapter is to provide the reader with sufficient information to understand in depth the principles, operation, design tradeoffs, and performance of machines to the degree necessary to use them effectively.

In order to draw the submicron patterns for which electron-beam lithography is suited, the electron beam must be focused to a diameter of $0.01-0.5$ μm. Furthermore, in order that the time required to expose the resist be short, the current density in this focused spot must be on the order of $10-100$ A/cm^2. Most thermionic electron emitters can provide a current density (with reasonable life) of a few amperes per centimeter squared, from a cathode on the order of $10-100$ μm in diameter. Therefore, the electron beam must be demagnified by a suitable electron-optical lens system; the diameter demagnification required is seen to be as high as 10^4. In addition, this focused beam must be directed with high precision, by a beam deflection system, to any chosen point in the scan field in response to control signals from the pattern generator. The technology of such machines for electron-beam lithography has its origin largely in the scanning electron microscope that was first introduced commercially in the early 1960s. In fact, many of the lithography machines now in use are scanning electron microscopes that have been modified to make them more suitable for pattern writing. However, over the past several years machines have been designed and built especially for lithography; such custom design is especially important for high throughput machines.

A schematic diagram of a complete electron-beam lithography system

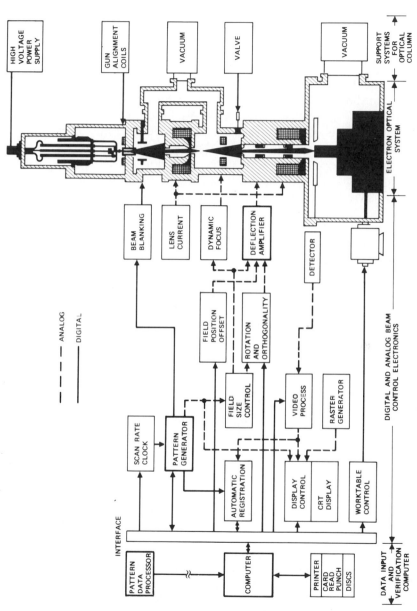

FIG. 3.1 Block diagram of an electron-beam lithography system. [From Speth *et al.* (1975).]

is shown in Fig. 3.1 (modified from Speth *et al.*, 1975). This system consists of four main subsystems, viz.: (1) the means for data input, usually a tape or disk memory system and a teletypewriter, and a computer that controls the pattern generator and other beam control units; (2) the several elements that carry out the computer commands for beam control and provide feedback data for pattern display; (3) the electron-optical column; and (4) the support systems, including vacuum pumps, power supplies, etc., for the electron-optical column. The principal components that are involved in the generation of the patterns to be written and the deflection and control of the beam are shown in Fig. 3.1 by the heavy border. The principal elements of this system will be discussed in this chapter.

As illustrated in Fig. 1.7, there are three generic classes of applications for an electron-beam machine, and the optimal design of the machine depends on which of these ways the machine will be used. A machine intended for the fabrication of masks for photolithographic reproduction, with linewidths typically $1-2$ μm or greater, will be designed to produce a relatively large ($0.25-1$-μm) beam diameter and must exhibit great precision in pattern location over an entire wafer size mask so that the sequential masks in the set can be registered accurately. A machine designed for laboratory use in the direct writing fabrication of developmental devices or of masks for high resolution replication must provide the smallest possible spot ($0.01-0.1$ μm) so that device structures with the highest possible resolution can be fabricated, but the patterns can usually be reregistered on each scan field. The device throughput of this type of machine can be moderate. A machine built for the production of devices by direct writing must be capable of the highest possible throughput; therefore, very fast exposure and stage motion are required. Obviously a machine capable of producing a very fine spot can be used to write patterns with broad lines, e.g., for a photolithographic mask, but it will be very slow; therefore, its use for this purpose will not be economical. As a result, the design of electron-beam lithography machines is tending to be specialized to the intended use.

II. THE ELECTRON-OPTICAL COLUMN

A. *Types of Columns*

The electron-optical column is the heart of the electron-beam microfabrication system; all of the other subsystems shown in Fig. 3.1 are to control or support the electron-optical subsystem, which is the essential active element of the system. The electron-optical column consists of a source of electrons (the cathode), one or more lenses, means for beam blanking, beam limiting apertures, and the deflection unit. These elements

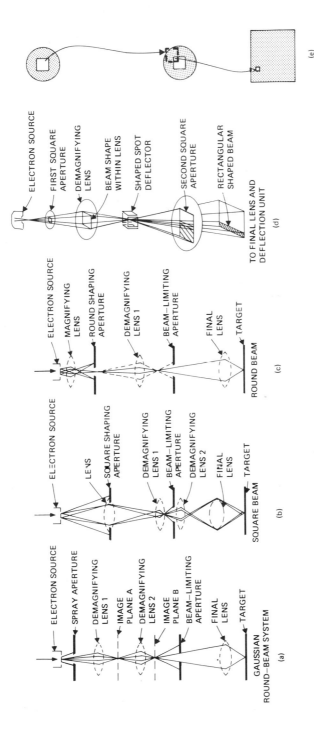

FIG. 3.2 Illustrations of the beam forming parts of several forms of electron-optical columns used in electron-beam microfabrication systems; (a), (b), and (c) are modified from Chang *et al.* (1977); (d) adapted from Pfeiffer (1978).

can be arranged in different ways in the column, depending on the purpose of the particular column and somewhat on the preferences of the designer.

Figure 3.2 shows several configurations of the beam forming elements of an electron-optical column that are in current use. Figure 3.2a shows the configuration adapted from scanning electron microscopes. In this type of column the cross-over region of the beam (to be discussed later—see Fig. 3.5) is imaged by three demagnifying or condenser lenses onto the target, with two intermediate image–object planes (*A* and *B*). A spray aperture is placed after the gun to collect those electrons on the outer fringe of the beam emerging from the gun, thus preventing them from striking the column walls or from forming a low density cloud surrounding the main beam spot on the target. A subsequent beam limiting aperture after the second lens serves the same purpose, viz., to shear off the fringe electrons at that plane. Because of the transverse thermal velocities of the electrons emitted from the cathode, the spot produced by this type of column will exhibit a gaussian, not rectangular, current density profile (see Fig. 3.3). This type of column is capable of creating the smallest spot diameter, e.g., down to ≈ 100 Å.

The type of column illustrated in Fig. 3.2a is capable of producing only a round spot, whereas the microelectronic device patterns to be drawn are usually composed of rectangles. Therefore, such a pattern can be drawn more rapidly by the use of a beam with a square (or even rectangular) cross section. In Fig. 3.2b a square aperture has been placed in the beam in the first lens. The subsequent demagnifying lenses image this square aperture onto the target, thereby causing the spot at the target to have a

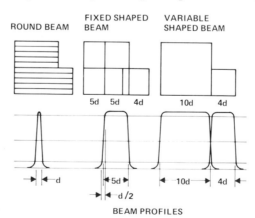

FIG. 3.3 Illustrations of the techniques of exposing patterns by the use of a small round (Gaussian) spot, shown on the left, vis-a-vis a fixed or shaped aperture. The graphs in the lower part of the figure represent the current density profiles in the beam. [From Pfeiffer (1978).]

square cross section. Because electron trajectories are rotated as well as focused by a magnetic lens, the strength of the lenses (i.e., the coil current) after the shaping aperture must be accurately stabilized to prevent rotation of the square image on the target. This complication can be avoided while still achieving a more uniform spot at the target if the shaping aperture is round, so that a circular spot is imaged onto the target, as shown in Fig. 3.2c. This configuration is superior to that in Fig. 3.2a if the target spot diameter desired is greater than the minimum (gaussian) diameter that is characteristic of the optical system.

The column configurations shown in Figs. 3.1 and 3.2 contain different numbers of lenses, viz., two, three, and four. The choice of the number of lenses to be employed depends on the purpose of the instrument, e.g., in order to achieve a high degree of demagnification, or to have available a large variation in demagnification (i.e., beam diameter), a relatively large number of lenses is required. An electron-beam lithography system that is designed for a large beam with little size variation can involve only two lenses (or in special cases, one). The use of a small number of lenses results in a short column, with greater mechanical stability and freedom from effects of stray magnetic fields. Systems b, c, and d (Fig. 3.2) offer an advantage in spot stability because a physical object, viz., the aperture, is imaged onto the target to form a spot, in contrast with (a) in which the crossover is imaged. The crossover position can vary because of instabilities in the gun.

The configuration of electron-optical column with the highest writing speed, but with corresponding increased complexity, is shown in Fig. 3.2d. In principle this technique is capable of creating any rectangular (and square, of course) shape desired in the spot; furthermore, the spot shape and size can be adjusted electronically and therefore rapidly. In this type of column, a first intercepting square aperture causes the beam to have a square shape. The first lens images the first aperture onto a second plane containing a square aperture. The position of this image on the second plane can be varied electronically by the deflection unit. That is, the square beam can be positioned to overlap any desired portion of the second aperture (see Fig. 3.2e). The transmitted electrons will be shaped with a cross section given by the overlap part of the second aperture and the image of the first aperture. This transmitted beam is then imaged onto the target by a subsequent deflection unit and final lens. In this way the size and shape of the beam at the target can be varied while keeping the electron-beam current density constant. This variable aperture approach and variants thereof has been described by a number of authors, including Goto *et al.* (1978), Pfeiffer (1978), Stickel and Pfeiffer (1978), and Thomson *et al.* (1978).

The way in which this variable shaped beam can be used to draw a pattern is shown in Fig. 3.3, in comparison to the many pass technique required by a small round spot. The resulting decreased writing time for the variable spot is evident.

The means for forming a small electron-beam spot on a target were discussed above. In order to use this electron beam to create a pattern, it must be deflected in a controlled manner so as to expose the desired areas of the resist. Beam deflection is usually accomplished by bending the beam by the use of magnetic coils. The choice of magnetic, versus electrostatic, deflection results from the lower deflection distortion that magnetic coils provide and the freedom from instability due to electrostatic charging on electric deflection plates by stray electrons impinging on surface contaminant films. The three generic classes of magnetic deflection units are illustrated in Fig. 3.4. The method used in scanning electron microscopes is shown in Fig. 3.4a, which offers the advantage, for that application, of close final lens-to-target spacing. With the resulting short focal length lens, the spherical aberration is lower and the spot diameter smaller. The double deflection shown is produced by two sequential opposing magnetic coils arranged so that the beam passes through the center of the lens so as to reduce off-axis aberration effects. The disadvantage of this technique is the relatively small scan field possible without spot distortion. The scan field area can be increased by placing a single coil inside of the final lens, so that it is closer to the target (Fig. 3.4b). There is a disadvantage in this arrangement because of the eddy–current coupling between the alternating fields of the scan coils and the magnetic materials of the lens. This coupling can result in a time delay in the deflection; that is, the beam position may not accurately track the deflection signal. It will

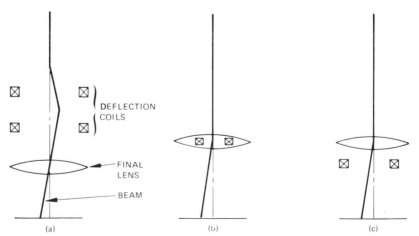

FIG. 3.4   Three arrangements of magnetic deflection coils: (a) prelens deflection; (b) inlens deflection; (c) postlens deflection.

be shown later that this problem can be corrected; therefore, the configuration in Fig. 3.4b is a currently used approach. A third possible configuration, shown in Fig. 3.4c, involves placement of the deflection coil between the final lens and the target. This last arrangement allows larger scan field sizes, but requires a longer focal length lens with attendant greater spherical aberration. Various hybrid combinations of these basic configurations are also possible.

In order to turn the beam on when it is in the correct position to expose the resist and off at other times, it is necessary to include a beam blanking unit in the electron-optical column (refer to Fig. 3.1). This unit consists of electrodes or coils for electrostatic or magnetic deflection of the beam so that it is totally intercepted on an electrode. This blanking unit is, therefore, usually placed either at a beam cross-over position, between the gun and the spray aperture, or preceding a shaping aperture. This blanking unit can be the cause of instability or drift of the electron beam, due to electrostatic charging of electron-beam polymerized organic contaminants on the edge of the aperture. This unit and its driving amplifier must be designed to provide very fast deflection speed, so that the time between beam on and off is no longer than about 5 ns, in order to avoid writing speed limitation.

B. *Electron-Optical Design Relationships*

This section presents a summary of analytical methods that are useful in the design and optimization of performance of the electron-optical column. For more information, the reader is referred to the literature references cited, especially Mulvey (1967), Wells (1974a), and Grivet (1965a).

In principle, the first-order design of an electron-optical column involving several lenses and limiting apertures can be carried out by simple graphical techniques to establish the desired object and image planes, lens positions and focal lengths, and aperture sizes and positions. A more elegant and revealing method is the use of a matrix representation of the electron-optical elements. This method provides a means for making design tradeoffs but is cumbersome unless a computer is used for the calculations. This first-order electron-optical formalism commonly neglects the effects of space charge and aberrations; the former are usually negligible in all but very high beam current systems, but the latter are not. However, the effects of aberrations can be included as a correction to the first-order treatment. Under these conditions, the linear electron-optical characteristics of each element of the beam transport system can be expressed by a transformation which relates the radius, or off-axis position, and slope of trajectories at the output end of each optical element to these quantities at the input plane. This transformation takes the form of a matrix; by simply multiplying together the matrices of each optical element, the complete electron-optical characteristics of the beam transport system can, in principle, be determined.

In those usual situations where the electrons move close, and with small angle, to the axis, the familiar paraxial ray equation can be applied to determine the trajectories. This equation is a linear homogeneous second-order differential equation that has solutions of the form

$$r_i = a_{11}r_o + a_{12}r'_o$$
$$r'_i = a_{21}r_o + a_{22}r'_o \tag{3.1}$$

where r and r' represent transverse position and slope in the r plane ($y^2 + x^2 = r^2$), and the subscripts o and i refer to the object and image planes, respectively. This formulation is valid in regions where the electron energy is constant, i.e., downstream of the electron-gun anode. Therefore, each electron-optical unit of the beam transport system can be characterized by an input plane (which is the object) and an output plane (at which the image is formed), at each of which the transverse position and slope (or effective momentum) of the ray are specified. The optical coupling between these two planes can then be represented by the above system of linear equations, or more compactly by using the matrix notation (Halbach, 1964; Fert, 1952)

$$\begin{pmatrix} r_i \\ r'_i \end{pmatrix} = \underbrace{\begin{pmatrix} a_{11} & a_{12} \\ a_{21} & a_{22} \end{pmatrix}}_{M} \begin{pmatrix} r_o \\ r'_o \end{pmatrix} \tag{3.2}$$

If M_{kl} denotes the matrix representing the optical element between the kth and lth planes of the system, the total beam transport system can be characterized by the product of the unit matrices*

$$\begin{pmatrix} r_i \\ \cdot \\ \cdot \\ \cdot \\ r'_{ix} \end{pmatrix} = M_{kl} \cdots M_{34} \cdot M_{23} \cdot M_{12} \begin{pmatrix} r_o \\ \cdot \\ \cdot \\ \cdot \\ r'_o \end{pmatrix} \tag{3.3}$$

The matrix elements can be expressed in terms of the parameters of the electron-optical elements (Wilson and Brewer, 1973; Dahl, 1973; Banford, 1966; Steffen, 1965). For example, using this technique, the spot diameter at the target (the final image plane) can be represented in terms of the beam conditions at the initial object plane (e.g., the beam crossover) and

* The reader is cautioned that the matrices must be multiplied in the correct sequence. If the object plane is at the beginning of the system (the entrance to unit 1, 2) the sequence is as shown in Eq. (3.3).

the parameters of the several electron-optical elements in the beam transport system.

C. The Aberration Free Beam

In order to discuss the behavior of an *ideal* electron beam, assume that the gun forms a real crossover outside of the anode. This ideal crossover is a point; therefore, the current density over the cross section of the beam can be represented as a delta function, as shown by the left inset drawing in Fig. 3.5. A magnetic lens (or series of lenses) is placed and adjusted to form an image of the beam from the crossover plane onto the target (shown by the solid rays in Fig. 3.5). If this lens has a magnification M,[†] the spot diameter on the target will be equal to the diameter at the crossover divided by M. Furthermore, if this lens is free of aberrations, it will form a stigmatic image;[*] that is, any ray passing a given point in the crossover plane will be imaged at a corresponding point in the image plane (the target), independent of the angle of the ray through that point in the object plane (shown by the dashed lines). Under these conditions the distribution of current density in the spot at the target will be a faithful reproduction of that at the cross-over.

Unfortunately, this ideal beam cannot exist even in an aberration free

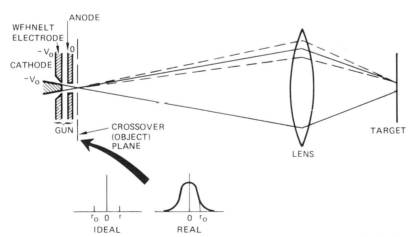

FIG. 3.5   Electron trajectories in an elementary gun focusing lens electron-optical column. The dashed lines denote trajectories of electrons emitted with a transverse velocity component.

---

[*] Numerically, $M = (a_{11})^{-1}$ in the matrix in Eq. (3.2).

[†] This condition is expressed mathematically by letting the term a_{12} in the matrix of Eq. (3.2) be zero, so that r_i does not depend on r_0'.

optical system. The reason for this nonideal behavior is that electrons emitted from a cathode held at a finite temperature will have a distribution of initial velocities and directions with respect to the cathode surface. That is, the electrons are not all emitted in a direction normal to the cathode, but with a Maxwellian distribution in magnitude and direction; this distribution has an equivalent temperature equal to that of the cathode. Because of this component of velocity transverse to the direction of acceleration that results from the electric field in the gun, the electrons will drift sideways (both radially into and out of the circular beam). By the time the electrons reach the crossover plane this transverse drift has resulted in a variation of current density with radius that is Gaussian* rather than uniform, as shown in the right inset drawing in Fig. 3.5. Since the lens forms a stigmatic image of the beam shape at the crossover, the current density distribution at the target will also be Gaussian. The existence of this transverse initial emission velocity, with consequent modification in the beam profile, is one of the principal limitations on the formation of small, high density beams.

Langmuir (1937) has analyzed the effects of transverse thermal emission velocities on the focusing of a beam of charged particles. This subject has been discussed also by Pierce (1949), Moss (1968a), and Meltzer (1957). The result of Langmuir's analysis is an equation relating the maximum current density (J_m) that can be focused toward a spot within a convergence half angle α:

$$J_m = J_c \left(1 + \frac{eV_0}{kT_c}\right) \sin^2\alpha \approx \frac{J_c V_0 \alpha^2}{T_c/11,600} \tag{3.4}$$

where V_0 is the potential corresponding to the electron energy, k Boltzmann's constant (1.37×10^{-23} j/°K), T_c the cathode or electron source temperature, and J_c the cathode current density. This relation is called the Langmuir limit and is independent of the type of electron-optical system used to focus the electrons. It does not assure that the current density J_m can be achieved; it merely expresses an upper limit. As a practical matter, some of the electrons with high transverse velocity must be collected on a beam defining aperture in order for the rest of the electrons to be focusable with current density J_m into a cone angle 2α. This tradeoff has been analyzed by Pierce (1949).

The term *Gaussian beam diameter* (d_G) is usually used to denote the diameter of the beam in the absence of aberrations, i.e., one distorted from ideal only by the effects of transverse thermal velocities. The current density in this beam will depend on radius as $J = J_p \exp -(r/\sigma)^2$,

---

* With an equivalent temperature that is given by the cathode temperature multiplied by the ratio of emitting area to cross-over area (Cutler and Hines, 1955).

where σ denotes the standard deviation of the distribution; σ is given by $(kT_c/eV_0)^{1/2}$ multiplied by a term that depends on the geometry of the gun and beam [see, e.g., Cutler and Hines (1955)]. The total current in this beam is given by $I = \pi\sigma^2 J_p$. For some purposes the actual Gaussian beam is treated as an equivalent beam of uniform current density J_p and diameter d_G, carrying equal current as the Gaussian beam ($I = \frac{1}{4}\pi J_p d_G^2$). Then $d_G = 2\sigma$ (σ is the radius on the Gaussian distribution at which the current density has decreased to e^{-1} of its peak value) and 63% of the current in the Gaussian beam is within this diameter d_G.

The Gaussian beam diameter can be related to the parameters of the gun and the focused beam by making use of the Langmuir limit equation [Eq. (3.4)]. In this case, if the diameter is defined arbitrarily as that circle encompassing 80% of the beam current, then the current density can be written

$$J = \frac{0.8 I_0}{\frac{1}{4}\pi d_G^2} \leq \frac{J_c V_0 \alpha^2}{T_c/11,600}$$

so that

$$d_G = (1/\alpha) \left[I_0 T_c/(1.14 \times 10^4 J_c V_0) \right]^{1/2} \qquad (3.5)$$

Another quantity that is useful in characterizing electron guns and beams is called the brightness. In light optics the brightness or luminous intensity is defined as the flux per unit solid angle emitted by a luminous source. By analogy the brightness B of a source of charged particles is defined as the current density J per unit solid angle Ω:

$$B \equiv J/\Omega \qquad (3.6)$$

The units of this parameter are amperes per square centimeter per steradian. If the current is emitted from (or converges toward) a small area A_s through a cone of included half angle α,

$$B \approx J/(\pi\alpha^2) \qquad (3.7)$$

if α is small. If the beam moves through a region of constant potential, e.g., downstream of the gun anode, the brightness is conserved, i.e., the brightness of the beam at the target will be approximately equal to its value from the gun.* The brightness can be related to the gun parameters by using the Langmuir limit equation [Eq. (3.5)]:

$$B = J_m/(\pi\alpha^2) = J_c V_0/(\pi T_c/11,600)$$

Thus, the maximum attainable brightness in a beam is determined by the

---

* This invariant can be derived, e.g., from the Lagrange–Helmholtz relation to show that the product of linear and angular magnifications is a constant (in a constant potential region) (Grivet, 1965b).

emission current density J_c, the cathode temperature T_c, and the accelerating potential on the gun anode V_0. This value can be increased in any subsequent electron-optical transformation only by accelerating the electrons to higher energy.

By inserting the above equations into Eq. (3.5), the gaussian beam diameter can be related to the beam brightness B:*

$$d_G = (1/\alpha)(I_0/3.08B)^{1/2} \qquad (3.8)$$

The cathodes in electron guns of the type discussed here are usually operated temperature limited, i.e., the emission current density is limited by the temperature of the cathode, not by the space charge of electrons between the cathode and anode. However, for reference, in guns operated under space charge limited conditions, the term *perveance* is used to characterize the gun structure. Perveance is defined as the current divided by the three-halves power of the accelerating voltage.

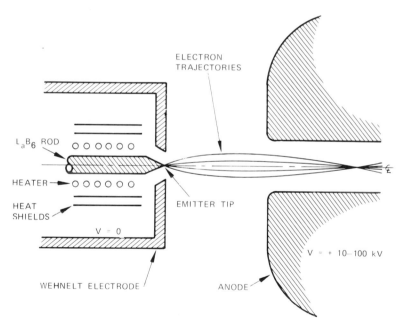

FIG. 3.6 Cross section of electron gun showing typical electron trajectories forming a crossover downstream of the anode. This form of gun uses a lanthanum hexaboride cathode but guns with other forms of cathode have similar geometry.

* For reference, it is noted that the term 3.08 in Eq. (3.8) would have been 2.47 if 100% of the current in the beam had been used in the derivation of Eq. (3.5).

D.   *The Electron Gun*

The electron gun serves to generate the desired solid cylindrical beam for subsequent action by the other elements of the electron-optical column. While the detailed design of guns used in electron-beam lithography systems differ in detail, this generic class of guns generally resemble the drawing in Fig. 3.6 (see, e.g., Wells, 1974). The gun consists of an electron source or emitter and two or more electrodes held at different potentials; the anode, usually at ground potential, will accelerate the electrons to their final velocity from a cathode held at negative potential corresponding to the desired beam energy. The purpose of the Wehnelt electrode, held at an appropriate potential close to that of the emitter, is to force the electric field lines, especially near the emitter tip, to be of such a shape that the intensity of the electric field at this tip is the proper value and the electrons pursue trajectories so as to form a beam passing through the anode aperture. This beam can be convergent, as shown in Fig. 3.6, so that a crossover is formed. In systems of the type illustrated in Fig. 3.2a, this crossover is imaged onto the target by the subsequent lenses. In those kinds of systems in which a physical aperture is imaged (Figs. 3.2b,c,d), a somewhat different form of gun must be used, one that will provide uniform current density over the aperture. The beam divergence required to attain this uniform illumination can be obtained by proper gun design and/or by the use of a magnifying lens.

It is seen in Eq. (3.4) that a tradeoff must be made between the maximum current density at the target J_m and the convergence angle (α). It will be shown later that a small value of α is desirable to reduce aberrations. However, a small value of α implies low J_m unless the cathode current density J_c and/or the beam voltage V_0 is high. There are other constraints on beam voltage (Chapter 2) so that J_c must be made high.

In order to provide a beam of high current density confined in a small included angle from the axis, the gun must exhibit a high value of the brightness parameter that is used to characterize these guns. This condition means that the electron current density at the emitter must be large and the emitting area small.

Three types of electron emitters are used as electron sources. In scanning electron microscopes and some microfabrication systems, the emitter consists of a tungsten hairpin, which is a piece of tungsten wire bent so as to present a sharp radius and thereby small emitting area at the position of the emitter tip. This wire is heated to $\approx 2800°K$, by passing current through it, to provide thermionic electron emission. Such cathodes exhibit a work function of about 4.5 eV and current densities of ~ 10 A/cm² at 3000°K, corresponding to a brightness of about 5×10^4

$A/cm^2/SR$. The lifetime of these filament emitters is typically 10–50 hr. While their mechanical stability (e.g., tendency to vibrate and maintain position) is marginal, the emission stability (uniformity and constancy of emission current density) is superior to the brighter sources. Another form of thermionic emitter is made of a rod of lanthanum hexaboride (LaB_6) machined to a sharp tip (radius ~ 1–10 μm). The work function of LaB_6 is ~ 2.4 eV, significantly lower than tungsten, so that the LaB_6 emitter can provide comparable emission at a lower operating temperature. Typical values of the emission parameters are 100 A/cm^2 at 2000°K for a brightness of $\sim 10^6$ $A/cm^2/SR$ with a 10 μm tip radius. The LaB_6 emitter is used extensively in modern high current electron-beam systems. The operation of this type emitter is somewhat more sensitive to ambient pressure in the gun region; longer life and more freedom from evaporation products accrue from operation in a good vacuum (10^{-6} Torr or better). Under such conditions, several hundred hours lifetime is typical.

The third generic class of electron source is the field emitter. In its simplest form, this emitter consists of a tungsten rod that is ground to a sharp tip (or a wire that is electrolytically polished to a small tip radius). The gun configuration—especially the Wehnelt electrode—must be arranged so that an electric field value of $\sim 3 \times 10^7$ V/cm is present at the sharp tip (radius ~ 0.1–1 μm) (Good and Mueller, 1956), at which the current density will be $\geq 10^2$ and brightness up to $\sim 10^8$ $A/cm^2/SR$. It is, of course, possible to heat a field emitter and thereby making it easier for the electrons to escape than under the high electric-field condition alone. This form of emission is called thermionic field (TF) emission. Either a tungsten or LaB_6 emitter can be operated under this condition, but the most effective such source is the zirconium-coated tungsten TF cathode reported by Swanson and Martin (1975). This emitter exhibits a low work function (2.6–2.8 eV) and has been shown to provide current densities up to $\sim 10^7$ A/cm^2 and brightness values of 10^9–10^{10} $A/cm^2/SR$ at ~ 1400°K. This cathode is also more stable under high vacuum conditions, i.e., $p \leq 2 \times 10^{-8}$ Torr. The characteristics of electron guns using field emitter sources has been studied by Wardly (1973) and by Broers (1972, 1973). Because of the high sensitivity of field emitted current to electric field and therefore anode voltage, guns employing field emitter sources frequently use two anodes, one to adjust the current and a second to set the total accelerating potential of the beam. The beam from a gun employing a field emitter will generally exhibit either a small diameter crossover or no crossover (beam is divergent), so that magnification is required to form the spot (in the latter case the virtual source area is imaged onto the target).

In the operation of an electron gun for microfabrication, the time stability of current and beam position are important considerations. Obviously the heater and high voltage power supplies must exhibit a high degree of stability. In addition, variations in the work function of composite cathodes such as the LaB_6 and Zr/W can occur due to changes in temperature, pressure, and ambient contamination. As with any low work function surface, the emitting facets of the polycrystalline LaB_6 emitter are susceptible to selective contamination that can increase the work function, resulting in instabilities in current and emission uniformity. Some machine applications require extreme areal uniformity of emission, e.g., for the illumination of an aperture that is to be imaged onto the target. In such cases, the superior uniformity of a tungsten emitter makes it the better choice, despite the lower brightness. The lateral and axial position of the emitter tip with respect to the Wehnelt electrode can affect the transverse position of the spot at the target and the current and trajectories, respectively. For example, a 0.001 in. lateral shift in tip position can seriously alter the location of the writing spot. A high operating temperature can result in severe evaporation of contaminants that can induce voltage breakdown and charging of column elements, and thermal stress resulting in emitter movement.

The electron-optical properties of the field emitter gun have been analyzed by Wiesner and Everhart (1973) and by Worster (1970). They find, for example, that the spherical aberration coefficient $C_s \sim 0.4$–0.7 mm, depending on the shape of the Wehnelt electrode face. Some gun designs produce a crossover in or near the gun, as shown in Fig. 3.6; other designs can result in beam divergence without a crossover.

Another parameter of importance is the longitudinal energy spread among the electrons in the beam; a large energy spread will result in a large focused spot because of the chromatic aberration in the focusing lenses. Wells (1974) reports that a tungsten hairpin emitter shows ~ 1.6–3 eV spread, about 2–3 eV for LaB_6 and 0.22 for the tungsten field emitter. Swanson and Martin (1975) show that the energy spread from a Zr/W emitter is less than 0.9 eV. This spread in electron energy is generally due to patchiness on the emitter, i.e., electrons emitted from microscopic regions of different work function will have slightly different total energy after acceleration.

There is another effect that causes significant energy spread in high current beams; this energy spread can form a limit on spot size through the chromatic aberration of the lenses. In high density regions of the electron beam (e.g., at a crossover), the coulomb interaction between individual electrons in the beam can give rise to an exchange of energy between them. The collective effect of these many interactions is an increase in energy spread of the beam. This phenomenon is called the Boersch effect (Boersch, 1954) and has been analyzed by Loeffler (1969), Zimmerman (1970), and Knauer (1979), with experimental confirmation by Pfeiffer

(1971). Knauer shows that the energy spread is proportional to

$$[(Jr_0/\alpha^2)/eV_0^{1/2}]^{1/2}\{1 + [kT_b/(eV_0\alpha^2)]\}^{-1/4}$$

where T_b is the temperature of the electrons in the beam. When the second term in the bracket is small, this equation reduces to $(Br_0)^{1/2}/V_0^{1/4}$ from Pfeiffer, where B and r_0 represent the gun brightness and radius of the cross-over. Therefore, as gun brightness is increased to provide faster writing speed, the design must produce a smaller crossover or excess energy spread will be observed. Since the energy spread due to this Boersch effect and that discussed above due to thermal or work function effects are statistically independent, the total energy spread is equal to the rms sum of the two terms.

Typical values of this sum are ~ 1 eV for a LaB_6 emitter, ~ 3 eV for a tungsten hairpin emitter and 2 to 3 eV for a field emitter. The Boersch effect can, of course, take place at any subsequent crossovers in the electron-optical column; this interaction can increase the energy spread at the target to ~ 2.4 and 4.5 eV, respectively. This effect can form a serious spot size limitation in high current systems.

E.   Magnetic Lens Characteristics

The magnetic lenses that focus and demagnify the electron beam are the most critical elements in the electron-optical column. The characteristics of the lenses determine to a large degree the size, shape, and current capability of the electron beam. The user of an electron-beam system must understand these characteristics in order to obtain the best performance from his instrument.

A magnetic lens in its simplest form is illustrated in Fig. 3.7. A coil of N turns, carrying current I_c, creates a magnetic flux density of approximately uniform magnitude B_0 on the axis over the length of the gap L_g in the surrounding iron shell. An electron entering this lens with velocity corresponding to potential V_0 will interact with the radial component of magnetic field, causing the electron to rotate around the axis. The angular velocity component, in interaction with the axial component of the magnetic field, causes the electron to be focused inward (all magnetic lenses are convergent). In the absence of aberrations all electrons are focused toward a point on the axis a distance f from the center of the lens. If this focal length f is large compared with the axial length of the field L_g, the focal length is given approximately by

$$f \cong 8V_0/(L_g B_0^2 \eta) \tag{3.9}$$

where $\eta = e/m$. Therefore, focal length is reduced by creating a high magnetic field (i.e., a large value of the exciting ampere turns in the coil,

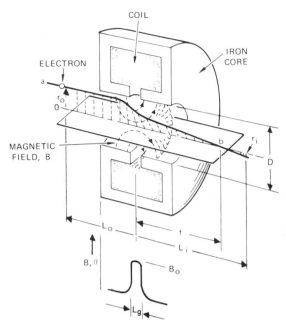

FIG. 3.7 Cross section of a simple magnetic lens and the trajectory of an electron ray in this magnetic field. Note the rotation of the trajectory around the axis as the electron passes through the lens.

NI_c) and a low voltage. In passing through a magnetic lens the electrons are rotated by an angle θ, given by

$$\theta = [\eta B_0^2/(8V_0)]^{1/2} L_g \tag{3.10}$$

Since all electrons are rotated through this angle, in principle any geometrical shape that is characteristic of the beam cross section at entrance will be rotated and the shape preserved. For example, if the beam has a square cross section at entrance, it will be square near the focal point but now rotated through an angle with respect to the original orientation. In practice, due to lens aberrations, the shape of the image will be distorted in this rotation.

The magnification of this ideal symmetrical lens is given by (see Fig. 3.7)

$$r_0/r_i \simeq L_0/L_i$$

where L_i and L_0 are the distances from the center of the lens to the image (the spot) and the object, respectively. Therefore, in order to obtain a small spot, the target on which the pattern is to be drawn must be close to the lens. That is, the distance from lens to target, called the *working distance*, must be short compared with the distance from the object (e.g., to the next lens). Typical distances in a microfabrication system with a thermionic source are $L_i \sim 2-5$ cm and $L_0 = 25-15$ cm, giving a magnification in the final lens of $\sim \frac{1}{12} - \frac{1}{3}$. Graphs and tables showing focal length and other lens characteristics for a variety of lens geometries are given in El Kareh (1970).

In practice, a magnetic lens does not exhibit exactly the characteristics of the ideal lens described above. Specifically, the beam is not focused to a spot which is a perfect demagnified image of the object (the entering beam), but aberrations in the lens cause distortions of the beam. Several of the more important of these distortions will be described. More complete information can be found in the extensive electron-optics literature.* In addition to these effects, the focal characteristics of magnetic lenses can change due to thermal drift as the temperature changes with variation in coil current.

F. Aberrations

As a result of the aberrations present in all real lenses and other electron-optical components, the rays that represent the electron trajectories will not behave in the simple manner described above. Rather, they will be displaced so that the focused spot will be larger than expected: it can be off axis; the beam may not be in sharp focus over the entire image plane; the spot can be distorted in shape; etc. In general, aberrations can be inherent in the configuration of electric or magnetic fields of the lens and can be caused by mechanical effects such as off-axis rays, ellipticity of the lens opening, tilt of the lens, etc., or by electronic effects such as variation in power supply voltage, in magnetic lens excitation current, stray magnetic fields, etc. These effects can manifest themselves in a distortion of the *shape* of the beam or change in the *position* of the beam from its desired location. Any deviation in the shape or position of the beam from those the machine user desires will cause distortion of the high resolution patterns that are written. These aberration effects (together with deflection aberrations to be discussed later) must therefore be of first-order concern to both the designer and user of electron-beam lithography machines.

Certain forms of aberrations produce an enlarged beam spot instead of a point focus. This smallest spot diameter d is called the disk of least confusion or aberration disk; it is related to the convergence angle of the beam at the target α by an equation of the form

$$d \propto C\alpha^n$$

* See, e.g., Grivet (1965, Chapter 16, "Practical Considerations," and Chapter 7, "Theory"); Klemperer (1953, Chapters 6 and 8); Cosslett (1950, Chapter V).

where $n = 1, 2, 3$. However, in optical systems with cylindrical symmetry, the even powers vanish for geometrical aberrations. C is the aberration coefficient. The most common forms of aberration are described below in the usual order of their importance.

Spherical aberration is a defect caused by focusing fields that are invariably stronger near the electrodes that produce them, usually resulting in a focal position of edge electrons that is closer to the lens than the focal position of paraxial rays (Fig. 3.8). As illustrated in Fig. 3.8, aberrations will result in a minimum beam diameter, viz., the disk of least confusion. This minimum diameter results from the crossing of several electron trajectories passing through the lens that do not come to a focus at the same axial position. In the following equations the convergence half-angle α_i refers to the image space, i.e., at the target end of the beam. The disk of least confusion due to spherical aberration, of diameter d_s, is given by

$$d_s = \tfrac{1}{2} C_s \alpha_i^3 \tag{3.11}$$

where C_s is the spherical aberration constant, usually related to the paraxial focal length f by $C_s = K_s f$; K_s is dependent on the excitation and on the lens geometry. The spherical aberration effect is lower for lenses

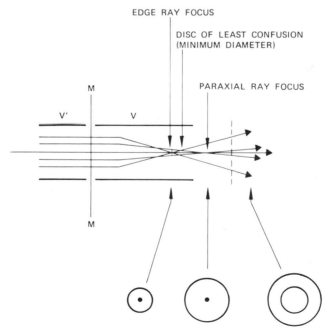

FIG. 3.8 Typical paths of electron trajectories focused by a lens that exhibits spherical aberration. For cylindrically symmetric lenses, C_s is always negative, i.e., the outer ray crosses the axis closer to the lens than the paraxial ray, as shown here.

with short focal length. Graphs of K_s versus excitation for several lens geometries are given by Fert and Durandeau (1967); generally $0.5 < K_s < 1.5$ for high excitations.

It is essentially impossible to eliminate spherical aberration from a beam by any subsequent electron-optical action. It is therefore of great importance to design and operate the elements for minimum C_s. This criterion is especially important in the final lens, where the attainment of the smallest beam diameter can be limited by spherical aberration in this lens. Assuming that the spherical aberration coefficient of a given final lens has been minimized by proper design, the effect of this aberration on spot diameter can be reduced, at the expense of beam current, by placing a limiting aperture in or before the lens. This aperture will reduce the convergence angle α of the focused beam, and thereby the effect of spherical aberration. However, it is seen from Eq. (3.4) that this change will reduce the maximum current density that can be focused toward the target. These kinds of tradeoffs between resolution (spot diameter) and writing speed (current density) are an integral part of the optimization of machine design and operation for a given application.

The importance of the final lens in any series of lenses can be seen from an equation for the total aberration resulting from two lenses in series; the effect of additional lenses can obviously be determined by repeated use of the relation for two lenses. Liebmann (1949) has derived a simple relation for the spherical aberration coefficient C_s of two lenses, each exhibiting a value of spherical aberration coefficient C_{s1} and C_{s2}, with focal lengths f_1 and f_2, spaced distance L apart (between principal planes). This equation is (expressed in terms of $K_s = C_s/f$)

$$K_s = \frac{K_{s1} f_2^2 + K_{s2}(L - f_1)^2}{(f_1 + f_2 - L)^2} \qquad (3.12)$$

In the typical case where the final lens is substantially stronger than the other (i.e., say $f_1 \gg f_2$ and $f_1 \gg L$), this relation reduces to

$$K_s = (f_2/f_1)^2 K_{s1} + K_{s2} \qquad (3.13)$$

Thus, the aberration of the stronger lens (number 2—the final lens—in this case) exerts the greater effect on the aberration of the system. However, the aberration of the combined system is almost always greater than that of one lens alone. The coefficient C_s can be found by using the relation for the total focal length of the lens combination $f = f_1 f_2/(f_1 + f_2 - L)$ and $C_s = K_s f$, together with Eq. (3.12).

Chromatic aberration in a lens refers to the sensitivity of the focal properties to the velocity with which the particles enter the lens. A higher velocity particle will come to a focus farther from the lens than a particle with lower entrance velocity. This effect can be understood easily for the simple magnetic lens described above. The dependence of lens properties on electron velocity follows directly from the Lorentz force on a moving charged particle in a magnetic field ($\mathbf{F} = e\mathbf{v} \times \mathbf{B}$). This effect results in the direct dependence of focal length on electron energy or potential as shown in Eq. (3.9). This effect is illustrated in Fig. 3.9. It is seen that a disk of least confusion exists, as in the spherical aberration case; this disk will be of diameter

$$d_c = C_c \alpha_i \, \Delta V / V_0 \qquad (3.14)$$

where C_c is the chromatic aberration constant, frequently expressed as $C_c = K_c f$, which shows that chromatic aberration is also greater in lenses with longer focal length. Fert and Durandeau (1967) show that K_c varies between 0.75 and 1 with changes in excitation for a variety of lens geometries. ΔV and V_0 represent the total energy spread and the mean energy of the incoming electrons. Values of the constants C_c and C_s are given for magnetic lenses by Mulvey and Wallington (1969).

It is seen that chromatic aberration is not only a function of the lens characteristics but of the incident electrons; this defect is usually referred to as an *electronic aberration,* in contrast to the other geometrical or mechanical defects. Since the lens characteristics depend on the applied voltage, the focused spot can exhibit a form of chromatic aberration if these voltages vary because of power supply ripple or drift. These lens characteristics also vary with magnetic field and therefore, with excitation current. The chromatic aberration relation is sometimes written

$$d_c = C_c \alpha_i \left(\frac{2\Delta B}{B_0} - \frac{\Delta V}{V_0} \right) \qquad (3.15)$$

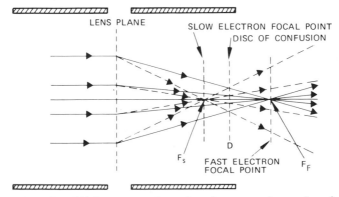

FIG. 3.9 Trajectories of high energy (—▶—, fast electron; --▶--, slow electron) and low energy electrons in a lens, illustrating the effect of chromatic aberration in the lens.

to reflect all of these variables. As seen from Eq. (3.9), the variations with energy spread and magnetic field are opposite and the latter is twice as great. These contributions can be minimized by adequate control of the power supplies. However, the effect of axial thermal velocities and the energy spread due to the Boersch effect cannot be reduced by machine control. It is therefore important to design and operate lenses for the minimum value of C_c. In operation the minima in C_s and C_c do not occur at the same excitation, (the minimum in C_s generally occurs at an excitation ~40% higher than that for minimum C_c) nor with exactly the same lens geometry (although both parameters are reduced as L_g/D is made larger, $L_g/D \geqslant 2$—see Fig. 3.7). Therefore, a careful tradeoff is necessary considering both types of aberration (Mulvey and Wallington, 1969).

The electric field configuration in the gun also forms a lens that affects the electron-beam characteristics. In field emitter guns, the spherical and chromatic aberration in this lens can limit the quality of beam formation and therefore the spot size.

A potentially serious form of astigmatism in the focused spot can result if the diameter of the openings in electrostatic or magnetic optical elements are not circular, or are displaced or tilted with respect to the optical axis. In these cases, the elliptical shape of the resulting electric or magnetic field will cause an aberration called ellipticity astigmatism. The resulting focused spot will, to first order, be elliptical rather than circular in cross section. The disk of confusion will be given by

$$\delta_e = C_e \alpha_i \qquad (3.16)$$

For a noncircular aperture the ellipticity constant C_e will be given to the right order of magnitude by δa, where δa is the difference between the axes of the ellipse which forms a limiting diaphragm (Grivet, 1965a, p. 428). This general form of aberration is quite common in charged particle optical systems; it can be identified by the observation of two line or elliptical foci (instead of round spots) which are 90° apart on an observation screen and are of different focal length.

While some of these effects are, strictly speaking, not due to ellipticity astigmatism, they should be of serious concern in the design, construction, and operation of electron-optical systems. The most careful optical analysis and paper design can be rendered meaningless if not implemented with a high degree of mechanical fabrication and assembly precision; the electron-optical column must be aligned with extreme accuracy to reduce these mechanical errors. Grivet (1965a, p. 436) gives equations relating the mechanical displacement or tilt of the principal aperture of a lens to the ellipticity constant. If this aperture is displaced off-center by an amount Δe with respect to the optical axis,

$$C_e = C_s(\Delta e/f)^2 \tag{3.17}$$

where C_s is the spherical aberration coefficient. If a circular lens is tilted at an angle β with respect to the optical axis,

$$C_e = C_s\beta^2 \tag{3.18}$$

The error Δe actually present can be estimated in practice by varying the potential V on a lens by an amount ΔV; the lateral displacement on a screen should be

$$\Delta y = GK_c(\Delta V/V)\, \Delta e \tag{3.19}$$

where G is the total magnification and K_c is the chromatic aberration constant.

For numerical examples, consider a lens with focal length 20 cm, $C_s = 20$ cm, $\alpha_i = 10^{-3}$ rad. The effect of a transverse displacement $\Delta e = 0.001$ in. $= 25$ μm will be a radius of confusion $\delta_e \cong 3 \times 10^{-10}$ cm, i.e., negligible in usual electron-optical systems. The effect of tilt, however, is more serious; for $\beta = 0.01$ rad ($\sim 0.6°$), $\delta_e = 2.0$ μm, which would form the limitation in spot size.

This form of astigmatism can be corrected by the use of a stigmator which, in its simplest form, is an n-pole element of opposite electric or magnetic fields arranged around the beam (see, e.g., Klemperer, 1953, p. 128; Archard, 1954, p. 97). All electron-optical columns employ stigmators for correction of these mechanically induced aberrations. A quadrupole stigmator which can be arranged in the form of orthogonal hyperbolic electrodes or magnet pole pieces (Courant *et al.*, 1952) is illustrated in Fig. 3.10.

With the potentials arranged as in Fig. 3.10, the rays in the y plane act as if they are passed through a lens element with equal drift spaces of length L_s^y on each side of a *convergent* lens. Similarly, the x plane rays experience drift lengths L_s^x and a *divergent* lens. Thus, an entering beam of elliptical cross section, with the long axis in the y direction, can be caused to become circular at some plane downstream of the stigmator. Essentially all electron-optical columns include a stigmator with controls available to the operator. If it is found necessary to increase the degree of stigmatic correction with time of machine usage, it is an indication that something is changing in the column that increases the beam astigmatism. This evidence suggests that the column be cleaned, aligned, or the emitter replaced. For greater control than is possible with a quadrupole stigmator, eight electrodes can be arranged to form an octupole stigmator,

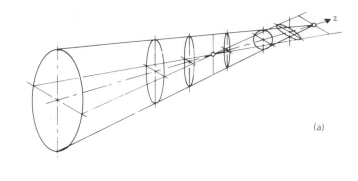

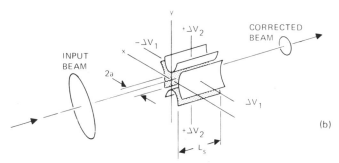

FIG. 3.10   (a) Beam cross sections at several planes, to show the effect of astigmatism. (b) The four pole electrostatic stigmator used to correct astigmatism in an electron beam.

which can correct higher order astigmatism and lower order astigmatism with arbitrary angular orientation (Septier, 1966).

In passing through a limiting aperture, a beam will be diffracted to form a spot of radius

$$\delta_d \cong 0.6\lambda/\alpha \tag{3.20}$$

where $\lambda = 12.25/(V_0)^{1/2}$ Å, for electrons. This effect will be a limitation only in the very highest resolution electron-beam systems.

There are several other forms of aberrations that can form higher order limitations on the electron-optical column performance. Complete descriptions can be found in the electron-optics literature referenced above. All of the important aberrations have been evaluated for specific electron-optical configurations by Chang et al. (1976b), Mauer (1977), and Munro (1975).

G.   Effects of the Aberrations

Four effects that can limit the minimum achievable on-axis spot diameter were identified above. These effects are due to transverse thermal velocities, chromatic aberration in the lens, spherical aberration in the lens, and diffraction by any limiting aperture. Wells (1974b) shows that, to the degree these four effects are statistically independent, the equations relating spot diameter for each effect can be combined in quadrature to yield the total beam diameter d_b. Therefore, from Eqs. (3.11), (3.14), (3.8), and (3.20), the resultant equation for spot diameter from a thermionic source with subsequent focusing lenses is given by*

$$d_b^2 = \frac{1}{\alpha^2}\left[\frac{54.02 \times 10^{-16}}{V_0} + \frac{I}{3.08B}\right] + \alpha^6 \left(\frac{1}{4}\, C_s^2\right) + \alpha^2 \left(C_c\,\frac{\Delta V}{V}\right)^2 \quad (3.21)$$

This equation and its individual terms are plotted for typical values of the parameters in Figure 3.11. It is noted that the minimum beam diameter is created at an optimal value of convergence angle α. In a well designed electron-optical column with low energy spread in the beam (low brightness), the principal effects that influence spot size are the transverse thermal velocities and spherical aberration in the final lens.

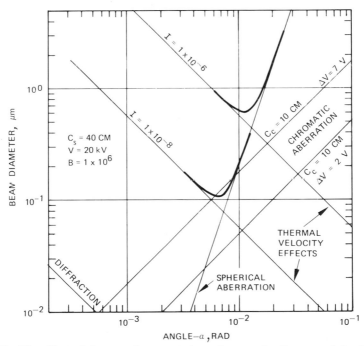

FIG. 3.11 The effect of the more important aberrations on the diameter of the focused spot, from Eq. (3.21). The $\Delta V = 7V$ line was used with $I = 1 \times 10^{-6}$ A, and the $\Delta V = 2V$ line with the $I = 1 \times 10^{-8}$ A data.

* Broers (1972) shows that a similar, but not identical, equation is representative of a field emitter gun that employs only electrostatic focusing by the gun electrodes.

The dependence of current density on the electron-optical parameters of the machine is given by the above equation. If the effects of chromatic aberration and diffraction are neglected, so that the spot diameter is determined only by transverse thermal velocities and spherical aberration,* the convergence angle which will produce a minimum spot diameter can be found from Eq. (3.21):

$$\alpha_{opt} = [I/(2.31BC_s^2)]^{1/8} \tag{3.22}$$

where B represents the source brightness. From this equation the spot diameter at the optimal value of α is given by

$$d_b = 0.73(I/B)^{3/8}C_s^{1/4}, \tag{3.23}$$

the current density by

$$J = 1.94d^{2/3}B/C_s^{2/3} \tag{3.24}$$

The exposure time per spot was shown in Chapter 1 to be given by $\tau = S/J$. By using Eq. (3.24), the minimum exposure time per spot (beam diameter), under the optimization conditions described above, is then

$$\tau_{min} = S/J \cong 0.517SC_s^{2/3}/(d_b^{2/3}B) \tag{3.25}$$

Under machine design or operating conditions where the energy spread in the beam is large, e.g., when a field emitter source is used or the beam carries high current so that the Boersch effect is important, the optimal convergence angle and resultant spot size can be determined more by the chromatic aberration of the final lens and the gun parameters than by the spherical aberration. Then, by considering only the chromatic aberration and transverse thermal velocity terms in Eq. (3.21), the following equations for the optimum convergence angle and exposure time can be derived:†

$$\alpha_{opt} \cong \{0.325I/[B(C_c \, \delta V/V)^2]\}^{1/4} \tag{3.26}$$

$$\tau = 0.255SC_c^2(\Delta V/V)^2/(Bd_b^2) \tag{3.27}$$

It is seen that to first order, in either case [Eq. (3.25) or (3.27)], to achieve a given linewidth at minimum exposure time, either resist sensitivity S, source brightness, or the aberration of the final lens can be varied to decrease τ. However, there are fundamental resist constraints, limits on lens quality, and secondary beam effects which limit this tradeoff, as dis-

---

* Other optimization relations are given by Wells (1974, Chapter 4) and Broers (1972).

† In those beams for which the Boersch effect is important, the energy spread is found to depend on the angle α (Knauer, 1979); in these cases, Eqs. (3.26) and (3.27) assume a slightly different form.

cussed above and in Chapters 1 and 2. That is, exposure time cannot be made arbitrarily small.

H. Beam Deflection System

By using a properly designed gun and lens configuration as described above, it is possible to create, on the optical axis, an electron-beam spot that is small enough (e.g., 200–500 Å diameter) that it will not form a limit on the resolution of patterns to be written. However, in order to write these patterns it is necessary to deflect the beam over an area of the target called the scan field. This deflection must be highly linear, without serious hysteresis, and with minimum degradation of the on-axis spot size and shape. That is, the user of the microfabrication system would like the spot to move precisely to a given point on the target in response to a prescribed input deflection voltage, independently of the past time history of deflection signals, and to be able to draw as fine a line at the edge of the scan field as on the axis. Furthermore, the resolution attainable with the lens and deflection coil (including dynamic correction) must be consistent with the bit accuracy desired in the scan field, e.g., at least 2000 to 4000 resolvable lines. Unfortunately, because of the complex nature of the electromagnetic or electrostatic deflection fields, and their interaction with the beam and with the surrounding environment in the column, these goals cannot always be met. The deflection system can introduce serious errors that can be minimized by design and corrections, but not all can be eliminated. Therefore, the deflection system represents a serious limitation on the area and resolution of the pattern achievable.

There are basically two ways to deflect an electron beam, viz., by the use of electric fields and by magnetic fields. In the former method an electric field is created transverse to the axis of the beam. In the simplest case this field is created between two parallel plates arranged symmetrically with respect to the beam, with appropriate potentials applied to them. This electrostatic deflection technique is, at least in principle, capable of higher deflection speeds, an important feature in electron-beam machines designed for the fastest writing speed. The deflection rate is limited by the capacitance of the plates and the driving impedance of the deflection amplifier, and ultimately by the transit time of the electrons through the deflecting field region. There are two significant disadvantages in this form of deflection, viz., electrostatic deflection causes greater aberration of the beam, (see e.g., Moss, 1968b) and there can be time instabilities in the deflection that result from electrostatic charging by electron impingement of insulating contaminants (e.g., condensed pump oil, evaporation products of the cathode) on the surfaces of the electrodes (Lin and Beauchamp, 1973). For these reasons most (but not all) modern electron-beam systems use magnetic deflection.

The usual magnetic deflection system consists of two orthogonal pairs of air core coils arranged around the electron beam, each pair oriented so as to create an approximately uniform magnetic field in the beam flow region. A simplified diagram of one pair of deflection coils is shown in Fig. 3.12. The electron motion, with velocity v_z, across the magnetic flux lines of density B_x results in the Lorentz force $F_y = ev_z \times B_x$, which causes a bending of the electron trajectory in a circular path. When the electrons leave the region of uniform flux, they continue in straight lines toward the target, but at an angle θ with respect to the initial direction. The first-order

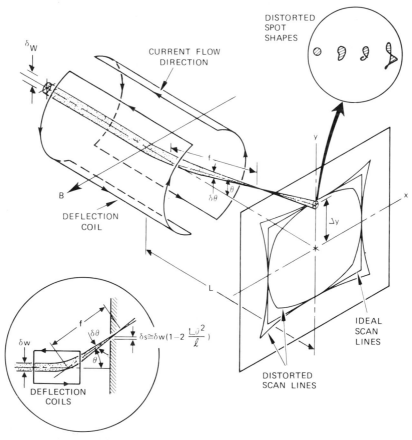

FIG. 3.12 Schematic illustration of magnetic deflection of an electron beam, showing the types of scan and beam distortions that can result from the deflection.

equation for deflection angle is

$$\theta = \eta B_0 l / v_z \tag{3.28}$$

where l is the length of the magnetic field region traversed. Thus, the deflection angle and therefore distance $\Delta y \simeq L\theta$ is to first order linearly related to the magnetic flux density B_0 and thereby to the current in the coil.

The maximum scan rate that can be achieved can be limited by the resonant frequency of the deflection coil. The design of this coil is in turn restricted by the current capacity of the driving amplifier, the power dissipation from the coil, the drive voltage, and the desired deflection angle. These tradeoffs are discussed by Jones and Owen (1978).

There are a number of higher order effects that result in nonlinearity in the scan angle and in distortion of the deflected spot. If perfectly linear signals are supplied to the input of the deflection amplifiers so as to write, for example, a square pattern on the target, this square can be skewed in shape as shown in Fig. 3.12. This distortion can be caused by a nonlinearity in the deflection amplifiers, magnetic material near the scan coils, nonorthogonality of the deflection coils (so that B_x is not perfectly perpendicular to B_y), a dc ambient magnetic field transverse to the column, or in extreme cases by electrostatic charging of some point in the beam flow region, such as the target. However, in a well designed system, including carefully integrated focusing lens and deflection coils, these errors can be made tolerably small (Munro, 1975). Figure 3.13 shows the magnified deviation of position of the electron spot from a postlens magnetic deflection unit (Reeds et al., 1978). This beam position data was taken with a laser interferometrically controlled stage. It is seen that the beam in this column can be positioned to an accuracy better than 0.8 μm over a 2×2 mm scan field.

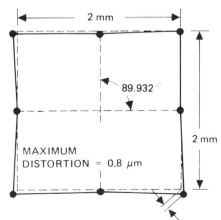

FIG. 3.13 Plot of measured vs. desired positions of an electron beam that has been deflected to the outer edges of a 2 mm × 2 mm scan field. [From Reeds et al. (1978).]

The shape of (and therefore current density distribution over) the deflected spot will be distorted from its on-axis condition by several different effects. The first class of effect is due to noise or ac signals. Noise in the deflection amplifier or other elements can create a randomly smeared out beam which can either enlarge or distort the spot. In general, this effect is negligible. Electromagnetic interference, in the form of ac signals in the deflection amplifier or ambient ac magnetic fields, caused by close by transformers or motors, will result in a beam that traces out tiny Lissajous figures. If the beam is not purposely deflected, this effect will appear as an increase in size or distortion in shape. However, since this effect is time dependent, if the beam is deflected, for example along a straight line, the transverse ac motion of the beam can create a scalloped edge to the pattern. These two effects can in general be controlled by care in grounding the machine, shielding of the electronic components, magnetic shielding of the column, machine location in an environment free of ambient ac magnetic fields, etc.

The second class of beam distortion is due to higher order interaction products between the electron beam and the magnetic field of the deflection coils. These effects are more fundamental and have been treated analytically* by Thomson (1975) and by Owen and Nixon (1973) and experimentally by Amboss (1975) and Chang and Viswanathan (1978). The simplest and most troublesome of these aberrations is due to the lens effect introduced by the deflection field. This deflection defocusing action causes a change in spot size as the beam is deflected over the scan field, as illustrated in Fig. 3.12. The focusing action can be explained to first order by noting that the electrons at the upper and lower edges of a deflected beam of finite width (δw in Fig. 3.12) with convergence angle $\delta\theta$ will follow slightly different path lengths in the magnetic field. Therefore, they emerge at slightly different angles. Because of this angular difference, the beam diameter in the y direction will be altered from the value it would have on the axis (which, of course, is dependent on the focusing action of the final lens). Furthermore, it is clear that this focusing action of the deflection coil takes place only in the direction of the deflection, that is, the distortion introduces an astigmatism into the beam. The change in diameter from its value on axis is given by $\delta \simeq \theta^2 L \, \delta\theta$ (Moss, 1968b); that is, the deflection defocusing is proportional to the square of the deflection angle. Furthermore, this effect is considerably less in magnetic deflection systems than in electrostatic deflectors. Fortunately, spot diameter changes and astigmatism can be corrected dynamically by measuring the

---

* A comprehensive treatment of deflection distortion as applied to cathode ray tubes has been given by Hutter (1970) and Kaashoek (1968).

errors and programming the final lens current (or preferably a fast subsidiary coil) and the stigmator to effect the desired correction. Other aberrations such as coma cannot be reduced to zero, but can only be minimized by proper design of the optical system. Also, it is seen from Eq. (3.28) that the deflection is sensitive to the electron velocity. Therefore, there will be a chromatic deflection distortion due to energy spread in the beam. This effect will increase the spot size. The treatment of these latter effects is beyond the scope of this book; the reader is referred to the electron-optics literature referenced above.

III. MACHINE DESIGN AND OPERATING STRATEGIES

A. Introduction

The characteristics of the several elements that make up the electron-optical column were presented in the previous section. This electron-optical subsystem, plus the wafer stage, beam control electronics, computer, and several support subsystems such as the vacuum system and power supplies, make up the total lithography machine. These pattern writing subsystems can be designed and used in any of several ways, depending on the purpose of the machine. This section will describe several forms that electron-beam lithography machines can take and the corresponding pattern writing and computer control strategies that can be employed. With this information, the potential user can understand and compare the several machine options available.

The types of machines can be divided, by intended usage, into two generic classes, viz., those intended for laboratory R&D work, and those intended for high throughput production of microelectronic devices. These classes differ principally in their throughput capability and the degree of automation that is incorporated. For example, a laboratory type machine should have high flexibility and good resolution, but certain high throughput features such as a multiple-wafer loading chamber and a fast wafer stage may not be economically justifiable. By contrast, a production machine can be designed for a narrow range of parameters, e.g., spot size, so that the throughput can be optimized for these values. However, this specialized design can restrict the range of linewidth and feature size. The production class of machine can be further subdivided into those intended for mask fabrication and for direct writing on the wafer. While in principle any well designed machine could perform either function, these two applications do differ sufficiently so that, at least to date, different forms of machines have evolved for each use.

Laboratory machines with reasonable writing speed for exploratory device development and machines for fast mask exposure are now commercially available from several sources. The production type machine presents a considerably greater challenge in design and choice of writing strategy; furthermore, its characteristics will be a principal determinant of the economic utility of electron-beam lithography. Therefore, the production class of machine will be emphasized here.

Even though the highest resolution capabilities of electron beams are usually not required in mask fabrication, electron-beam mask exposure systems have already proven their value. The effect of improved quality in an electron-beam exposed master mask is evident in each of the many wafer exposures that are made from one master. Furthermore, the shorter time involved in the one step mask fabrication possible with electron-beam exposure can significantly shorten the time required to introduce a new device design. Systems that will expose a 3 in. mask with half-micron address structures (2 μm patterns) in about 30 min, or quarter-micron address structure (1 μm features) in 90 min are commercially available today. As shown in Chapter 5, these masks, with fewer defects, better registration, and better linewidth control, cost less than conventionally exposed masters.

A practical direct exposure production system is a more difficult problem. High speed is much more important for exposing wafers than for masks. In direct writing, each wafer must be exposed between four and ten times, while a single master mask for each level of the device may be used in an optical printer to expose many hundreds of wafers. A system that would expose a single level on a 3-in.-diameter wafer with a 1-μm feature pattern in about 4 min and 0.5-μm feature pattern in about 7 min would be a reasonable target for limited production use in the early 1980s.

B. Machine Throughput and Economics

Production electron-beam exposure systems must compete economically with alternative patterning systems. Economic advantage can derive from better resolution, improved pattern quality, or from lower direct costs. For example, the higher resolution of electron-beam systems can lead to smaller devices or a higher scale of integration with significant economic advantages. Improved exposure quality, i.e., lower defect density, tighter linewidth control, and more accurate registration can improve yields. On the other hand, the serial exposure of pattern features in an expensive electron-beam system will usually cost more in capital and labor than exposure with parallel methods. Therefore, the extra costs of production electron-beam exposure must not exceed the economic value of the devices produced in order for this method to be used. Present commercial electron-beam mask exposure systems may be considered economic in direct writing if they will make devices with half the dimensions at similar yields for about twice the total wafer processing cost. In this way, about four times as many devices, with higher operating speed and lower power consumption, are made on each wafer for only twice the cost—a clear economic advantage (Pease *et al.*, 1975). However, the capital required for a significant production volume is still too large to make direct writing with the mask machines an attractive investment in the rapidly changing technology. Economic justification for electron-beam direct writing in large scale production is at least as important as in mask making. Therefore, both classes of machines must be designed, procured, and used with due consideration for economic value.

The most important factor that affects the economics of production of an electron-beam lithography machine is the number of wafers that can be exposed per unit time. Other factors affecting the economic equation are, of course, the capital cost of the machine and the costs of its operation and maintenance.* However, these costs will not vary widely between machines, whereas the throughput of a machine designed for full scale production can be one or two orders of magnitude higher than that for a laboratory type machine. Therefore, the machine-dependent parameters that determine wafer throughput will be described here, to provide a basis for analysis of the cost of wafer production. Of those machine-related factors affecting throughput, the beam and resist parameters that determine wafer exposure time, together with the associated overhead times, represent the most fundamental considerations. The speed of certain electronic and mechanical components, such as the wafer holding stage and the automatic registration subsystem, can also form limitations on writing time; these factors will be presented after the discussion on exposure time.

The total time required to expose a wafer (one mask level) with a vector scan type machine can be represented approximately by the equation

$$T_{W} = K \left[\frac{SC_{s}^{2/3}}{Bd_{b}^{2/3}} \right] + \frac{A_{wafer}}{A_{scan}} [t_{stage} + t_{reg}] + t_{load} \qquad (3.29)$$

The first term [in brackets—from Eq. (3.25)—for a spherical aberration limited optical system] represents the time to expose one spot and is composed of the resist sensitivity S (C/cm²), the spherical aberration coeffi-

---

* Another important element is the process yield; this subject was discussed in Chapter 1.

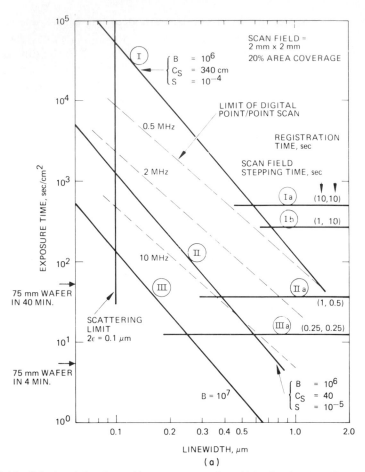

FIG. 3.14   Calculated time for writing patterns vs. linewidth, showing the effect of several machine variables. Refer to text for description.

cient C_s (cm) of the final lens, the current density in the beam [as expressed by the beam brightness B (A/cm²/SR)] and the spot diameter d_b (cm). The factor K is composed of the product of 0.52 (a numerical factor so that the bracketed term is expressed in seconds) times the number of spots of diameter d_b necessary to cover 1 cm² times the fraction of wafer area that is written. This first term assumes point-by-point exposure and is obviously related to the parameters of the electron-optical column and the resist employed. To achieve high writing speed, a fast resist (small value of S) and high beam brightness must be used. The second term expresses the times required to move the stage between scan fields and to register on each scan field. The sum of these times is multiplied by the

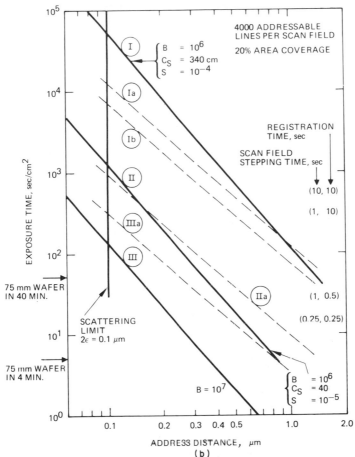

FIG. 3.14b   See legend for Fig. 3.14.

number of scan fields on a wafer. The last term represents the time to load a wafer onto its holder for exposure, pump down of the exposure chamber and other related overhead times. This term can be minimized by the use of a multiple wafer loading system so as to amortize the total overhead time over several wafers.

The individual components of exposure time described by Eq. (3.29) above are plotted in Fig. 3.14, which shows the dependence on linewidth of the time required to expose 1 cm² of resist, together with the effect of other important machine parameters. The solid diagonal lines represent the electron-beam-dependent term in the above equation; they are moved downward as the resist sensitivity is increased and beam brightness increased. The horizontal solid lines represent the beam-independent factors, particularly the stage and registration times that would be required in a step and repeat system. As stage travel speed is increased and registration time decreased, these lines move downward. The total exposure time is the sum of these individual components. This graph is drawn for linewidth equal to beam diameter. In order to attain best edge resolution, it is frequently desirable to use a beam of diameter equal to from one-third to one-fourth of the width of the line, with corresponding increase in writing time. The vertical line representing the scattering limit (the linewidth in resist for zero beam diameter) is drawn at 0.1 μm. This is not a lower bound; it is an arbitrary choice that is in at least qualitative agreement with experimental observations with normal substrates. The diagonal lines are drawn for 20% area coverage and a spot overlap so that the number of spots per square centimeter n_s is given by $(2/d_b)^2$. Furthermore, the assumption, implicit in these lines, that beam brightness is constant as spot diameter is changed may not be valid for all electron-optical systems, and in any case is valid only when the convergence angle is optimized for each value of beam current [Eq. (3.22)] which is in turn dependent on spot diameter. For example, this representation may not be correct for a system using a field emitter source, in which chromatic aberration can be significant. Nevertheless, this simplification illustrates the general dependence of writing time on beam and resist parameters.

The curves in Fig. 3.14a were calculated for certain individually demonstrated values of electron-gun quality (specifically the source brightness) and of spherical aberration in the final lens. Curve I represents an early electron-beam fabrication machine, assuming 10 s and 10 s stage repositioning and beam registration times, respectively (curve Ia). Decreasing the stage repositioning time between scan fields to 1 s results in curve Ib; it is noted that this improvement results in a reduction in writing time at linewidths greater than ~0.7 μm. Curve II was calculated for a resist ten times more sensitive than that of curve I, and an improved final lens. It is seen that this change results in a substantial reduction in writing time at very narrow linewidths, but little change would be realized in the >0.2 μm regime if the same stage and registration times (curves Ia and Ib) were used. Therefore, these latter times must be reduced to about the values shown on curve IIa. Finally, curve III represents the writing time achievable with a 10× brighter gun and faster stage–registration. Even in the curve III situation, representing a machine that has not yet been built but is technologically possible, the stage–registration times form the limit for linewidth greater than about 0.25 μm.

It is noted in Fig. 3.14a that, as the beam-dependent characteristics are improved with a fixed scan field size, the intersection between the two solid lines moves to the left, i.e., to narrower linewidth. Under this condition the stage and registration times begin to dominate for more of the range of linewidths, i.e., only at narrow linewidth is the writing speed dominated by the beam and resist. This situation means that the stage and registration times must be made low by the use of a high speed stage and automated registration techniques. This design feature is particularly important in the 0.5–2 μm linewidth regime and under conditions where the ratio S/B is small. These stage motion and registration time considerations are particularly applicable to the vector and raster scan type machines, in which one scan field is written completely, then the wafer is stepped to the next scan field. There is another type of writing strategy, discussed below, that avoids these move-and-reregister times. In order to prevent the wafer loading time from becoming dominant in any machine as beam, resist, and stage improvements are made, a multiple wafer holder–loader with suitable vacuum interlock must be used.

The lines in Fig. 3.14a representing the time for relocation and final reregistration of the stage between scan fields are horizontal, as shown, when the scan field size is fixed. If the number of resolvable lines per scan field were fixed instead (Fig. 3.14b), the scan field size would increase with linewidth so that these time limits would vary inversely as the square of the linewidth. Under this latter condition the step and repeat times would become a more severe limit at small linewidth (i.e., more scan fields). The use of a shaped spot would reduce the beam–resist-dependent time, placing even further emphasis on stage and registration system development to achieve high throughput.

In order to achieve the exposure speed shown in Fig. 3.14, the beam deflection system must be capable of moving the beam with the appropriate scan velocity. In the digital point-by-point exposure mode, the beam must be held fixed for a time τ_s [given by Eq. (3.25)], then stepped to the next adjacent spot. The incremental stepping rate f_s is then slightly less than τ_s^{-1} and the time per square centimeter $T = \eta_s \tau_s \approx (2/d_b)^2 \tau_s = 4/(d_b^2 f_s)$. Light dashed lines corresponding to several stepping rates are drawn on Fig. 3.14a.

An illustration of a typical chain of electronic subsystems that form the beam deflection system is shown in Fig. 3.15. This system consists of a clock to generate the timing pulses for a generator that forms the digital deflection data, which is converted to the deflection signal (a staircase) by the digital to analog (D/A) converter, amplified, and used to drive the beam deflection coils. Two D/A converters are used in some types of vector scan systems in order to increase writing speed. The high resolution converter can be used to form the outline of a pattern and a faster, but lower resolution, unit used to drive a larger beam to fill in the central area of the feature. In this point-by-point writing approach, the distance that

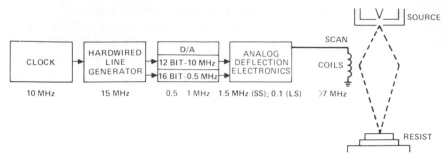

FIG. 3.15   Functional diagram of the pattern generator and beam deflection components. The numbers indicate typical values of bandwidth. SS denotes small signal incremental bandwidth; LS denotes large signal (i.e., for a large deflection step) bandwidth.

the beam is moved due to a change of one bit into the D/A converter is called the address structure. Some typical (1978) values of small signal incremental bandwidth or pulse rate are shown for each component. In this example, the 16 bit D/A converter is the lowest frequency component and will, therefore, form the electronic limit on scan rate. In order to prevent a limitation due to spot deflection rate, all elements of the deflection electronics must be designed so that they can handle a stepping rate in excess of that necessary to expose the resist. Therefore, as beam and stage–registration parameters are improved, the bandwidth of the deflection electronics must also be increased. It is seen that a total system approach to the design of the electron-beam machine must be adopted in order to minimize total time to write a wafer level and thereby maximize throughput.

In order to expose a resist of higher sensitivity and/or expose with a beam of higher brightness, the required beam scan velocity may be higher than is possible by the digital point-by-point technique. Then elementary areas of the pattern can be written by the use of a raster scan, for which the beam slew rate rather than the address rate is usually limited by the bandwidth of the deflection amplifier or scan coils rather than the D/A converters. Alternatively, if a variable aperture system, as described earlier, is employed, the exposure times can be reduced significantly. In general, for a given gun brightness the total current density in the small shaped spot and a larger shaped beam will be equal, so that the exposure time per pixel will be the same for a small round spot as for a larger square spot. A partitioning analysis of integrated circuit patterns with 0.5 μm minimum features shows that only a small percentage (e.g., $< 10\%$) of the written pattern area is composed of features less than 1 μm in size; most of the features are in the 1–2 μm range. Therefore, the exposure time of a given pattern with a variable aperture system can be significantly shorter (e.g., $\frac{1}{3}-\frac{1}{7}$) vis-a-vis that time required by the use of a round spot. Furthermore, because the number of individual exposures in the variable aperture case will be a small fraction of the number required by the use of a small round spot, the rate of deflection will be lower, with less challenge to the deflection electronics.

The general trend of all of the curves in Fig. 3.14 shows the resolution–writing time tradeoff alluded to above, i.e., more time is required to write a narrow line. The principal reasons for this tradeoff are: (a) the decrease in beam current density as the spot diameter is made smaller so as to expose a smaller feature [see, e.g., Eq. (3-24)]; (b) the finite number of resolution elements in a scan field, resulting in a smaller scan field size as the feature size is reduced, therefore in more scan fields per unit wafer area; and (c) the greater overhead time associated with deflection of the larger number of spots required to cover a given area with smaller features. The principal conclusions that can be drawn from the writing speed–resolution analysis (Fig. 3.14—for a fixed scan field size) are: (a) backscattering limits the ultimate resolution; (b) resist sensitivity and beam current density affect writing time principally in the <0.5 μm regime; and (c) the rate of stage motion forms the principal limit for larger linewidths. Under conditions where the scan field size is reduced with the linewidth, the step-and-repeat time can be a limit even at narrow linewidth. Implicit in these conclusions are the conditions that the deflection rate can be made fast enough that it does not form a limit, that the number of resolvable spots per scan line is limited to $\sim 10^4$ spots (faster, higher resolution D/A converters and lower noise deflection amplifiers and improved deflection coils could increase this limit), and that the resist can exhibit adequate resolution at the assumed sensitivity to reproduce the narrowest lines.

A more careful analysis of a realizable production level electron-beam lithography system that employs the variable aperture technique shows that a throughput of approximately three to six mask levels (75-mm-diameter wafers) per hour can be written with 0.5 μm minimum linewidth, depending on the exact feature size partitioning and area fraction written. Therefore, each lithography level will cost roughly $10 to $20, which includes operator labor, machine amortization, maintenance, and support overhead. While this value is many times the cost of a mask level printed by contact photolithography with 5 μm design rules, the number of functions that can be fabricated on a wafer can be up to 100 times higher and the lithography cost is still less than half the cost of a processed wafer. Therefore, assuming the yield values of the two processes to be comparable, the cost per function of devices fabricated by the use of electron-beam lithography writing directly on the wafer can be lower.

C. General System Strategies

Any strategy for a production type electron-beam system will emphasize speed (wafer throughput) consistent with the desired edge resolution and placement accuracy. There are a number of machine-related factors that affect throughput, as discussed in the previous section. It is clear that table stepping times and registration times can be as important as exposure times and that deflection bandwidth can be as important as cathode brightness and resist sensitivity in an electron-beam exposure system. Therefore, the design strategies of several types of production systems will be described in terms of the following parameters:

1. Speed at which an area of substrate (e.g., a scan field) can be accessed by table motion while retaining accurate dimensional control of pattern distortion and registration.
2. Speed at which a pattern can be written within an area in relation to cathode brightness and resist sensitivity.
3. Rates at which a pattern information can be processed to control an exposure system.

D. Area Coverage with Accurate Dimensional Control

Electron-beam exposure systems usually employ electronic deflection of the beam in combination with a mechanical stage to move the substrate under the electron column because the required resolution cannot be achieved over the large substrate area using beam deflection alone. Therefore, it is necessary to control the table motions and beam deflections so that patterns are accurately registered over the whole area of the substrate.

As shown in Section II.H, the size of the field over which the electron beam can be deflected is limited by several factors. In order to attain good pattern quality, the edge gradient of the electron-beam profile, the distortion of the exposed pattern, and the positional stability of the beam should all be held below a tenth of the minimum feature size to be patterned. Even when lens and deflection aberrations are designed to meet this criterion, fabrication tolerances on the electron-optical components and stabilities of structures and power supplies usually limit the field size to about 2000–6000 times the minimum feature size or 8000–20,000 times the address size. For example, the IBM EL-1 electron-beam exposure system (Engelke et al., 1976) employs a 2.5 μm square writing spot over a 5 mm square field (2000 times the feature size); the deflection is controlled by a sophisticated computer system for measuring distortion and compensating the scan (Loughran et al., 1976).

Most laboratory exposure systems and many production systems move the substrate in a step and repeat manner (Speth *et al.*, 1975; Varnell *et al.*, 1974; Ozdemir *et al.*, 1972; Chang and Stewart, 1969). In this mode, a field containing a circuit, or portion of a circuit, is exposed by deflecting the electron beam over the field while the table is held stationary. The table is then stepped to an adjacent field and the next circuit or portion is exposed. This operation is repeated until the area of the wafer is covered. The stage must be positioned with sufficient accuracy to allow registration, or in some cases precision abutment of adjacent patterns. Registration of the new scan field can be accomplished by precision location of the stage, adjustment of the stage position in response to electron-beam scanning of registration marks in each scan field, or usually by offset of the electron-beam pattern, in response to registration signals, to compensate for stage position errors. The wafers to be exposed suffer out-of-plane distortions in the several high temperature processing steps used in semiconductor device fabrication. Realistically, the electron-beam machine design should minimize the effects of these flatness errors. In many systems, the electron beam makes an angle as great as 0.05 rad with the normal to the substrate when deflected to the edge of the field. If the substrate is not flat, or is displaced from the best focal plane of the beam by 5 μm at the edge of the field, the beam will be displaced 0.25 μm from its proper position, as shown in Fig. 3.16. It is, of course, not possible to use vacuum chucks to flatten the wafer and so control the substrate height. In order to compensate for this wafer distortion, it is necessary in step and repeat systems to measure the position of two or more registration marks in each exposure field and use this data to adjust the x and y deflection gains in order to compensate for the pattern errors. In this way, proper

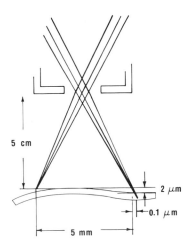

FIG. 3.16   Pattern error resulting from substrate height error with conventional (nontelecentric) deflection system.

registration can be attained on each of the different levels of directly written devices. But this approach requires that registration marks be etched into the substrate at each chip location either before or as part of the first processing step. These marks use a significant area of the substrate and are usually not acceptable on master masks.

The time required to cover a wafer will consist of the stepping time, the aligning time, and the exposure time for each step, multiplied by the number of steps required to cover the wafer. A 75 mm wafer, with 40 cm² area, will require 160 steps with a 5 mm square field and 4000 steps with a 1 mm field. If the table motion and registration time required for one step is 0.5 sec, the total time to cover a wafer would be 80s with 5 mm fields and 2000 with a 1 mm field, in addition to the pattern exposure time. The maximum system speed that can be achieved is therefore very dependent on the scan field size. It is seen that the time required to access the field increases rapidly as the feature size, and therefore the field, is reduced and is larger than acceptable for direct writing of features smaller than about 2 μm.

An alternative stage-and-exposure strategy has been developed for use on the EBES mask exposure system (Herriott *et al.,* 1975; Alles *et al.,* 1975). In this approach, a small electron-beam field is scanned to write a pattern on a stripe of a continuously moving substrate. Laser interfer-

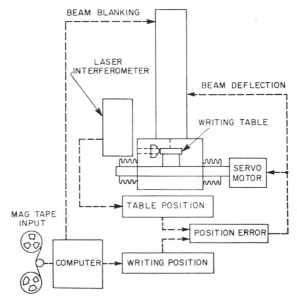

FIG. 3.17   Laser interferometer stage measurement with deflection compensation of stage errors.

ometers monitor the substrate motion and modify the beam deflection to compensate for any substrate position errors, as shown in Fig. 3.17. Because the electron-beam deflection angle and field is very small, the resolution, distortion, and stability of the electron beam in this approach are not seriously limited by aberrations, machine fabrication defects, or mechanical stabilities, and deflection signals are not significantly affected by D/A linearity, amplifier drifts, or power supply stabilities.

The error in beam position caused by out-of-plane wafer distortion is eliminated by the use of a telecentric electron-beam deflection system. A telecentric deflection system is one in which the electron beam remains normal to the substrate for any position in the deflection field (Alles *et al.*, 1975). Telecentricity is more easily achieved for small deflection fields than for large fields. In one approach, a doubly deflected beam crosses the axis of the final lens at the front focus of the lens. The beam is both imaged to a focus and bent by the lens so that it is normal to the substrate, as shown in Fig. 3.18. With this double deflection technique an error in the substrate height does not cause a shift of lateral beam location on the substrate. Furthermore, the depth of focus of the electron beam is nor-

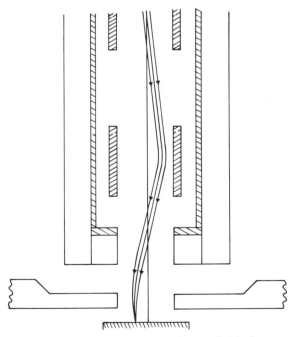

FIG. 3.18 Elimination of pattern errors due to substrate height by use of a telecentric system.

mally greater than 10 μm so that adequate focus can be maintained with normal substrate flatness and height control to achieve satisfactory resolution. Laser interferometers, together with small field telecentric lenses, can be used for accurate positional control in the presence of reasonable substrate quality.

This system achieves a positional accuracy better than 0.125 μm and does not require additional stepping time because the pattern is written on the moving substrate.

E. Pattern Writing Strategies

Three principal strategies can be used to expose the pattern information within the electron-beam field. The beam can be scanned along a path to expose an individual rectangle in the pattern and then jump to the next rectangle to build up the pattern, as shown in Fig. 3.19a. This technique is generally referred to as vector scan and has the significant advantage that only the exposed features are written. The exposed area is almost always less than half the substrate area and is usually about 20% or less. In the second method, called *raster scan,* the total area of the field is covered with a television type scan and the beam is turned on when the spot being covered should be exposed, as shown in Fig. 3.19b. The third method uses a variable shaped beam to expose a whole feature at one time before moving to the next feature.

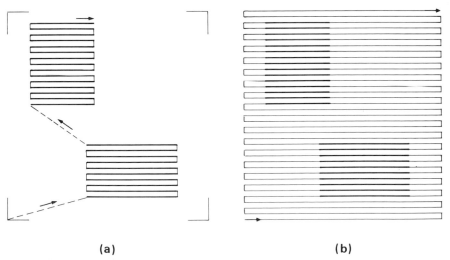

(a)   (b)

FIG. 3.19a   Vector scan to write only the feature area in electron-beam exposure.
FIG. 3.19b   Raster scan where beam is gated "on" to write desired pattern area. [From Chang *et al.* (1977).]

Within the general scan method called *vector scan,* a number of deflection strategies can be used to fill each feature, as shown in Fig. 3.20 (Speth *et al.,* 1975). For example, the beam may outline the feature and continue to spiral to the center (Fig. 3.20c) or it may outline the feature and then follow a raster or serpentine path to expose the center (Fig. 3.20b). The feature may be written by a small raster or serpentine scan without any outline scan (Fig. 3.20a). The outline scan has an advantage in that the center can be filled by using a larger beam if beam size can be changed rapidly without causing offsets (Figs. 3.20e and 3.20f). The outline scan may also be used with proximity correction that will be discussed later in this chapter.

It is seen that in the vector scan techniques, the vector defining the beam direction may have to change its direction after as few as five addresses of exposure. If the deflection bandwidth is not sufficient, delay must be introduced at this direction change until the beam has responded with sufficient accuracy. The bandwidth may be limited by capacitance or inductance of the deflection components and by the driving amplifiers. The response of magnetic deflection can also be severely limited by eddy currents generated in metallic system components that are penetrated by the magnetic fields. After a large jump to a new feature, these eddy cur-

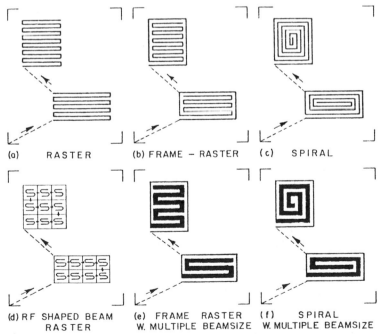

FIG. 3.20 Alternate pattern writing strategies used for vector scan in electron-beam systems. [From Chang *et al.* (1976).]

rents can require the introduction of delays of many microseconds to allow the beam to be positioned accurately before it can be turned on. The effects of such eddy currents can be reduced by cutting slits into any metallic components with which the magnetic fields can interact, so as to interrupt the resultant current flow, or by the use of ferrite shields and pole pieces.

Magnetic deflection is commonly used in electron-beam systems because of its better linearity and distortion, vis-a-vis electrostatic deflection techniques. Magnetic deflection systems have been made with 1-part-in-5000 linearity and stability. Air core deflection coils with a bandwidth of greater than 7 MHz have been built, but this component can represent a limitation on deflection bandwidth. Electrostatic deflection systems have better frequency response, but are generally limited to 1 part in 1000 in distortion for large deflection angles.

The raster scan method (Fig. 3.19b) has an advantage in that the scan is periodic and requires a lower deflection bandwidth. Peaking of the frequency characteristics of the drive system can be used to compensate for distortions in the scan. Another advantage of the raster scan is that the tone (polarity) of a pattern can be reversed by inverting the signal to the modulator. This will have the effect of changing a positive pattern into a negative, or vice versa. In this way, one tone of resist can be used for all masks, regardless of the type of processing. Raster scan is also compatible with a particularly efficient system for pattern data processing. However, this pattern technique requires a larger bandwidth in the beam blanking system in order to turn the beam on and off in a time that is short compared with that corresponding to the address size. In fact, bandwidth of the blanking system can be a limitation on edge resolution.

A third approach to writing patterns involves the use of a variable shaped beam (Trotel, 1978; Goto *et al.*, 1978; Pfeiffer, 1978; Thomson *et al.*, 1978). If the cross section of the focused electron beam can be changed rapidly to best suit the feature shapes to be patterned, the area exposure rate can be increased significantly because larger areas can be exposed at one time. As described earlier, this approach is implemented by illuminating a shaped aperture by an electron source and imaging this pattern onto a second shaped aperture. A deflection system can move the image of the first aperture so as to illuminate a portion of the second aperture. If the two apertures are squares as shown in Fig. 3.2, the combination will result in a rectangle with length and width dependent on the deflection of the first aperture image. Other aperture shapes (Fig. 3.21) can provide rectangles at 45° orientation, as well as some parallelograms (see also Thomson *et al.*, 1978).

The maximum size of a variable shaped spot is limited by space charge

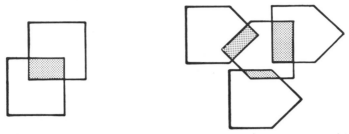

FIG. 3.21 Shaped apertures that can give rectangles and some parallelograms for variable shaped beam writing. [From Goto *et al.* (1978).]

effects at high beam currents (Pfeiffer, 1972). The interaction of adjacent electrons at the cathode and in the beam (called the Boersch effect) will shift the focus, increase the spot size, increase the energy spread in the beam, and increase the lateral spread in a deflected spot for electrons having different energies. The magnitude of these effects are dependent on the details of the system, but can be significant at total currents greater than a microampere. Furthermore, the electron-optical column required to implement the variable shaped spot approach is much more complex than a column to produce a round spot. However, despite these limitations, variable shaped beams can increase machine throughput significantly; therefore, this technique should have a major impact on production electron-beam systems.

F. Pattern Information Processing

Virtually all integrated circuits or discrete devices are designed or processed by the use of some type of computer aided design (CAD) technique. The total system must include an element for introducing this pattern information into the electron-beam system and processing the data to control pattern exposure.

The data processing for a vector scan system is quite straightforward. The output of the CAD system is usually a list of some fundamental shape, commonly rectangles or trapezoids, that make up the pattern.

Any polygonal feature such as that in Fig. 3.22 can be decomposed into a list of trapezoids having bases parallel to the x axis. Each of these trapezoids can then be exposed following a general trapezoid exposing strategy such as shown in Fig. 3.22. A computer program generates deflection signals to drive the scan along a sequence of lines parallel to the base with the ends terminated to correspond with the slopes of the sides of the trapezoid. The beam is usually turned off during the turnaround

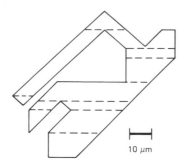

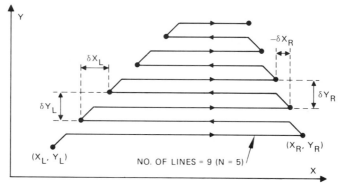

FIG. 3.22   Strategy for trapezoidal decomposition of pattern and writing of basic trapezoid.
[From Spicer *et al.* (1973).]

between adjacent scans. After exposing all of the individual trapezoids,
the total exposure is shown in Fig. 3.22.

Figure 3.23 shows a block diagram of an electronic circuit that will generate this type of scan (Ozdemir *et al.*, 1975; Spicer *et al.*, 1973; Patlach *et
al.*, 1978). The system must allow time for the beam to settle at corners,
this time being dependent on the length of a jump to new features, and
must turn the beam on and off to expose the desired pattern. Over a mil-
lion addresses may be exposed in a second; therefore, the system must
generate these deflection signals with broad bandwidths at very high
speeds.

The data processing for a raster scan system is very different from that
for the vector scan (Alles *et al.*, 1975). In this case, the features must be
sorted into the order in which they will appear in the scan. A memory
must then be used in one of two ways to convert from the feature description to the raster line description. The features can be put into a memory
in order of their position along the raster line scan and the individual bits

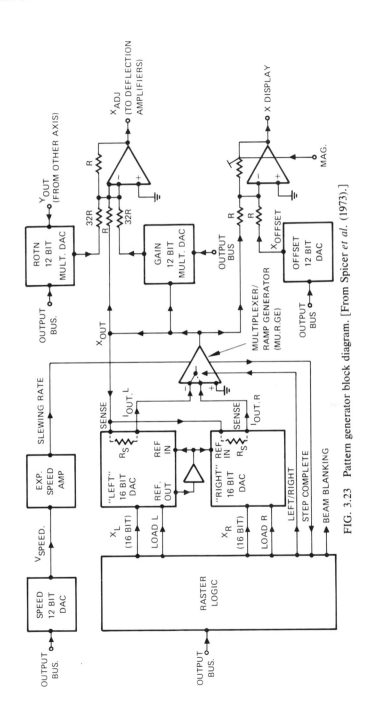

FIG. 3.23 Pattern generator block diagram. [From Spicer *et al.* (1973).]

determined from a sequential evaluation of those features. When each new line is to be started, any new features that are intersected by the line are added and completed features are removed. The position of these features along the line must be reordered frequently. In an alternate method a core or semiconductor memory array can be used to store an image of the pattern to be written. Each feature is written into this memory by changing the stored bits from 0 to 1 in the area representing the feature. After all features have been written, the memory can be read a line at a time to control the beam modulator as the beam follows a corresponding scan on the substrate. This method is particularly efficient when writing the repeated chips of a semiconductor pattern as the memory can be written once and then read repeatedly for the identical chips.

The feature-to-line scan conversion can be done ahead of the writing time either outside of the system or within the electron-beam system. If this decoding is done outside of the system, a great deal of information must be fed into the system. If the conversion is done inside the system, a dedicated memory large enough for a complete device pattern is required. Usually the pattern is entered into the system in a compact form, but in the order in which it will be written by the system. Small portions of pattern are expanded into a dedicated memory and then used to write that portion of the pattern. On EBES mask systems, the memory for one stripe of a chip is decoded once and then written from memory on all of the chips on the substrate before decoding the next stripe.

One of the important functions of the data processing subsystem is to effect a change in the exposure of any portion of a pattern feature that is located close to another, separate, feature. This process is called *proximity correction* and was discussed in Chapter 2. To review here briefly, the exposing electrons are scattered as they pass through the electron resist and some of those penetrating the substrate are scattered back into the resist (Chang, 1975; Parikh, 1978b; Chung and Tai, 1978; Nakata *et al.,* 1978). These back scattered electrons cause a tail of exposure extending as much as a few microns from each edge of a feature. Because of this exposure tail, the effective position of a feature edge will depend upon how much of the nearby area has been exposed. For example, the edge of a narrow isolated line will have a much smaller exposure from electrons scattered into it than the edge of a large solid block of exposure. Similarly, corners and ends of lines will have less scattered exposure. Variation in exposure (time or current) can be programmed into the machine, dependent on feature size and distance for the adjacent feature, to produce more precise linewidth control. A typical relation between exposure and linewidth or gap spacing is shown in Fig. 3.24. This first-order correction technique will not give correct feature dimensions for a mixed pattern of

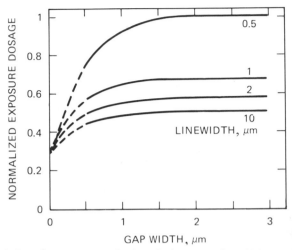

FIG. 3.24   Variation of exposure required to obtain proper linewidth as a function of gap width. [From Chang (1975).]

large and small features. However, some systems have been modified to correct this deficiency. For example, when a small feature is exposed in a vector scan system, a second scan around the outer edge can be used to enlarge the feature, or the dimensions of small features or parts of features can also be increased slightly to compensate for the reduced scattered exposure near their boundaries. This latter form of proximity correction is particularly adaptable to the variable shaped spot writing approach. However, this single-feature correction does not help when two or more features are close together. Scattering from one feature will affect the edge position for a close adjacent feature. It is possible in either a vector or raster scan system to make corrections in the pattern memory where the positions of all adjacent figures are known. However, this type of correction can probably be done best in the computer-aided design system using automated procedures and algorithms prior to being entered into the electron-beam exposure system.

Another important function that is performed by the pattern data processing subsystem is the processing of the registration data from the electron-beam scans of registration marks. It was shown earlier that the registration of two levels of pattern or the alignment of two or more fields on a substrate requires that the electron beam be able to sense accurately the position of a registration mark on the substrate (Miyauchi *et al.*, 1970; Wolf *et al.*, 1975; Wilson *et al.*, 1975; Stephani and Froschle, 1978; Stickel, 1978). These marks are generally topographical features such as raised areas (pillars) or depressions (trenches), or an area of different material than the substrate.* A detector is usually mounted beneath the pole piece of the final beam focusing lens to collect backscattered and secondary electrons from the substrate as the electron beam scans the mark. As the beam scans a registration mark, the change in secondary emission coefficient (if the mark differs in composition from the rest of the surface) and/or the topography of the mark affect the signal collected. When the electron beam penetrates a pillar on the substrate, electrons can escape more easily from the sides and can be collected in greater numbers than from the surrounding areas. When the beam penetrates the bottom of a trench, more electrons are trapped and fewer electrons escape to the detector. Therefore, the edges of the marks are usually the more significant sources of scattered electrons that produce signals for mark location. Many scans across the mark are made during the registration process and the detected signals are processed to find the center of the mark. The mark is usually a cross or L which is patterned in the oxide or silicon either as part of the first-level patterning or prior to patterning. The widths of the bars can range from 2 to 30 μm.

The signal from the backscattered electron detector or the conduction signal through the substrate is usually amplified and digitally encoded for computer processing. There are a number of different processing methods that can be used (Stephani and Froschle, 1978; Wilson et al., 1975; Stickel, 1978). In the simplest form, the location of the beam when the ac coupled signal crosses the axis on each side of the mark can be averaged for a number of scans to find the center of the mark. Spurious readings can be removed by assuring that each scan measures the correct mark width before including it in the average. Improved accuracy can be achieved by fitting each measured signal to a general characteristic signal before determining the mark edges to be averaged. This fitting method uses a larger fraction of the signal to determine the edge location and thus has better noise performance. A further improvement can be achieved by adding the curves from repeated scans in the computer memory before determining the edge position.

If the mark is formed in poorly conducting material, the first scan in the registration process may deposit charge in the region of the mark and so deflect the beam on subsequent scans, resulting in faulty mark location. For most accurate positioning, the scans are commonly spaced along the mark to eliminate this charging effect, or grounded metal films are deposited over the marks to discharge the surface. In most systems, the registration on a mark can be completed in a small fraction of a second to a 0.1 μm accuracy.

* Refer also to Chapter 2 for discussion of registration signal generation.

G. *System Construction and Operation*

The construction of electron-beam exposure systems involves the coordination of electron-optical technology in the column with precise stage translation in vacuum, computer measurement and control systems, and data processing systems. Electron column structures are basically similar to those used in scanning electron microscopes. However, stability and vibration resistance are more important in lithography systems because of the tight dimensional tolerances on the patterns. Tungsten and thoriated tungsten cathodes give excellent stability with moderate brightness. Lanthanum hexaboride (LaB_6) cathodes are brighter, but fluctuate in brightness as the polycrystalline structure is contaminated or eroded. Single-crystal LaB_6 has a higher brightness with lower noise because the orientation of the preferred emission from crystalline faces is stable (Shimizu *et al.*, 1978). Field emission cathodes give the highest brightness for small beam diameters and are showing increased beam current as new materials and processing are used, but these sources require very good vacuum conditions and have marginal stability (Swanson, 1975; Stille and Astrant, 1978). However, with further development, they can become important in the future.

Beam blanking is usually achieved with an electrostatic deflector that deflects the beam out of an adjacent aperture to turn the beam off. The deflector is frequently positioned at an image of the final writing spot so that the spot does not move as it is being turned off (Lin and Beauchamp, 1973).

The deflection coils are often encased in a ferrite shield to prevent the deflection signals from penetrating the lens pole piece and thereby creating eddy currents that will distort the pattern and limit the deflection response.

The wafer holding stages in many machines use roller bearings with vacuum pump oil lubrication. The use of magnetic materials in the stage can change the configuration of the magnetic flux lines and thereby deflect or distort the beam deflection pattern as the stage is moved. Therefore, material that is even partially ferromagnetic should be used only with great caution. An external air bearing $x-y$ stage has been used in some systems to eliminate moving magnetic materials near the beam and to provide very smooth stage motion.

Cleanliness is of vital importance in electron-beam exposure systems. Polymerized hydrocarbons deposited in sensitive regions of the electron-optical column can collect stray charges that will deflect the beam and destroy beam stability. Ion pumps with sorption roughing are frequently used with careful vacuum techniques to maintain clean systems for long periods. Oil diffusion pumps require very careful trapping to eliminate oil buildup in the system.

Commercial computer technology is usually used for the control and data processing portion of the systems. However, high accuracy glitch free D/A converters and very stable power supplies are particularly critical components in large field step and repeat systems. The fastest state-of-the-art electronic logic is usually required in the pattern generators for high speed vector scanning; these subsystems are typically custom designed.

Automatic means for adjustment of beam focus, current, and deflection gains are usually included, particularly in a production system. A Faraday cup is used to collect the beam behind a target grid, allowing measurement of the total beam current when the beam is passing between the wires. Focus can be adjusted by measuring the slope of the cutoff as the beam is deflected across the edge of a wire. Deflection gain can be adjusted by measuring the deflection required to center the beam on two adjacent wires at a known spacing or to track a single wire while the stage is moved under laser interferometer control. These automatic parameter adjustments permit relatively unskilled operators to run the system in a reproducible manner.

Assuming that the electron-beam system has been designed and constructed properly, it is essential that this machine be installed in the proper environment and maintained regularly. The environment must be clean, free of vibration, free of electromagnetic interferance, and with small temperature variation. Installation must be in a clean room of the type appropriate to the best quality semiconductor device fabrication (class 100). Typically, the temperature should be controlled, with varying heat loads, to $\pm 2°C$, alternating magnetic field strength should be less than 5 mG (for any frequency), and the low frequency (50–60 Hz) floor vibration must not exceed ≈ 3 μm peak to peak. The input ac power must be regulated and filtered.

IV. STATE-OF-THE-ART MACHINE CHARACTERISTICS

The principal features and performance characteristics of electron beam machines that are in use and representative of the early 1979 state of the art are described here, from the published literature. These systems include one designed specifically for mask fabrication, a typical high resolution vector scan machine, and a machine with variable shaped spot that was designed for high throughput production use at modest resolution.

A. EBES Mask Exposure System

The EBES exposure systems (Alles *et al.*, 1974; Herriott *et al.*, 1975) were developed to provide fast, practical, and economical exposure of masks and special purpose direct fabricated devices. They were designed to give optimal performance in the 1–5 μm minimum feature range with $\frac{1}{2}$ and $\frac{1}{4}$ μm address structure. Small field telecentric beam deflection is used with a continuously moving air bearing table and laser interferometer feedback to the deflection system to provide fast area coverage with $\frac{1}{8}$ μm absolute accuracy over the 4 in. square patterning area. The chip pattern is broken into parallel stripes so that the pattern in one stripe can be decoded with a small computer during stage retrace and stored in a memory for repeated writing of the many identical chips. Raster scanning is convenient because it uses almost constant table velocity, can read information from the memory in a line-at-a-time fashion, and minimizes the frequency response required in the deflection system. The systems have demonstrated reliable performance in both mask making and exploratory direct writing in a number of installations.

A block diagram of the EBES system is shown in Fig. 3.25. This system uses a telecentric deflection technique, as shown diagrammati-

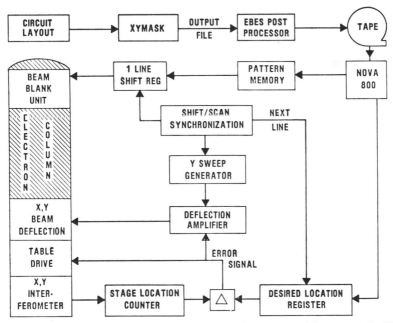

FIG. 3.25 Beam deflection system to compensate for stage position errors in EBES systems.

cally in Fig. 3.18. A vacuum stage moves the substrate continuously while the pattern is being written. The stage position is continuously measured by laser interferometers to an accuracy of $\frac{1}{32}$ μm and the difference between the actual and desired writing positions is corrected by beam deflection at a megahertz rate. This feedback system corrects for stage inaccuracy, stage response time, and vibration, and relates all written patterns to the accurate grid of the interferometer system. Since the deflection within the small field is accurate to better than $\frac{1}{8}$ μm, an overall positional accuracy of that value can be achieved.

The EBES system was designed to write repeated identical patterns in rectangular arrays. The chip pattern is divided into stripes 256-μm-wide for $\frac{1}{2}$ μm address writing. The features within one stripe are decoded and written into a bit image of the stripe in a core memory. This can be done slowly with random access during the stage retrace time between different stripes using the general system computer. The core memory is then read out in serial fashion to control the raster scanning of the stripe, as shown in Fig. 3.26. The memory is read repeatedly for each chip along the first row and then read in reverse for each chip as the stage returns along the next row. In that way, the first stripe of pattern is written at all chip locations on the substrate with the same chip orientation. Adjacent stripes are decoded in turn and written adjacent to the previous stripe on all chips. One-quarter micron address patterns are written in the same manner, but a scan of 128 μm is used with the same 512 addresses in a line of the reduced length scan. At the 20-MHz writing rate, the stage travels 2 cm/s and writes 2 cm²/min at the $\frac{1}{2}$ μm address and 0.5 cm²/min at the $\frac{1}{4}$ μm address size.

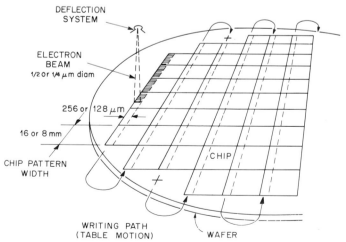

FIG. 3.26   EBES strategy for writing identical stripes of pattern on each chip of a wafer.

The stability of the system is very important to insure that adjacent stripes butt accurately and that all features are accurately placed. At regular intervals (and between the writing of stripes), the stage is driven so that the beam scans a registration mark on the stage. The position of the mark is measured and if the system has drifted since the previous measurement, the pattern is shifted by a compensating amount in $\frac{1}{32}$ μm. If the drift is above an acceptable level, the run is aborted.

When exposures are made directly on a wafer, the position of three or more registration marks on the wafer are ready by the electron beam. The pattern is shifted in x and y, the x and y gains are set, and the orthogonality is adjusted so that the pattern will align exactly at three points. If more than three points are read, a polynomial fit is used to control pattern distortion to fit at the measured point. Registration can be achieved regularly to 0.2 μm.

A diagram of the column components is shown in Fig. 3.27. A thoriated tungsten cathode is used because it has sufficient brightness, longer life, and better emission stability than the brighter cathodes. Forty nanoamps are obtained in a $\frac{1}{2}$ μm spot at 10 kV beam energy for mask writing. A

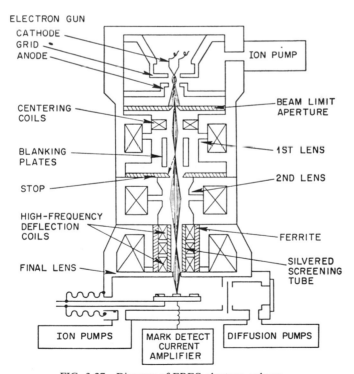

FIG. 3.27 Diagram of EBES electron column.

beam voltage of 20 kV is normally used for direct writing to penetrate insulating layers on the wafer and avoid deposition of charge on the surface
that would deflect the electron beam. The limiting aperture for the column
is near the cathode to minimize the effects of contamination and unwanted beam deflection due to charging. The beam is gated on and off
with a pair of electrostatic deflection plates located at a position that is
ultimately imaged on the writing surface to avoid spot motion as the beam
is blanked (Lin and Beauchamp, 1973). The blanked beam is deflected so
that it strikes a grounded aperture plate.

A dual prelens magnetic deflection system is used to deflect the writing
spot. About 30 μ s are required for the scan of the 512 addresses and 4 μs
for the flyback.

The vacuum stage uses an external air bearing $x-y$ motion that carries
the stage on the end of a cantilever beam. Stainless steel bellows are used
to seal the motion for vacuum in an arrangement that compensates the
atmospheric pressure on the stage motions. Torque motors drive ball type
lead screws for the two motions. All moving parts of the stage are non-
magnetic and the motors are mounted far from the electron column to
minimize magnetic fields. The laser interferometer Porro prisms are
mounted directly on the stage. The air bearing system provides very
smooth friction free motions that minimize vibrations and optimize servo

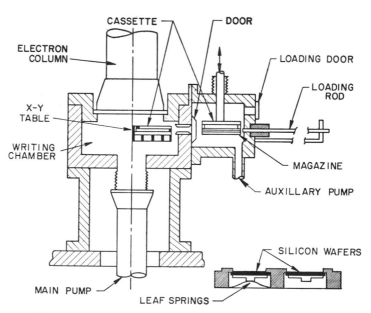

FIG. 3.28   Loading system (EBES) (cross section of cassette).

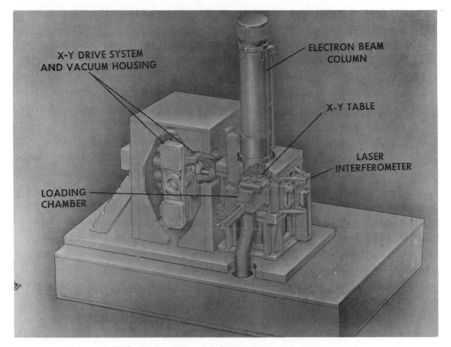

FIG. 3.29 Diagram of EBES system structure.

performance. Out-of-plane motion and orthogonality are maintained to ±2.0 μm.

A loading chamber is constructed on the side of the exposure chamber with a vacuum door between them as shown in Fig. 3.28. An elevator in the chamber allows two cassettes to be carried so that one can be removed from the stage, the elevator moved to the other position, and an unexposed cassette loaded into the system. An automatic loader has been developed to permit unattended operation overnight.

Ion pumps and sorption roughing pumps are used to maintain 10^{-6} Torr in the exposure chamber, 10^{-7} in the column, and 10^{-8} or better in the cathode region. An automatically cycled oil diffusion pump system with liquid nitrogen trap is used to evacuate the loading chamber to 10^{-5} before opening the vacuum door to the exposure chamber.

The EBES system uses automatic computer programs to control beam brightness, beam centering, beam focus, x and y deflection gain, and rotation of the scan. When used with an automatic loader, the system will maintain system adjustment for unattended overnight exposure of many masks. An overall illustration of the system is shown in Fig. 3.29.

An electron-beam exposure system that is equipped with a laser interferometer can be used for coordinate measurement to measure errors in a pattern or wafer distortion (Lieberman, 1978; Chang and Viswanathan, 1978). In order to do this, an array of registration marks are included in the pattern on a wafer. The stage is driven to each mark and each registration mark read with the electron beam. Laser interferometer measurements of the location of each mark are used in the computer system to automatically plot an output graph of the distortions. A typical plot obtained by the use of an EBES system is shown in Fig. 3.30. The rectangular dotted pattern is the nominal array position and the solid plot shows the actual position on a greatly exaggerated scale. The scale is 0.68 μm per box width and 0.40 μm per box height in this example. This technique has been used extensively to study distortions of silicon wafers in processing, to study distortion of x-ray and other masks, and to evaluate the performance of electron-beam systems. The substrate can be rotated 90° to examine orthogonality errors, as well as separate errors in the writing and reading system.

The use of the EBES systems for mask fabrication is described more fully in Chapter 5. However, in summary these systems have been used for over four years to expose COP and PBS electron-resist coated chrome mask blanks in a routine manner for LSI masks. A 3 in. mask requires between 30 and 40 min for exposure, depending on the test patterns, alignment marks, labeling, and shop control features. Since the system omits blank lines, low density patterns are written significantly faster than these times, with table velocities ranging up to 5 cm/s. Mask defect densities are about 0.2 defects/cm² (vis-a-vis typically 1–2/cm² with conventional mask fabrication methods) as measured on an optical automatic mask inspection system (AMIS) that detects many more defects (2.5 μm square minimum) than a human inspector will normally find. The systems have been used in order to attain better linewidth control, lower distortion, faster turnaround, and lower costs than is possible using alternate mask fabrication techniques.

B.   Vector Scan System

Several electron-beam exposure systems that have been developed for direct writing are based on the vector scan pattern writing strategy. This pattern writing strategy was illustrated in Figs. 3.19 and 3.20. As mentioned earlier, vector scan is distinguished from the raster scan method by the restriction of the beam deflection to only the areas to be exposed. A number of vector scan systems have been developed; a few, laboratory type, are commercially available. The detailed characteristics of these

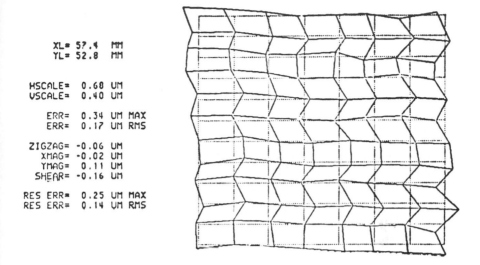

```
XL= 57.4  MM
YL= 52.8  MM

HSCALE=  0.68  UM
VSCALE=  0.40  UM

    ERR=  0.34  UM MAX
    ERR=  0.17  UM RMS

ZIGZAG= -0.06  UM
  XMAG= -0.02  UM
  YMAG=  0.11  UM
 SHEAR= -0.16  UM

RES ERR=  0.25  UM MAX
RES ERR=  0.14  UM RMS
```

ROWDATA:	AVG		SLOPE		BOW			
	-0.10	UM	-0.17	UM	-0.04	UM		
	-0.01		-0.17		-0.06			
	-0.06		-0.11		-0.03			
	0.02		-0.17		-0.05			
	-0.04		-0.13		-0.03			
	-0.01		-0.11		0.01			
	0.04		-0.09		0.02			
	0.04		-0.14		0.05			
	0.05		-0.17		0.04			
	0.04		-0.28		-0.00			
	-0.02		-0.19		0.05			
	0.05		-0.16		0.09			

COLDATA:	AVG		SLOPE		BOW		ZIG	
	-0.08	UM	-0.26	UM	-0.10	UM	-0.04	UM
	0.03		-0.19		-0.19		-0.06	
	0.08		-0.17		-0.10		-0.05	
	0.02		-0.16		-0.09		-0.05	
	0.07		-0.19		-0.05		-0.04	
	-0.04		-0.15		-0.06		-0.06	
	-0.04		-0.14		-0.11		-0.09	
	-0.03		-0.12		-0.04		-0.13	

FIG. 3.30 Electron-beam coordinate measurement output plot.

systems vary according to the purpose of the machine and the judgment or experience of the designer. For example, they may or may not incorporate a laser interferometer for precision stage control; only the more recent designs make use of a shaped beam or variable aperture feature.

One of the more advanced systems, viz., a laboratory type machine, illustrative of the state-of-the-art, will be described here.* It is a medium

---

* Descriptions of other vector scan machines have been given by Trotel (1976) and Beasley *et al.* (1978).

speed lithography system for submicrometer device and integrated circuit fabrication. This machine was designated VS-1 by its developer, and the details are reported in three companion papers, by Chang (1976a), Wilson *et al.* (1976), and Chang (1976b). The system block diagram is similar to that shown in Fig. 3.1. The electron-optical column employs three magnetic lenses, an LaB_6 emitter, and electrostatic blanking plates mounted at the plane of the cross-over in the first condenser lens. This location minimizes spot shift during blanking. A double magnetic deflection system, similar to that shown in Fig. 3.4a, is used except that in this case the deflection coils are mounted inside of the final lens. A beam limiting aperture, with three interchangeable aperture sizes, is provided below the gun. The condenser lenses image the source, in the manner illustrated in Fig. 3.2a. The gun brightness is 1×10^6 A/cm²/SR at 25 kV; several hundred hours life can be achieved routinely. The spot diameter is variable upwards from 0.05 μm and can produce a current density of more than 300 A/cm in the focused spot. The minimum feature linewidth is 0.1 μm for a single pass of the exposing beam. The linewidth is usually made equal to four spot diameters in order to obtain best edge resolution.

The pincushion pattern distortion of this system has been measured to be about 0.05 μm over a 2 mm $\times$ 2 mm field. The scan field size is 2000 times the minimum feature size, e.g., 5 mm $\times$ 5 mm for 2.5 μm lines. A 9-cm-diameter wafer can be accommodated on the stage, which can travel 10 cm $\times$ 10 cm. The target chamber includes an air lock for rapid wafer changing.

As mentioned earlier, one of the critical features of the vector scan approach lies in the effect on the pattern position and integrity of eddy currents induced in metallic walls surrounding the deflection coils. These eddy currents are greatest when the beam is caused to jump from the end of one pattern to the beginning of the next pattern. In the system described here, the eddy current suppression was effected by using ferrite material in both the final lens pole pieces and in a cylinder located between the deflection coils and the lens. In this way, the pattern position error was made negligible.

The hardwired pattern generator allowed any of the three writing strategies illustrated in Figs. 3.20a, 3.20b, or 3.20c to be used. A significant decrease in writing time, especially for larger feature sizes can be realized by using a small beam for pattern edge delineation and a larger beam for fill-in (Figs. 3.20e and 3.20f). The beam stepping rate is changed to correct for the proximity effect. This system has been operated at a beam stepping rate up to 10 MHz.

The registration signals were generated in the usual way by scanning the beam over a bench mark, but the signal-to-noise ratio was enhanced by processing the signal obtained from the backscattered electrons. This processing consisted of digitizing and storing the signal traces obtained from repeated scanning (e.g., up to 1000 times), with each new digitized signal added to the sum in the computer memory. In this way, the signal-to-noise ratio was improved and level-to-level registration accuracy better than $\pm \frac{1}{8}$ μm was observed (Wilson *et al.*, 1975).

This system was exercised by fabricating several types of devices, including an operational 8K-bit FET memory chip described by Yu *et al.* (1975). The minimum linewidth in this device was 1.25 μm, yielding an array density of 0.8 Mbits/cm², on a chip 1.1 mm × 1.6 mm. The fractional area coverage of this memory pattern varied from about 1.4 to 30%, depending on the mask level, with an average value of 22%. This value is higher than normal for integrated circuits because of the high density nature of this memory circuit. An SEM micrograph of a portion of the array is shown in Fig. 3.31. The beam writing time for the four mask levels on this chip was about 1.4 s. Overhead times account for about 0.4 s/chip, for a total of ~ 1.8 s/chip. As an experiment, this array was shrunk by a factor of two in both linear dimensions and all four levels exposed with satisfactory lithography. Level to level registration of ± 0.1 μm was achieved consistently.

C. Raster Scan Production Machine

The raster scan pattern writing strategy has been used in a direct writing production type electron-beam lithography system described by Yourke and Weber (1976). Since this machine was intended for production use, the attainment of high throughput, together with a high degree of automatic control and stabilization, were primary design considerations. In order to achieve high throughput, the electron-optical column was made to produce a square beam spot of 2.5 μm on a side. This size was chosen equal to the minimum feature size desired. As shown earlier in this chapter, use of this square spot allows much faster exposure than would have been possible by the use of a small round spot. Because of the large size of the spot, the beam current is high, viz., 3 μA, which causes high energy spread due to the Boersch effect and aberration problems. These machine features require some special characteristics in the electron-optical column, which is shown schematically in Fig. 3.32 (Mauer *et al.*, 1977). The electron source is a tungsten filament, with a brightness of 3×10^5 A/cm²/SR at 25 keV. The tungsten emitter was chosen over the brighter lanthanum hexaboride source because the illumination of the spot shaping aperture by the latter type source is nonuniform. The gun contains a turret of sixteen such tungsten filaments that can be rotated

FIG. 3.31 Portion of 8192-bit MOS memory array fabricated by direct writing electron-beam lithography. One-micrometer minimum feature size. Memory array density = 0.8 Mbits/cm². [From Yu *et al.* (1975). Photo courtesy IBM.]

into place and the beam centered under automatic servo control, without breaking vacuum. Each filament exhibits a lifetime of 30–40 hr.

The electron-optical column of this machine (Fig. 3.32) is seen to include four lenses and two beam shaping apertures. The condenser lens images the gun crossover, through the 400-μm-square beam shaping aperture, into the first demagnifying lens. This lens demagnifies the beam, which then passes through a circular aperture that passes only the central emission cone from the source. In this way, the current density in the final spot is caused to be more uniform. The final projection lens images the square beam forming aperture onto the wafer to create the 2.5 μm square spot. The maximum half angle of convergence of the beam at the target is

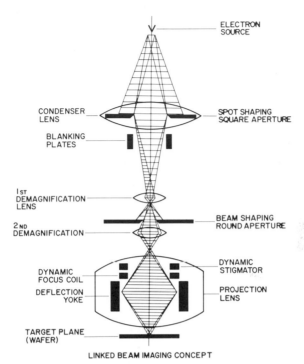

FIG. 3.32 Schematic illustration of the electron optical column in the EL-1 electron-beam machine. [From Mauer *et al.* (1977).]

7.5×10^{-3} rad. The scan field is 5 mm $\times$ 5 mm. The beam is deflected by a deflection yoke located inside of the final lens, as illustrated in Fig. 3.33. This yoke creates a double deflection, as shown, to achieve normal incidence by the electrons onto the wafer. Dynamic focus and stigmators are provided to correct for deflection distortions. An automatic deflection distortion correction allows 10,000 resolved lines over the 5-mm field with a deflection accuracy of 30 ppm (Engelke *et al.*, 1977). The electrostatic plates located within the final lens allow small, high speed, positional correction of the deflected beam. Even with a 7.5 eV energy spread in the beam, the total geometric and chromatic aberrations after correction are 0.8 μm. A sophisticated beam control and stabilization system provides means for automatic servocontrol of such critical adjustments as beam centering on the square forming aperture, filament temperature for beam current stability, and beam focus. These control systems result in a stability of $\pm 1\%$ in total beam current and uniformity of spot illumination within 5%. The exposure time per chip layer depends on the circuit being written, but is typically 1 s.

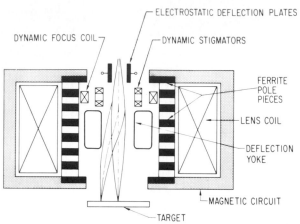

FIG. 3.33   Schematic of final lens and deflection systems used in the EL-1 machine. [From Mauer *et al.* (1977).]

Three beam deflection modes are used, illustrated in Fig. 3.34. The registration signals are generated by a raster scan over a limited area in each corner of the scan field, as shown in Fig. 3.34a. The exposure or pattern writing mode is a bidirectional raster scan over the scan field (Fig. 3.34b). In this mode the beam is blanked on and off by use of the electrostatic blanking plates shown in Fig. 3.32.

In the third mode (Fig. 3.34c), implemented during table motion, the beam is deflected in a square so as to scan a cross-wire system to provide the signals for automatic beam focus control (Doran *et al.*, 1975).

Fast and accurate overlay registration of the multilevel exposure patterns that make up an integrated circuit has been achieved with the aid of an automatic registration system (Davis *et al.*, 1977). In this registration technique, the area of one chip is devoted to large alignment marks that provide the inputs for wafer registration, effected by moving the wafer table in response to error signals. The error in initial mechanical location of the wafer on the table is $\sim \pm 75$ μm; the wafer registration routine can position a chip with a maximum error of ± 7.5 μm. Four alignment marks (two orthogonal pairs of 5-μm-wide bars spaced 30 μm apart) are located in each of the four corners of each chip for chip registration. These marks occupy about 1% of the chip area. The electron beam automatically locates and scans each pair of resist-covered marks 30 times. The backscattered electrons are detected by energy sensitive solid state detectors. The resulting signals are filtered, processed, and summed to provide a single digital signal to indicate mark position. This data is used to adjust the ori-

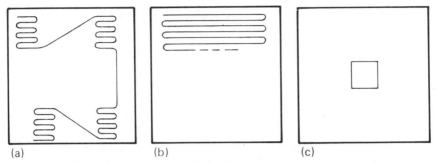

(a)   (b)   (c)

FIG. 3.34   Illustration of the three scan modes in the EL-1 system used for (a) registration (time = 200 ms), (b) pattern exposure (time ~ 1 s for 5 mm field), and (c) automatic focus scan (implemented during stage motion).

entation and scale of the writing scan field to compensate for linear distortions in each field. The results of this technique have been shown by many tests over extended periods of time to result in 3σ errors less than about 0.5 μm in overlay position. The registration time for each chip is 150 ms. The system has also shown the ability to register on 0.5-μm-deep alignment marks that are covered by 4 μm of resist with a random error in mark location of 0.2 μm.

The production system described above has been operating in a production environment for more than two years, with an up-time greater than 85%. The time required for table motion, automatic focus, etc., for each scanfield is 250 ms. Automatic wafer handling and loading is provided. The throughput is twelve 82-mm-diameter wafer levels per hour, or more than 2000 chips per hour. A photograph of the system is shown in Fig. 3.35.

D.   Trends in Machine Development

It is clear that needs are developing for the high level of performance from discrete devices and integrated circuits that can be met only by the use of high resolution fabrication techniques. These needs are seen first in specialty applications, such as military electronic systems, but will develop eventually in the larger commercial market. As discussed in Chapter 6, there are several promising batch replication techniques under development that could, in principle, satisfy the production needs of high resolution microelectronic devices. However, at the time this is written, no fully satisfactory submicrometer production replication process has

FIG. 3.35 Photograph of the EL-1 production electron beam system described in the text.
[Courtesy IBM.]

been demonstrated. Therefore, the development of electron-beam
lithography machines for direct writing is being pursued by a number of
system organizations and machine suppliers. The goals of this work are
high throughput and submicrometer feature size.

An indication of the possible acceptable throughput of a production
machine and the implication of this throughput on machine design can be
obtained as follows. An advanced projection photolithographic printer is
expected to expose 100 5 in. wafer levels per hour with 2 μm minimum
features by using a very fast negative resist. If the desired integrated circuit patterns are merely scaled by a factor of four, to $\frac{1}{2}$ μm minimum feature size, there could be sixteen times as many functions created on this
same size wafer. Therefore, a production rate of six 5 in. wafer levels per
hour with the smaller features would produce the same number of higher
performance functions per hour.

It was shown earlier that high beam current density (brightness) coupled with a sensitive resist are necessary in order to attain a reasonable

exposure time per wafer level. Beam currents approaching a microampere can be obtained in a small circular spot from a thermally assisted field emission cathode or in a large shaped beam from a thermal cathode. In both of these cases, the performance will be seriously affected by Coulomb forces between the electrons in the beam. These forces both shift the focus and spread the lateral size of the beam. They also increase the energy spread, causing lateral chromatic aberration in lenses and deflectors. These effects are proportional to the current and length of the column and inversely proportional to the solid angle illuminating the image, and will limit the maximum useful current in electron-beam systems.

It is not clear that improvement can be assumed in the sensitivity of resists. Furthermore, there are features of resists other than sensitivity that are important. For example, the less sensitive resists tend to have better processing characteristics and are more rugged than the more sensitive materials. However, a breakthrough in resists could extend the ultimate throughput and resolution limits of electron-beam lithography significantly.

Whereas high beam current density coupled with a sensitive resist and shaped spot capability may be necessary in order to attain a reasonable exposure time per wafer level, achievements in these technical areas do not necessarily assure high throughput. For example, the stage motion and registration times in a vector scan system can become limiting factors.

Therefore, the challenge in system design is to reduce the overhead times and use the available current and resist sensitivity most efficiently in writing patterns. Vector scan is an obvious choice over raster scan to use the beam current most effectively on the low density patterns of real devices. Small field continuous scan systems have lower overhead times than step and repeat systems; also, the small field usually permits the use of a larger numerical aperture to reduce electron interactions and reduces deflection range to minimize the effects of energy spread on resolution. Higher machine stability and the use of servocorrection techniques will reduce the frequency of registration required, and therefore lower the overhead times in a vector scan machine. Also, some step-and-repeat time can be saved by writing "on-the-fly," a technique in which the electron beam is caused to track the stage motion so that the exposure can continue during the acceleration and deceleration phases of stage motion. Judicious combination of these several advanced features can lead to machines with production level throughput. These issues are summarized in Table 3.1, in which the principal design features of presently available

TABLE 3.1

Machine Design Options

Subsystem	Present commercial machines		Future production machine	
	Approach	Limitation	Approach	Advantage
Beam forming (gun and lenses)	Small gaussian spot	Slow writing— fast electronics	Variable shaped spot	Fast writing speed— lower speed electronics
Deflection system	Magnetic	High inductance— limited speed	Magnetic/electro-static	High speed
Wafer stage	Step and repeat	Step-and-repeat time— high acceleration	Write on-the-fly	Higher speed— reduced settling and motion time
	Continuous scan with raster writing	Extra writing time on low density patterns	Continuous scan— vector writing	Low overhead times
Registration	Register on each scan field	Registration time	Register once per cluster of several scan fields	Fewer registrations— less time consumed

commercial machines are compared with those features that should be available in a few years.

It is seen that the choice of a circular spot or a shaped beam is strongly dependent on the electronics. A circular spot requires extremely high speed deflection and modulation circuits to pattern submicron devices at practical rates. The electronics requirements for a shaped beam system are considerably less severe. The data rate for the shaped spot system will be significantly less than for the circular spot system. However, the column necessary to form a shaped beam system is longer, which leads to greater electron interaction effects.

It appears that the development of a direct write shaped beam system with a throughput of at least 5–4 in. wafer levels per hour with submicrometer patterns will be challenging but achievable. Calculations suggest that the throughput limit due to electron interactions and resist sensitivity will be in the range of ten wafer levels per hours. However, in order to approach this latter limit the machine design strategy must involve very low overhead times.

REFERENCES

Alles, D. S., Ashley, F. R., Collier, R. J., Gere, E. A., Herriott, D. R., Johnson, A. M., and Thomson, M. G. R. (1974). *Proc. Int. Electron Devices Meeting, Washington, D. C.* (abstract only), pp. 21–22.

Alles, D. S., Ashley, F. R., Johnson, A. M., and Townsend, R. L. (1975). *J. Vac. Sci. Technol.* **12**, 1252–1256.

Amboss, K. (1975). *J. Vac. Sci. Technol.* **12**, 1152–1155.

Archard, G. D. (1954). *Proc. Int. Conf. Electron Microsc., London* pp. 97–105.

Banford, A. P. (1966). "The Transport of Charged Particle Beams." F.& FN Spon, London.

Beasley, J. P., Spencer, D. B., and Beelaard, R. A. (1978). *Proc. Symp. Electron Ion Beam Sci. Technol., ECS* pp. 98–107.

Boersch, H. (1954). *Z. Phys.* **139**, 115.

Broers, A. N. (1972). *Proc. Symp. Electron Ion Beam Sci. Technol.* pp. 3–25.

Broers, A. N. (1973). *J. Vac. Sci. Technol.* **10**, 979–982.

Chang, T. H. P. (1975). *J. Vac. Sci. Technol.* **12**, 1271–1275.

Chang, T. H. P., and Stewart, A. D. G. (1969). *Symp. Electron Ion Laser Beam Technol., 10th, Gaithersburg, Maryland.*

Chang, T. H., and Viswanathan, R. (1978). *J. Vac. Sci. Technol.* **15**, 878–882.

Chang, T. H. P., Wilson, A. D., Speth, A. J., and Ting, C. H. (1976a). *Proc. Symp. Electron Ion Beam Sci. Technol., ECS* pp. 392–410.

Chang, T. H. P., Speth, A. J., Ting, C. H., Viswanathan, R., Parikh, M., and Munro, E. (1976b). *Proc. Symp. Electron Ion Beam Sci. Technol., ECS* pp. 377–391.

Chang, T. H. P., Hatzakis, M., Wilson, A. D., and Broers, A. N. (1977). *Electronics* May 12, pp. 89–98.

Chung, M. S. C., and Tai, K. L. (1978). *Proc. Symp. Electron Ion Beam Sci. Technol., ECS* pp. 242–255.

Cosslett, V. E. (1950). "Introduction to Electron Optics," 2nd ed. Oxford Univ. Press, London and New York.

Courant, E. D., Livingston, M. S., and Snyder, H. S. (1952). *Phys. Rev.* **88**, 1190.

Cutler, C. C., and Hines, M. E. (1955). *Proc. IRE* **43**, 307.

Dahl, P. (1973). "Introduction to Electron and Ion Optics." Academic Press, New York.

Davis, E. D., Moore, R. D., Williams, M. C., and Woodard, O. C. (1977). *IBM J. Res. Dev.* **21**, 498–505.

Doran, S., Perkins, W., and Stickel, W. (1975). *J. Vac. Sci. Technol.* **12**, 1174–1176.

El-Kareh, A. B., and El-Kareh, J. C. (1970). "Electron Beams, Lenses and Optics." Academic Press, New York.

Engelke, H., Loughran, J. F., Michail, M. S., and Ryan, P. M. (1976). *IEDM Tech. Digest* **437**.

Engelke, H., Loughran, J. F., Michail, M. S., and Ryan, P. M. (1977). *IBM J. Res. Dev.* **21**, 506–514.

Fert, C. (1952). *J. Phys. Radium* **13**, 83A.

Fert, C., and Durandeau, P. (1967). "Focusing of Charged Particles," Vol. 1, Chapter 2.3. Academic Press, New York.

Good, R. H., and Mueller, E. W. (1956). *Handb. Phys.* **21**, 176–231.

Goto, E., Soma, T., and Idesawa, M. (1978). *J. Vac. Sci. Technol.* **15**, 883–886.

Grivet, P. (1965a). "Electron Optics." Pergamon, Oxford, England.

Grivet, P. (1965b). "Electron Optics," p. 68. Pergamon, Oxford.

Halbach, K. (1964). *Amer. J. Phys.* **32**, 90.

Herriott, D. R., Collier, R. J., Alles, D. S., and Stafford, J. W. (1975). *IEEE Trans. Electron Devices* **ED-22**, 385–392.

Hutter, R. G. E. (1970). *IEEE Trans. Electron Devices* **ED-17**, 1022–1031.

Jones, G. A. C., and Owen, G. (1978). *J. Vac. Sci. Technol.* **15**, 896–900.

Kaashoek, J. (1968). *Philips Res. Rep. Suppl.* **11**, 1–114.

Klemperer, O. (1953). "Electron Optics." Cambridge Univ. Press, London and New York.

Knauer, W. (1979). *Optik (Stuttgart)* **54**, no. 3, 211–234. Also presented at the *Electron, Ion, Photon Beam Symp., Boston, Massachusetts, May 30*.

Langmuir, D. B. (1937). *Proc. IRE* **25**, 977.

Lieberman, B. (1978). *J. Vac. Sci. Technol.* **15**, 913–916.

Liebmann, G. (1949). *Proc. Phys. Soc. B* **62**, 213.

Lin, L. H., and Beauchamp, H. L. (1973). *J. Vac. Sci. Tech.* **10**, 987–990.

Loeffler, K. H. (1969). *Z. Angew. Phys.* **27**, 145–149.

Loughran, J. F., Michail, M. S., Ryan, P. M., and Engelke, H. (1976). *Technical Digest, IEDM, Washington, D. C.,* p. 437.

Mauer, J. L., Pfeiffer, H. C., and Stickel, W. (1977). *IBM J. Res. Dev.* **21**, 514–521.

Meltzer, B. (1957). *J. Electron Control* **3**, 355.

Miyauchi, S., Tanaka, K., and Russ, J. C. (1970). *IEEE Trans. Electron Devices* **ED-17**, 450–457.

Moss, H. (1968a). "Narrow Angle Electron Guns and Cathode Ray Tubes," p. 205. Academic Press, New York.

Moss, H. (1968b). "Narrow Angle Electron Guns and Cathode Ray Tubes," p. 116. Academic Press, New York.

Mulvey, T. (1967). "Focusing of Charged Particles" (A. Septier, ed.), Vol. I, Chapter 2.6. Academic Press, New York.

Mulvey, T., and Wallington, M. J. (1969). *J. Sci. Instrum.* **2**, 466–472.

Munro, E. (1975). *J. Vac. Sci. Technol.* **12**, 1146–1150.

Nakata, H., Kato, T., Murata, K., and Nagami, K. (1978). *Proc. Symp. Electron Ion Beam Sci. Technol., May 21* pp. 393–405.

Owen, G., and Nixon, W. D. (1973). *J. Vac. Sci. Technol.* **10**, 983–986.

Ozdemir, F. S., Wolf, E. D., and Buckey, C. R. (1972). *IEEE Trans. Electron Devices* **ED-19**, 624–628.

Ozdemir, F. S., Buckey, C. R., and Wolf, E. D. (1975). *J. Vac. Sci. Tech.* **12**, 1246–1250.

Parikh, M. (1978a). *J. Vac. Sci. Tech.* **15**, 931–933.

Parikh, M. (1978b). *Proc. Symp. Electron Ion Beam Sci. Technol.* pp. 382–392.

Patlach, A. M., Jaskar, P. R., and Studwell, T. W. (1978). *J. Vac. Sci. Technol.* **15**, 874–877.

Pease, R. F. W., Ballantyne, J. P., Henderson, R. C., Voschenkov, A. M., and Yau, L. D. (1975). *IEEE Trans. Electron Devices* **ED-22**, 393.

Pfeiffer, H. C. (1971). *Record Symp. Electron, Ion Laser Beam Technol., 11th, Boulder, Colorado, May 12–14* San Francisco Press, San Francisco, California.

Pfeiffer, H. C. (1972). *Proc. Ann. Scanning Electron Microsc. Symp., 5th, Chicago, Illinois* p. 113.

Pfeiffer, H. C. (1978). *J. Vac. Sci. Technol.* **15**, 887.

Pierce, J. R. (1949). "Theory and Design of Electron Beams" Van Nostrand-Reinhold, Princeton, New Jersey.

Reeds, J. W., Amboss, K., Fralick, R., Wolf, E. D., and Wallman, B. (1978). *Proc. Symp. Electron Ion Beam Sci. Technol.* pp. 179–183.

Septier, A. (1966). "Advances in Optical and Electron Microscopy," pp. 204–274. Academic Press, New York.

Shimizu, R., Shiniki, T., Ichimura, S., Kawaii, S., and Tanaka, T. (1978). *J. Vac. Sci. Technol.* **15**, 922–926.

Speth, A. J., Wilson, A. D., Kern, A., and Chang, T. H. P. (1975). *J. Vac. Sci. Technol.* **12**, 1235–1239.

Spicer, D. F., Roger, A. C., and Varnell, G. L. (1973). *J. Vac. Sci. Technol.* **10**, 1052–1055.

Steffen, K. G. (1965). "High Energy Beam Optics." Wiley (Interscience), New York.

Stephani, D., and Froschle, E. (1978). *J. Vac. Sci. Technol.* **15**, 906–908.

Stickel, W. (1978). *J. Vac. Sci. Technol.* **15**, 901–905.

Stickel, W., and Pfeiffer, H. C. (1978). *Proc. Symp. Electron Ion Beam Sci. Technol., ECS* pp. 98–107.

Stille, G., and Astrant, B. (1978). *J. Vac. Sci. Technol.* **15**, 921.

Swanson, L. W. (1975). *J. Vac. Sci. Technol.* **12**, 1228–1233.

Swanson, L. W., and Martin, N. A. (1975). *J. Appl. Phys.* **46**, 2029–2046.

Thomson, M. G. R. (1975). *J. Vac. Sci. Technol.* **12**, 1156–1160.

Thomson, M. G. R., Collier, R. J., Herriott, D. R. (1978). *J. Vac. Sci. Technol.* **15**, 891–895.

Trotel, J. (1976). *Proc. Symp. Electron Ion Beam Sci. Technol.* pp. 325–331.

Trotel, J. (1978). *J. Vac. Sci. Technol.* **15**, 872–873.

Varnell, G. L., Spicer, D. F., Rodger, A. C., and Holland, R. D. (1974). *Proc. Int. Conf. Electron Ion Beam Sci. Technol., 6th, San Francisco, California* p. 97.

Wardly, G. A. (1973). *J. Vac. Sci. Technol.* **10**, 975–978.

Wells, O. C. (1974). "Scanning Electron Microscopy," Chapter 4. McGraw-Hill, New York.

Wiesner, J. C., and Everhart, T. E. (1974). *J. Appl. Phys.* **44**, 2140–2148. with addendum **45**, 2797–2798 (1974).

Wilson, A. D., Chang, T. H. P., and Kern, A. (1975). *J. Vac. Sci. Technol.* **12**, 1240–1245.

Wilson, A. D. *et al.* (1976). *Proc. Symp. Electron Ion Beam Sci. Technol., ECS* pp. 361–376.

Wilson, R. G., and Brewer, G. R. (1973). "Ion Beams," p. 191ff. Wiley, New York.
Wolf, E. D., Coane, P. J., and Ozdemir, F. S. (1975). *J. Vac. Sci. Technol.* **12,** 1266–1270.
Worster, J. (1970). *Int. J. Electron.* **28,** 117–128.
Yourke, H. S., and Weber, E. V. (1976). Technical Digest, pp. 431–436. IEDM, Washington D. C.
Yu, H. N., Dennard, R. H., Chang, T. H. P., Osburn, C. M., Dilonardo, V., and Lukn, H. E. (1975). *J. Vac. Sci. Technol.* **12,** 1297–1300.
Zimmerman, B. (1970). *Adv. Electron. Electron. Phys.* **29,** 251.

4

Device fabrication by electron-beam lithography

RICHARD C. HENDERSON

HUGHES RESEARCH LABORATORIES
MALIBU, CALIFORNIA

I. BACKGROUND

Research on high resolution lithography has been an active subject for the past decade. Much of the work has been machine and process oriented, aimed at developing the lithographic and processing tools neces-

217

sary in order to fabricate high resolution devices; these aspects have been discussed in Chapters 1–3. However, the ultimate purpose of this research is to evolve various forms of microelectronic devices with high-resolution features. Therefore, much development work has focused on experimental and prototype device fabrication, which includes development of new processing techniques, in order to make high resolution devices and to characterize the physical laws that govern device behavior.

The motivation for this research on high resolution devices arises from the superior performance that smaller devices can provide. The particular goal has varied with the type of device. For example, the desire for higher operating speed or lower power consumption has provided the impetus for work on field effect transistors (FETs), surface acoustic wave devices, charge coupled devices (CCDs), and bipolar transistors. Moreover, some devices could not be made at all without a high resolution capability. An example is the Josephson junction microbridge. Finally, a substantial effort has been devoted to reduction of the size of LSI circuits for logic, large capacity memory storage, etc. Here a major benefit is cost saving, achieved by increasing the number of functions per unit area. In addition, smaller circuitry should make possible larger systems, because of higher reliability (through fewer chips) or smaller volume.

In order to verify the theoretical promise of smaller devices, experimental samples must be built and tested. But, in the case of high resolution devices, the fabrication of such prototypes has required the use of new lithographic tools in addition to changes in other aspects of device processing. As a result, electron-beam lithography has been used extensively to make many different kinds of prototype devices that are beyond state-of-the-art of photolithographic methods.

While the direct writing electron-beam approach (exposing directly on the wafers) has been but one of several available·high resolution options, in practice it has been the one most widely used. This has occurred because the electron-beam machines offer relatively straightforward solutions to the problems of accurate generation and overlay of high resolution patterns. The other options, viz., the high resolution replication techniques such as x ray, ion beam, or projection electron lithography, should offer the economic advantage of higher throughput compared to digitally controlled electron-beam machines; therefore, they will find application in production.

In order to use any of the high resolution lithography techniques, changes must be made in the methods of device fabrication, and this requires development in many disciplines. For example, particular attention must be devoted to the techniques of pattern generation and alignment. The principles of device scaling must be understood and applied correctly. The factors affecting undercutting and associated etching phenomena must be controllable. The sensitivity of the smaller devices to the wafer processing must be known. The remaining sections of this chapter will treat the details of these processing changes and will review the state-of-the-art in devices made with electron-beam lithography.

The next section will compare photolithography with electron-beam lithography, specifically pointing out the difference between the two techniques. Section III will examine the lithography tasks of resist coating, alignment, and pattern transfer with respect to electron-beam lithography. In addition, this section will discuss the processing ramifications of substrate alignment marks. Section IV will review a number of devices that have been constructed with electron-beam lithography, including the performance improvements that have resulted, as well as the problems that have arisen. Section V summarizes some of the constraints on electron-beam lithography based on the experience gained from device fabrication.

II. COMPARISON OF PHOTO- AND ELECTRON-BEAM LITHOGRAPHY

A comparison of the processing steps for conventional size devices made with photolithography with high resolution devices made using electron-beam lithography will clarify the different features of these two lithographic techniques. The differences are fundamental, even though general descriptions of either process are similar. That is, in both cases the sample must be coated with resist, the pattern aligned, exposed, and developed, and subsequently the pattern must be etched and the resist stripped. Moreover, the techniques utilized with these various steps are often similar. For example, coatings of both electron resist and photoresist are usually formed by spinning the wafers after applying the appropriate polymer solution. Also, both types of resist films are usually baked in order to harden the films and to promote adhesion to the substrate. After exposure, both resist types can be developed by immersion, spray, or combinations thereof. Finally, many of the typical etchants used in photolithography find applications with electron-beam lithography.

Despite this apparent similarity, in actual practice processing a high resolution device is quite different compared with processing a conventional size device. One fundamental difference is that smaller devices tend to be more sensitive to subtle process effects. For example, etch processes have been found (Henderson et al., 1979) that have slightly faster or slower etch rates at the edges of resist features. Even electron-beam exposure has been found to affect the chemical etch rate of MoAu alloy films used for transistor leads (Pankratz *et al.*, 1973).

Another factor is the need for greater absolute control of linewidth, alignment accuracy, and line profile in high resolution device fabrication. This demand for greater relative control arises because the relative dimensional control must be maintained. For example, referring to Fig. 4.1, consider the effects upon scaling by 20-fold of a 5 μm × 10 μm feature in a film 1-μm thick (e.g., the gate of an FET). A designer might typically allow a 10% error in the size of this feature; but, maintaining this degree of error as the feature size is scaled down by a factor of ten would decrease the allowable absolute error from 0.5 μm to 500 Å. Hence, in absolute terms, the edge roughness of features, as well as the feature-to-feature size variation, must be more tightly controlled with high resolution devices.

In the same manner, to maximize the improvement in device packing density obtainable with high resolution features, tighter control of alignment is also necessary. Where structures coincide, such as a contact via to a gate, the minimum linewidth of the overlapping feature must account for both misalignment (arising from the lithographic tool) and for variation in feature size (due to the processing). This allowance can be a worst case provision. However, both misalignment and feature size variation are sta-

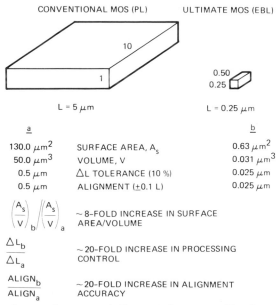

FIG. 4.1   Area, volume, tolerance, and alignment changes resulting from a 20-fold reduction in feature size for electronic devices.

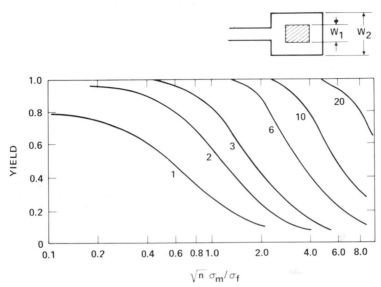

FIG. 4.2   Overlap yield versus the normalized ratio of the standard deviation of misalignment σ_m to the standard deviation of feature size σ_t, as a function of the ratio $\Delta W/\sqrt{2}\sigma_t$ [From Lynch (1977).]

tistical quantities, so it is possible to trade off yield with decreasing area by tightening the design tolerance to less than the worst case. Figure 4.2 (Lynch, 1977) shows such a relationship, where σ_m is the standard deviation in misalignment, σ_f is the standard deviation in feature size, and ΔW is the difference in size between the two aligned features. The alignment analysis shown in Fig. 4.2 quantifies the need for improvement in the absolute value of alignment and dimensional control which was depicted in Fig. 4.1. Assume a given set of values of σ_f, σ_m, and ΔW in Fig. 4.2 and consider the changes implied when the features are scaled by some parameter $1/K$ $(K > 1)$. There are three possible cases:

(1) ΔW scales as $1/K$, but σ_f and σ_m are constant;
(2) ΔW and σ_f scale as $1/K$, but σ_m is constant;
(3) ΔW, σ_f, and σ_m all scale as $1/K$.

It is seen from Fig. 4.2 that for any arbitrary starting point, scaling via case (1) causes the yield to degrade dramatically down a line $\sigma_m/\sigma_f = $ constant. Only for case (3) is there no yield degradation. Thus, as device size decreases, there are compelling reasons to improve alignment and feature size control to the same degree that the size is reduced.

Another difference between processing conventional and high resolution devices is the greater height-to-width aspect ratio for features of smaller devices. This ratio changes because the thickness of the etched films are usually not decreased in the same proportion as are the lateral dimensions, since it is difficult to make continuous, pinhole-free films that are very thin. Very thin films also make step coverage more difficult. And, in the case of conductors, shrinking all three dimensions by the scaling factor $1/K$ increases the resistance of the line by K, which reduces circuit performance. For these reasons, the thickness is generally made as large as is compatible with the processing. But as the aspect ratio increases, the patterning is generally more difficult.

A major difference in the processing of conventional and high resolution devices arises because the optimal device structure (vertically) may change in order to maximize benefits from smaller lateral dimensions. This change may require that the entire process for device fabrication be modified, and extensive research may be necessary, first to find out the changes that are necessary, and second how to achieve them.

For example, to make a smaller metal-oxide semiconductor (MOS) transistor of optimal design requires changes in oxide thickness, substrate doping, and junction depth. In turn, each of these changes requires modifications in the nonlithographic procedures involving thermal and doping treatments, and these changes must be well controlled and characterized.

Because of such differences, it is not possible to obtain a high resolution device by simply substituting electron-beam lithography for photolithography and continuing to use an existing set of procedures. There are several other reasons why this cannot be done, due to the differing nature of electron-beam and photolithography procedures. For example, process changes may be required because of the differences in the physical properties of the electron resist vis-a-vis the optical resist. A relatively common experience is that some well characterized etchant proves inoperative with the desired electron resist, so alternatives must be found. Moreover, the desired type of processing may change; for example, the lift-off technique discussed in Chapter 2 may be preferred to etching. This lift-off technique is widely used in electron-beam lithography because of the natural undercut profile obtained from properly exposed electron-beam–resist patterns, but its use is not so straightforward in optical lithography.

The use of electron-beam lithography rather than photolithography can require changes in the substrate processing in several other ways. For example, the change of the exposing media from photons to charged particles can require a ground path when exposing electron-beam patterns on insulators. Moreover, the electron beam can induce damage which would require more elaborate changes in the processing, such as special anneals.

The techniques employed for pattern-to-pattern alignment with electron-beam lithography can also require processing changes. With optical lithography, relatively simple etched structures will provide the necessary alignment features. And, by simple change of wavelength, these marks can be seen without exposing the photoresist that covers the wafer. In contrast, the resist covering electron-beam alignment marks is practically always exposed during the alignment step. Moreover, the alignment marks used with electron-beam lithography generally require better definition than those used for photolithography, and must be of a nature that allows them to be "seen" by a scanning electron beam. These needs can lead to material incompatibilities between the alignment feature and the substrate, restrict temperatures or processes, or require extra masking steps and so forth.

Clearly, the impact of all these differences in processing, required by the introduction of electron-beam lithography into device fabrication, is a need for careful design of the process sequence.

III. CHARACTERISTICS OF ELECTRON-BEAM LITHOGRAPHY

The previous section discussed the similarities and differences between wafer processing with conventional and high resolution lithography. This section will review some specific developments that have been carried out in order to implement electron-beam lithography in device fabrication. Each of the sequential operations that constitute lithographic processing (sample coating, alignment, exposure, etc.) will be examined. For each of the operations, the use of electron-beam lithography has required specialized developments which will be discussed below.

The interrelationships of the various component operations that are referred to by the phrase electron-beam lithography may be visualized from Fig. 4.3. Here, an electron-beam machine is shown exposing a pattern on a semiconductor wafer. Note that electronic data controls the beam deflection and blanking. These data must be generated off-line. Methods of doing this are discussed in Section III.A. The wafer depicted in Fig. 4.3 is usually coated with a polymer film. Some of the necessary properties of this resist coating, as well as the specific polymers that have been used for prototype device fabrication are discussed in Section III.B. Notice also in Fig. 4.3 that the electron-beam scan field must be aligned to previously defined patterns on the wafer. The corrections required to effect this alignment are described in Section III.C. In order to implement these corrections, the machine must be able to sense alignment marks on the wafer

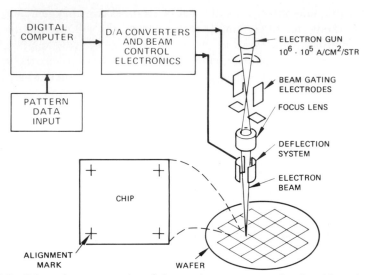

FIG. 4.3   Schematic representation of electron-beam exposure showing chip registration.

as depicted on Fig. 4.3. The various kinds of alignment marks that have been used are discussed in Section III.D. Because wafer processing can affect the properties of these alignment marks, care must be exercised in the choice of materials. Several alignment mark strategies are discussed in Section III.E. Finally, the exposed pattern must be developed and the resulting image transferred to the substrate. While some of this information has been presented in Chapter 2, ramifications of pattern transfer particularly significant for device fabrication are discussed in Section III.F.

A. Pattern Data

Before device fabrication can begin the corresponding pattern data must be composed. There are several alternative ways to do this composition. Figure 4.4 depicts one method that is relatively straightforward to implement. Assume that an idea or symbolic design exists; the device designer uses these data to generate a layout. This layout can be a drawing using different colors on line segments to depict the various pattern levels (i.e., the exposures). For example, FET structures basically require four pattern levels: first an isolation pattern, then a gate, followed by contact vias and then interconnecting metal. Each of these patterns is separately exposed and etched into the semiconductor wafer, so that the drawing must display them as independent steps.

The drawing must be accurate since it is used to define the actual size of the device features. Mylar grid paper, on which accurate grid lines already exist, can be used. The designer then indicates the grid lines that delineate the features desired.

The next step, as shown in Fig. 4.4, is to digitize the pattern. In this operation a machine records the apices of every corner of all features on each of the pattern levels. By indicating which apices are interconnected, the drawing is decomposed into a collection of polygons of arbitrary shape. Instead of a visual image, the layout now consists of numerical data.

However, the electron-beam pattern generator may not be able to accept data of a general polygon form. Either rectangles or trapezoids are usually required (Spicer *et al.,* 1973). Consequently, another operation is required to fragment the polygon data (refer to Chapter 3). Here, software routines are used to decompose the arbitrary polygons into the more lengthy data set composed solely of the allowed shapes. The result of this operation is data that are usually specific for the electron-beam machine to be employed.

The final collection of data can be fairly large. Several hundreds of thousands of shapes is not an uncommon amount for complex integrated circuits! When it is considered that each rectangle requires at least four values for the x and y coordinates of two opposing corners and that the values of these coordinates require five or six digits, it is seen that the stream of data being fed to the electron-beam pattern generator can be enormously high. Consequently, data compaction schemes are desirable, for example, by inputting the coordinates of a few rectangles together with an algorithm for generating repeated placement in various desired locations throughout the scan field.

Of course, the method depicted in Fig. 4.4 is only one of several possible alternatives. It is possible for the designer to work directly at a computer terminal using a language that instructs the peripheral equipment to

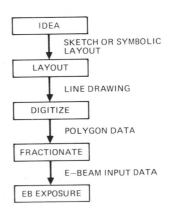

FIG. 4.4 Schematic representation of the process steps required to obtain pattern data for electron-beam exposure.

generate the final data input required for the pattern generator. In this way drawings, polygons, and fractionated data are eliminated. Even this automation of the design process can be carried a step further with the designer inputting only symbolic data. If a sufficient library of component layouts exists, then computer algorithms can take over the function of placing the parts and interconnecting them. However, the scheme depicted in Fig. 4.4 serves the purpose here of indicating generally how pattern data can be generated for the electron-beam machines.

B. Resist Changes

Having generated the desired design, fabrication activities can start. For the lithography portion of fabrication, polymer resist films must be applied to the substrates. These polymer films should have several properties to be ideal electron-beam resists. Typically such a resist

(a)   forms continuous, pinhole-free coatings, with easily varied, but highly uniform thickness;

(b)   requires a relatively low electron dose for exposure;

(c)   produces high resolution structures;

(d)   has reproducible physical and chemical properties batch-to-batch;

(e)   yields patterns with dimensions that are relatively insensitive to minor fluctuations in exposure dose or development;

(f)   adheres tenaciously to a variety of substrates;

(g)   is impervious to plasma or solution type etchants;

(h)   remains structurally stable against ions used for implants or sputter etching;

(i)   does not degrade (e.g., flow) due to temperature increases.

Obviously, it is improbable that any one material would possess all these ideal properties. For this reason, relatively few resists have been found generally useful in a variety of devices, whereas numerous resists have been employed for specialized applications. Table 4.1 lists the preferred electron-beam resists that have been employed in practice for device fabrication, together with their

(a)   type (exposed positive resists are dissolved by developers and exposed negative resists are insoluble),

(b)   sensitivity (the electron charge per squared centimeter required to expose), and

(c)   compatibility with device processing.

When electron resists such as those in Table 4.1 are used on insulating substrates, an additional charge dissipating coating must be applied. This

TABLE 4.1

Properties of Electron-Beam Resists

Resist name and acronym	Type	Sensitivity (C/cm)	Minimum resolution (μm)	°C Thermal stability [a]	Process compatibility
Epoxidized Poly-butadiene	Neg	5×10^{-8}	2	100	Fair
Poly(diallyl ortho phtholate) PDOP	Neg	10^{-6}	2	150	Good
Poly(glycidyl meth-acrylate)	Neg	5×10^{-7}	1	100	
Poly(glycidyl meth-acrylate-co-ethyl acrylate) COP	Pos	10^{-6}	0.5	150	Good
Poly(butene-l-sulfane) PBS	Pos	10^{-6}	0.5	80	Fair
Shipley AZ-2400	Pos	2×10^{-5}	1	120	Good
α-Cyano ethyl-acrylate α-amide ethylacrylate FMR-E	Pos	5×10^{-7}	0.5		
Poly(methyl meth-acrylate) PMMA	Pos	5×10^{-5}	<0.1	120	Excellent

[a] Temperature at which pattern deformation may be experienced.

coating can be a few hundred angstroms of a metal such as gold or aluminum, and the coating can be applied either on top of or beneath the resist film. The electron-beam currents are low enough that the resistance of the conducting film can be relatively high and simple specimen clamps can provide a discharging path to ground. Before etching, however, the conducting film must be removed. This is often achieved with a light sputter etch when the conducting layer is beneath the resist. When the film is on top of the resist, it must be removed before development, but the etching media must not disturb the resist.

C. Corrections for Alignment

Most electronic devices require definition of several overlay patterns. Consequently, after coating the sample with resist, the second basic step of a lithographic process is to align the pattern. This alignment must account for the rigid body motions of displacement and rotation, because the substrate has been removed between exposing succesive patterns. In addition, with electron-beam lithography changes in magnification may be required, either because of drift in the machine electronics, or process induced wafer distortion. Another correction required is orthogonality. The pattern data may be drawn using perfectly orthogonal axes, but inevitable mechanical inaccuracy in the machine or wafer results in an actual pattern that may not be truly orthogonal.

All the above corrections can be made with relative ease by adjusting the gain and offset of the electron-beam deflection amplifiers. These required changes may be calculated by formulas that involve simple linear combinations of the x and y coordinates of the desired beam deflection point. There are additional corrections necessary due to the barrel, pincushion, and trapezoidal type distortions that arise with electron-beam deflections. Indeed, these latter corrections may be accounted for with x and y terms to second order or greater. However, the general approach is to minimize the higher order terms by centering the beam as closely as possible to the optical axis and limiting the possible range of deflection. Then the pattern data can be modified electronically to correct for the linear terms.

The alignment problem for the linear terms may be treated by the techniques of mapping in complex variable theory (Churchill, 1960). For this approach, each electron-beam spot with complex coordinates z in the reference (x, y) plane is mapped to a corresponding point w in the image (u, v) plane. Alignment is equivalent to finding the mapping function f such that

$$w = f(z) \tag{4.1}$$

The function f may be constructed in a straightforward manner by considering individually the linear functions of x and y. For example, the transformation

$$w'' = ax + ia_0 y \tag{4.2}$$

corresponds to magnification (or compaction) in both x and y directions. If $a = a_0$, Eq. (4.2) represents a uniform change. The more extensive transform

$$w' = ax + by + (a_0 y + b_0 x)i \tag{4.3}$$

accounts for both nonorthogonality and rotation. If $b_0 = 0$, Eq. (4.3) represents skew alone (aside from the a coefficients). Figure 4.5 shows an example of both magnification and nonorthogonality. It is easily shown that if $a = a_0$, $b = -b_0$, and $a^2 + b^2 = 1$, then Eq. (4.3) represents pure rotation. Finally, a complex constant $c + ic_0$ can be added to account for translation. Therefore, the alignment function f that consists of x or y to only linear powers is

$$w = (ax + by + c) + (a_0 y + b_0 x + c_0)i \tag{4.4}$$

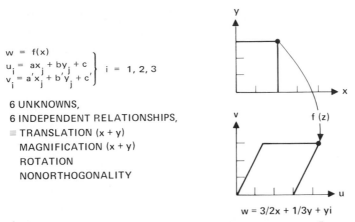

$$w = f(x)$$
$$\left. \begin{array}{l} u_i = ax_j + by_j + c \\ v_i = a'x_j + b'y_j + c' \end{array} \right\} \quad i = 1, 2, 3$$

6 UNKNOWNS,

6 INDEPENDENT RELATIONSHIPS,

≡ TRANSLATION (x + y)

   MAGNIFICATION (x + y)

   ROTATION

   NONORTHOGONALITY

$$w = 3/2x + 1/3y + yi$$

FIG. 4.5   Example of alignment change that requires magnification and skew corrections.

and the derivation above shows that this function accounts for x and y translation, x, and y magnification, nonorthogonality, and rotation.

There are six unknowns in Eq. (4.4), but any three points in the image plane will provide three equations for the independent variables u_1, u_2, and u_3 and three equations for v_1, v_2, and v_3 provided the reference coordinates (x_j, y_j) of these three points are known:

$$u_j = ax_j + by_j + c, \quad j = 1,2,3,$$
$$v_j = a_0y_j + b_0x_j + c_0 \tag{4.5}$$

Since there are six independent equations of the type (4.5), there will be unique values for the six unknown coefficients. These can be readily found with the method of determinants.

The transformation described above has been implemented in two basic ways. Many electron-beam machines expose one chip at a time, determining the corrections each time the stage moves (Varnell et al., 1973). (Usually, if the wafer is not distorted and the electron-beam system is stable, corrections for rotation, magnification, and nonorthogonality should be the same for each scan field.) Other types of machines treat the entire wafer. With this method, an accurate monitoring of the stage is required (typically through the use of precise interferometers).

Notice that the alignment process with electron beam-lithography differs fundamentally from the process used with photolithography, because the electron-beam pattern is stretchable electronically. With fixed photomasks, the only feasible adjustments are those that account for rigid body motion. This fixed nature of photomasks can limit the achievable alignment with whole wafer exposures because small displacements can arise in the step-and-repeat process in mask fabrication. Pattern adjustments are an important feature because wafer processing does induce distortion (Henderson, 1977; Gegenworth and Laming, 1977; Yau, 1978).

D. Alignment Marks

The three reference points required for solving Eqs. (4.5) are the coordinates of alignment marks. These alignment marks are simply surface features on the wafer that show a different backscattered electron characteristic when scanned by the electron beam (discussed in Chapter 2). This change in backscattered electron yield from the alignment mark to the substrate can generate a signal such as the number of detected backscattered electrons, or the amount of total specimen current. Video processing of this signal provides the (u_j, v_j) coordinates. Since the (x_j, y_j) coordinates are known from the pattern data, all the necessary values are known in order to calculate the a, b, and c coefficients.

Successful alignment marks have several requirements. For a given resolution and sensitivity of the detector, the electron signals must be sufficiently greater than the background to provide a workable signal-to-noise ratio. Also, these signals must not change drastically with additional steps in the processing, even though some degradation can be expected if the marks become overlaid progressively with additional films. Furthermore, because mark degradation is undesirable, the marks must be resistant to thermal treatments or etchants.

Generally, marks either are relief features etched into the substrate or are patterns of a material with a high atomic number relative to the substrate. As shown in Fig. 4.6, in the first case, contrast results from the greater yield of secondary electron emission as the beam scans an edge. This effect is referred to as topological contrast and results from the dependence of the backscatter coefficient on angle of incidence with respect to the substrate. On the other hand, when the atomic number of the alignment mark is greatly different from the substrate, the signal arises from the difference in the backscatter coefficient between two different materials. Note that as the beam moves near an edge, there is some shadowing of the ejected electrons which causes a corresponding dip in the signal strength. Another type of mark is a groove feature which has a signal similar to that from the mesa structure shown in Fig. 4.6.

No universal preference for alignment mark type appears to have emerged. Wolf et al. (1975), showed that Au on Si gave 20 times greater signal than 0.4 μm oxide steps on the surface. In fact, Au on GaAs has been used to make MESFET gates with only 0.1 μm misalignment (Ozdemir et al., 1976). For MOS devices, Ta alignment marks have proven to

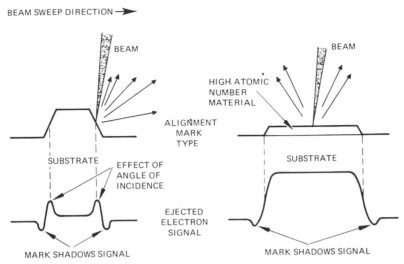

FIG. 4.6   Two types of electron-beam alignment marks for pattern registration.

be compatible with the wafer processing (Henderson *et al.*, 1978). On the other hand, Yau and Thibault (1978) prefer to use trenches 3–4-μm deep etched into the silicon substrate. Using a substrate current detector, these marks give S/N ratios of 6:1. Furukawa *et al.* (1978), with 30 keV incident electrons, have observed S/N = 10 from Si marks etched only 1.5-μm deep by using a highly sensitive scintillator type backscatter detector. Friedrich *et al.* (1977), also prefer silicon etched features, but use anisotropic etching to provide a sharpened edge and thereby enhance the signal. They found S/N ratios greater than 15 for both backscattered electrons (when the beam energy was greater than 20 keV) as well as secondary electrons (with less than 10 keV). Wilson *et al.* (1975) studied 4000-Å-high SiO_2.

The particular alignment mark choice is often dictated by process compatibility. For example, gold has a high atomic number relative to silicon, but the contamination introduced at the temperatures typical of silicon processing make it incompatible. Moreover, a high atomic number alignment mark is unusable when a thin film with a high atomic number must be patterned. In this case, a separate lithography step must be used to remove the thin film overlaying the area to be scanned for alignment.

E.   Alignment Methods and Strategies

The methods of determining the positions of alignment marks by use of the electron-beam generated signal have evolved from rather rudimentary to sophisticated techniques. An early method used the deflection electronics to continuously raster the mark era (Magdo *et al.*, 1971; Pease *et al.*, 1973). In the manner of a scanning electron microscope, the magnified images of the alignment marks were displayed on the CRT (cathode ray tube) viewing screen. Patterns were aligned by combinations of aperture positioning, stage movement, and electronic adjustments of the deflection and magnification controls. Modern systems, such as described in Chapter 3, utilize computer processing of the video signal as well as computer controls of the necessary corrections.

Moreover, signal averaging is now generally used which increases the S/N ratio as the square root of the number of scans. With the technique used by Wilson *et al.* (1975), the raw digital signal derived by scanning the alignment mark is repeatedly and synchronously added to the contents of a memory until a prescribed number of scans has been recorded. With other multiple scan methods (Alles *et al.*, 1975), the alignment mark edges are detected with each scan, and then these data are arithmetically averaged. The beam position is usually moved in selected increments along the alignment mark between successive scans. This approach allows for the rejection of data obtained from an alignment mark that is locally distorted by comparing new data with values from prior scans.

Alignment strategy also depends upon the type of detector used. Some systems use level detectors (Alles *et al.*, 1975; Chang *et al.*, 1976; Stephani and Froschle, 1978). Here the alignment mark edge position is defined as the point at which the electron signal rises (or falls) through a specified level. (See lower portion of Fig. 4.6.) This position can be set automatically at some fraction of the difference between the lowest and highest signal. Other systems use edge detection (e.g., Ozdemir *et al.*, 1973) by digitally differentiating the signal and defining the alignment mark edge position as the point of maximum differentiated signal.

The electron detectors can be solid state diodes, electron multipliers, or the scintillator type. Whether these detectors are used for secondary or backscattered electrons depends primarily on the electron-beam energy. Figure 4.7 reproduces the results of Friedrich *et al.* (1977), who showed that for etched alignment marks, the S/N ratio increases with electron energy for backscattered electrons when using a solid state diode detector. On the other hand, with a conventional scintillator detector for secondary electrons, the S/N ratio decreased with increasing energy. Thus, if the electron energy to be used is relatively low (~10 keV), secondary electrons are superior, but above 15 keV backscattered electrons are best.

There are three choices of alignment mark strategy: (1) a single set of marks could be used throughout all processing steps; (2) initially a number of sets could be defined and a fresh set used at each subsequent level; and

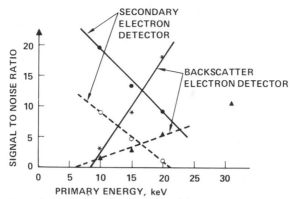

FIG. 4.7   Signal-to-noise ratio vs. primary energy for backscatter and secondary electrons using V-groove (———) and mesa-type (–––) alignment marks. [From Friedrich *et al.* (1977).]

(3) new alignment marks could be defined when patterning some intermediate level.

The last approach has the advantage of accuracy because, if the random error of alignment is ϵ, then ϵ is the error experienced in registering any subsequent pattern to the pattern that contains the intermediate alignment mark. On the other hand, the error is 2ϵ for alignment between any two levels that are referenced to a third one. However, typically the intermediate marks cannot provide as great an S/N ratio as an optimized alignment mark pattern, and thus the intermediate marks are used only in relatively special circumstances.

Defining a number of alignment marks at the beginning of the process can eliminate the problems associated with the resist exposure when the electron beam scans the mark location. Also, it is always useful to have a backup set of marks, particularly when exploring new processes. On the other hand, too many marks are wasteful of chip area, so from this standpoint it is desirable to reuse marks as often as possible.

When planning to reuse marks, it is best to totally expose the area neighboring the alignment mark as part of the pattern data. If only the registration line scans expose the resist over the alignment marks, then unwanted boundaries will arise from residuals of the patterned material. These boundaries can lead to spurious signals that will obscure the true alignment mark when attempting subsequent registration.

When negative resists are used, exposing the alignment mark area will create successive overlayers of the thin films being patterned when using (subtractive) etching processes. It must be determined that this approach will not impair the effectiveness of the marks. For positive resists, exposing the alignment mark neighborhood will cause etching of any exposed layers, and it must be determined that overetching will not attack the marks. These two situations are reversed, of course, when using additive processes such as electroplating or lift-off.

Residual material can be a problem when using poly methyl methacrylate (PMMA) and multiple alignment mark scanning. This material cross links if it is greatly overexposed ($\sim 10^{-3}$ C/cm^2). Thus, a negative resist scan pattern might be created over the alignment marks which, depending upon the subsequent processing, can leave unwanted material.

F. Pattern Transfer Methods

One of the most critical operations with high resolution lithography is the transfer of the pattern in the resist to the substrate. There are many different kinds of transfer. Transfer processes such as the lift-off method, electroplating, or ion implantation are referred to as additive. The different types of subtractive processes involve an etching medium such as dry plasma, a chemical solution, or an ion beam.

Several steps may be required before the pattern can be transferred to the substrate. After the resist has been exposed and developed, the transfer process may demand postdevelopment bakes to harden the resist. Often a substrate cleaning step is necessary. A common technique is to use an O_2 plasma descuming treatment that will remove residual resist films remaining in the pattern areas (Chang et al., 1976).

Naturally, given one of the pattern transfer processes and the material to be patterned, one type of resist may turn out to be more effective than others. Table 4.2 has been constructed by compiling results from several sources. This table cross-references the material successfully patterned, the process used, and the resist type.

For any particular process indicated in Table 4.2 the critical variables may differ from other entries. The amount of detail in each of these categories is sufficiently large that it cannot be treated completely here. However, some general characteristics have emerged from the literature. For example, the lift-off process consists of depositing a material on the resist film after the pattern has been exposed and developed. When the remaining resist is dissolved, it carries away the excess material, leaving behind a pattern where the deposited material contacted the substrate. This process is straightforward with positive resists because electron-beam exposure provides an undercut as long as the dose is sufficiently high (see Chapter 2). For successful lift-off, it is important that there be little or no continuity between the deposited material on the substrate and that on top

TABLE 4.2

Mask Material Used to Pattern Various Materials Using Different Techniques

	Solution etching	Plasma etching	Lift off	Electro plating	Ion sputtering
Al	COP PMMA		PMMA		
SiO	COP, PMMA PDOP, PBS				
Si$_3$N$_4$	SiO$_2$	COP, PMMA, PDOP			
Poly–Si		COP, PMMA, Al			
Au					TI-309
Permalloy			PMMA	PMMA	
GaAs	PMMA				
Nc			PDOP		
Si		COP, PMMA			
Ti	PMMA				

of the resist. For this reason, negative resists, which typically have rounded profiles, are not used with lift-off. The lift-off technique also limits the thickness of the deposited pattern to ~70% of the resist thickness (see Chang *et al.*, 1976). Moreover, for good separation, the deposition process should assure that the material impinges on the resist pattern at near normal incidence. Also, the substrate must be kept below the resist glass transition temperature. The undercut should not be too great (~5° is recommended); otherwise the minimum spacing between lines is limited. Also pennumbral shadows will alter the linewidth. Finally, before depositing the film, cleaning is mandatory to achieve good substrate adhesion. The O$_2$ plasma treatment is frequently used, but alternatively a light etch of the substrate material can be employed.

Electroplating is an additive process that can be used to build up patterns that are actually thicker than the resist film. Plating is a low temperature process, and the patterns can have very good adhesion to the substrate. On the other hand, many materials and alloys cannot be defined by this method, and it is reportedly difficult to maintain uniformity (Chang *et al.*, 1976). It is also important that the resist profile should not be undercut since in that case an upward force can be generated that will lift up narrow lines. Typically the resist must be cleared from a ring-shaped area surrounding the wafer periphery (for electrical contact); and, of course, there must be a conducting layer beneath the resist. The substrate patterns must be thoroughly cleaned before plating. Of the electron resists, PMMA and PDOP have been used successfully for electroplating.

IV. ELECTRON DEVICES MADE WITH ELECTRON-BEAM LITHOGRAPHY

The state-of-the-art with respect to devices that have been made by employing electron-beam lithography will be reviewed in this section. Device scaling studies will also be reviewed in the applicable cases. This discussion will highlight the principal results of various investigators, including applications, key findings, and fabrication problems encountered.

A. Silicon Bipolar Transistors

The silicon bipolar transistor was one of the earliest devices made with electron-beam lithography. However, despite several investigations, very little structure optimization or scaling rule definition has emerged. Rather, the thrust of most work has been to use bipolar transistors as a vehicle for high resolution processing. Most of the work reported to date has been on microwave transistors, although electron-beam-fabricated bipolar integrated circuits are beginning to appear (Evans et al., 1977).

Bipolar transistors emphasize some of the complexities with high resolution device fabrication discussed earlier in this chapter. For example, bipolar transistors are high current devices, and therefore the metallization must be thick (see Fig. 4.8). But this means that the fabrication process used must be capable of assuring a high aspect ratio, as discussed in Section II. Another problem reported (Kruger et al., 1975) was that definition of the metallization by use of the lift-off method showed the need for careful cleaning since otherwise poor adhesion and high contact resistance were found. Moreover, the metallization should run over an oxide (for low capacitance and isolation), and therefore there is a potential step coverage problem. One solution is to control the resist undercutting during the oxide etching to obtain a tapered edge profile (Kruger et al., 1975). Another approach reduces the step height by using silicon nitride features to mask the oxidation. This results in the structure shown in Fig. 4.8. The required alignment tolerances are very tight with bipolar transistors—typically a few tenths of a micron.

The reported performance of electron-beam bipolar transistors has been quite good. Kruger et al. (1975), report 2 dB better gain than the comparable transistor made photolithographically. Their devices can also generate 250 mW power versus 10–20 mW for similar but larger devices made with optical lithography.

Both Kruger et al. (1975) and Tsai and Yau (1978) reported that device yields were considerably higher with electron-beam-fabricated tran-

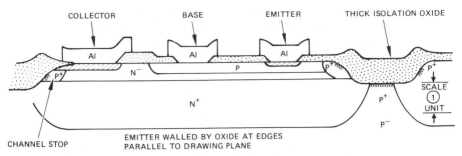

FIG. 4.8 Bipolar transistor device structure.

sistors, due to the superior alignment possible. In fact, Tsai and Yau (1978) find no more than 0.25 μm misalignment using only three alignment marks spanning an entire 2 in. wafer (see alignment discussion in Section III). They attributed this improved alignment to the ability of electron-beam lithography to adjust the exposed pattern. This improved device yield is very significant for microwave transistors because they require costly bonding before testing. (To minimize the capacitance, the probing pads are made so small that automatic probing is not feasible.)

B. Surface Acoustic Wave Devices

Another early device application for electron-beam lithography was the fabrication of surface acoustic wave (SAW) structures. Such devices consist of interdigitated metal fingers on a piezoelectric crystal (Fig. 4.9). When alternating voltages are applied to adjacent fingers, the crystal is stressed locally, which generates a surface sound wave. Other interdigitated electrodes can be used to sample, manipulate, or modify this signal. However, the dimensions of the electrodes (width and spacing) must be in submicrometers in order to operate at gigahertz frequencies.

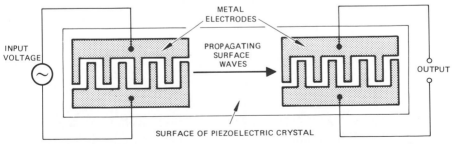

FIG. 4.9 Schematic diagram of the principal properties underlying the operation of a surface acoustic wave device.

Surface wave devices should be relatively simple to fabricate with a high resolution electron-beam system. Only one exposure is involved, and the substrate is flat, so step coverage is not an issue. However, the substrate is usually an insulator, so that a charge dissipating technique is required. Moreover, the absolute precision of electrode placement is critical because errors in position will affect the rf characteristics of the electrical filter that is formed by the SAW device. To achieve the desired precision, Wolf et al. (1973) found it necessary to sample the output of the D/A that controls the position of the electron beam and compare the actual signal with the desired one and thereby make a correction in deflection signal voltage. This technique reduced placement error to less than 500 Å.

Another fabrication problem that can arise with SAW devices is due to the electron-beam proximity effect. A broadband pulse compression filter will contain typically over a thousand electrodes in a 1 mm or longer array length. In this array, the electrode lengths are constant, but the spacing varies. Therefore, as the electrode spacing changes the contribution of electron dose received by exposing adjacent electrodes will change. This problem can be solved by changing the beam spot dwell time (through computer control) as a function of the local electrode spacing.

Also, the electrode structures must be aligned to the crystal axes. This has been achieved by shaping the crystals so that the edges, as well as the device surface, are crystal planes. Then simple scanning of the edge permits rotational alignment of the electrodes.

The lift-off method has been the technique chosen to define the metallization patterns (Wolf et al., 1973). Aluminum was used for electrode material, but there have been adhesion problems. Better results were obtained with either thin films of Ti (Wolf et al., 1973) or Cr (Broers and Hatzakis, 1971) underlaying the aluminum.

Several devices have been reported. Transducers on $LiNbO_3$ with 0.3 μm electrodes spaced 0.7 μm apart have operated at 1.75 GHz (Broers and Hatzakis, 1969). Pulse compression filters have been made with bandwidths up to 0.5 GHz centered at 1.3 GHz with electrodes 0.5-μm wide (Wolf et al., 1973). Several narrow band filters, some with multiple electrode taps, have been reported.

C. Schottky Barrier FETs

Prototype Schottky barrier field effect transistors have been made with electron-beam lithography on both silicon and GaAs substrates. Typical cross-sectional views are seen in Figs. 4.10 and 4.11. The majority carrier current between the source and the drain is controlled by the depletion of

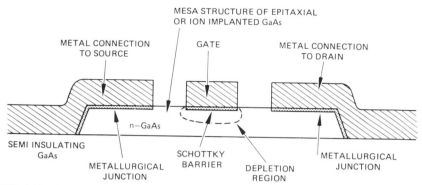

FIG. 4.10   Cross-sectional view of a Schottky barrier gate transistor using an n-type GaAs layer on a semi-insulating substrate.

the channel by the applied gate bias. Substrates with very high resistivity provide device isolation.

One application for these barrier FETs is high speed switching. In this case, very narrow gate electrodes are desired, as evident from the approximate formula for the maximum frequency f_0 of an FET which is given by

$$2\pi f_0 = g_m/C_g = q\mu_n N_D d^2/\epsilon_s L^2 \qquad (4.6)$$

Here, g_m is the transconductance, C_g the gate capacitance, μ_n the electron mobility, N_D the channel doping, ϵ_s the dielectric constant of the semiconductor, d the thickness of the channel, L the gate length, and q the electron charge. Equation (4.6) shows that with $N_D = 10^{16}$ and $\mu_n = 500$ cm^2/v s, Schottky barrier FETs with 0.5 μm gates on 0.2-μm-thick layers should show a cutoff frequency above 100 GHz.

FETs also demonstrate the need for tight alignment between the gate and the source–drain electrodes. This factor arises because the series re-

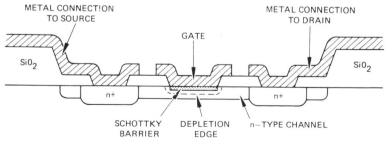

FIG. 4.11   Cross-sectional view of a Schottky barrier field effect transistor made on a p-type silicon substrate between 10^2–10^3 Ω cm.

sistance of the source R_s and drain R_d affects the channel conductance by

$$g_0 = g/[1 + (R_s + R_d)g] \tag{4.7}$$

where g_0 is the observed channel conductance and g the intrinsic conductance. To minimize R_s and R_d, the metallurgical contact to the semiconductor substrate must be placed as close as possible with respect to the gate electrode.

Another potential performance limit in a high resolution FET is the gate resistance and the associated RC time constant. Both the maximum available gain and the noise figure will be affected by gate resistance. For a given gate length and width this means the techniques used for gate metallization must be able to provide a high aspect ratio. Figure 4.12 (Butlin *et al.*, 1978) shows the calculated results for noise figure versus gate metallization thickness for both 0.5 and 0.3 μm gate lengths. As can be seen, aspect ratios >1 are necessary in order to minimize the effect of gate resistance.

Several investigators have used electron-beam lithography to make MESFET devices with submicron gate lengths (Butlin *et al.*, 1978; Ozdemir *et al.*, 1976). Figure 4.13 shows a GaAs Schottky barrier FET with a 0.5 μm aluminum gate (from Ozdemir *et al.*, 1976). Electron-beam lithography, in conjunction with the lift-off technique, was used to define the gate and the source–drain patterns. In their work, the gate was aligned to the source–drain pattern by defining alignment marks as part of

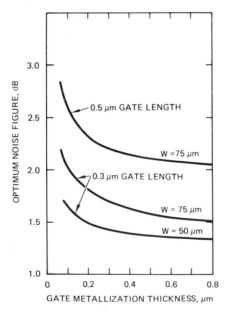

FIG. 4.12 Plot of noise figure vs. the thickness of the gate metal for different gate lengths and gate widths (w) after Butlin *et al.* (1978). $R_c = 1.0 \times 10^6 \ \Omega/\text{cm}^2$, $N_D = 1.3 \times 10^{17} \ \text{cm}^3$, 14 GHz.

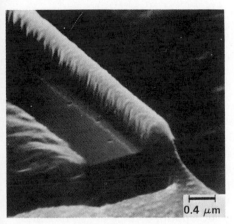
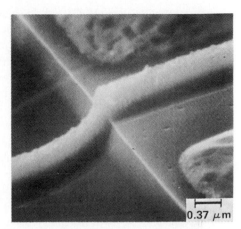

FIG. 4.13 SEM microphotograph of GaAs FET with Al Schottky barrier gate showing metallization step coverage of mesa edge.

the source–drain pattern. The stated alignment accuracy was ±0.1 μm. Care was taken to maximize the gate thickness consistent with the short gate length. Extrapolated S parameter measurements on these devices indicate a maximum oscillation frequency >100 GHz, and when incorporated into amplifiers have shown a maximum single stage gain of 11 dB at 33 GHz (Krumm et al., 1978).

Another potential application for Schottky barrier FETs is high speed, low power logic. This interest has developed because, compared to the metal-oxide semiconductor transistors (MOSFET), the MESFET devices (1) are more radiation tolerant, (2) operate with the higher bulk mobility rather than surface mobility, and (3) can operate at higher voltages without breakdown. Problems, however, are higher pinch-off voltage and the relatively tighter process tolerances required in the fabrication of making normally off transistors. Hence, in logic type circuits a diode level shifter is needed between the output of the preceding stage and input gate of the next.

To circumvent this latter difficulty, normally off MESFETs can be made by thinning the channel depth so that it is less than the depletion width arising from the gate barrier height determined by the Schottky metal. For example, the epitaxial GaAs layer can be etched using the gate resist pattern as a mask, prior to a lift-off process (see Fig. 4.10). This process would thin the layer in the channel region only, so that source and drain resistance would not increase. An alternative approach controls the layer thickness by the appropriate choice of ion implant conditions. This method has been applied to silicon MESFETs (Nuzillat et al., 1976) to make 1-μm gate structures with electron-beam lithography.

Darley *et al.* (1978) have also fabricated Si MESFETs using electron-beam lithography. They have made operating transistors with gate lengths as small as 0.25 μm. Ring oscillators with 1 μm gate lengths have operated with a power delay product as low as 1.2 fJ at a speed of 1.7 ns.

Several Si MESFET circuits have been built and tested. Using normally on transistors, Bobenrieth *et al.* (1972), have built an elementary NAND gate with stage delay of less than 200 ps and power consumption less than 1 mW. In later work, different designs of a three-input NOR gate version were made using 1 μm MESFET transistors for the basic elements (Nuzillat *et al.*, 1976). These gates are made by Cr lift-off which serves as an ion sputtering mask to etch the Schottky barrier metal, which was $SiPd_2$. Designs with normally on transistors could be optimized for speed, and those with normally off could be optimized for power. In fact, by combining normally on with normally off transistors on the same chip, very high performance was achieved. The power required was only 150 μW with 840 ps delay.

A question remains whether the gate length for silicon MESFETs in logic circuits can be reduced to submicrometer dimensions since in this range the source to drain leakage current increases. Computer studies (Nuzillat *et al.*, 1976) have indicated the maximum fan-in would be 1 for 0.5 μm gates. In this case, only inverters are feasible.

D.   Metal-Oxide Semiconductor Devices

Electron-beam lithography has been used extensively in the fabrication of metal-oxide semiconductor (MOS) transistors and circuits. A cross-sectional view of one type is shown in Fig. 4.14. Here a gate elec-

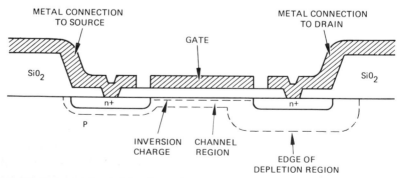

FIG. 4.14   Cross-sectional view of an *n*-channel MOSFET structure made on a silicon substrate.

trode, separated from the channel by a thin oxide layer (t_{ox}), controls the flow of carriers from source to drain. For the case in Fig. 4.14, a gate voltage V_g that exceeds the threshold voltage V_T depletes the substrate of the majority carrier holes and allows electrons to accumulate in the channel region. If the gate voltage is sufficient, an inversion layer of electrons forms at the oxide–semiconductor interface and provides a conduction path between the n^+-doped regions. A current will flow when the drain has an applied positive voltage V_D.

The device considered in Fig. 4.14 is termed n-channel, but there are several other possible types. A p-channel MOS transistor has n-type substrates and p^+-doped source and drains. And when both n and p types are combined in one circuit, it is termed complimentary MOS or CMOS. Moreover, either n- or p-channels can be depletion or enhancement mode, depending upon the doping in the channel. The device in Fig. 4.14 is enhancement mode, which means the transistor is normally off (when $V_g = 0$). However, the channel region could be doped with donor type impurities so that the channel is normally on (i.e., a sufficiently negative voltage must be applied to the gate in order to deplete the channel of electrons and turn the transistor off). This type is termed depletion mode. Also, the oxide can be a composite of dielectrics, e.g., a layer of Si_3N_4 over SiO_2. Finally, all these types of transistors can be made on silicon epitaxially grown on sapphire substrates (SOS).

The considerable interest in high resolution lithography for MOS devices arises from substantial payoffs in both performance and circuit packing density. This may be seen by scaling the length L and the width W of the transistor by the factor $1/K$ ($K > 1$) (Dennard et al., 1972). Then the number of possible devices per unit area increases as K^2. Therefore, for a given defect density the cost per scaled circuit should decrease substantially. Moreover, Table 1.1 (see Chapter 1) shows that the speed and power consumption also improve with scaling. In fact, the power–delay product (which is essentially the energy required for switching) decreases by the factor $1/K^3$.

Table 1.1 also shows that MOS devices must change in several ways as the lateral dimensions decrease. First (with three-dimensional scaling), the oxide thickness must decrease, and fabrication techniques must be determined that provide these thinner oxides with the same yield as oxides with conventional thicknesses. Moreover, the substrate doping must increase and the drain voltage decrease.

The variables in Table 1.1 are first-order approximations and more detailed calculations modify some of the values. For example, because the substrate concentration increases, the mobility decreases slightly. This will mean that the speed will not improve as much as $1/K$, but the power dissipation will decrease by somewhat more than $1/K^2$, so that the power–delay product remains at $1/K^3$. The breakdown voltage is another consideration. Typically this has a $1/K$ dependence which arises from the increase in the substrate doping. But the depth of the source–drain junction generally also decreases. The correspondingly smaller radius of curvature of the junction will lower the breakdown voltage even more than $1/K$.

The quality of the oxide is an influential factor in the performance of MOS transistors and an early concern was the degree to which electron exposure would irreparably damage the oxide. Indeed, Thibault and Pickar (1972) and El-Kareh and Pattletz (1976) have shown there is damage immediately after exposure, but that anneals at 400°C remove the damage. However, this was not the case for mixed dielectrics. Both Al_2O_3/SiO_2 and Si_3N_4/SiO_2 appear to have a residual damage which is characterized by shifts in the capacitance versus voltage curves. Also, the 400°C anneals used with these studies are not effective in removing all damage. Aitken *et al.* (1978) report that neutral traps remain in the oxide subsequent to electron-beam exposure and anneal. Their presence is revealed by stressing the capacitor gates sufficiently so that electrons are injected into the oxide, where they are captured by existing defects. Removal of these neutral defects requires anneals in excess of 550°C, but this is difficult when aluminum interconnection features have been defined.

Another factor which was discovered when small devices were made was that the threshold voltage was sensitive to the gate length (Yau, 1975). For conventional size devices, the equation for V_T is

$$V_T - V_{FB} = 2\phi_f - (Q_B/C_{ox}) = 2\phi_f + [2\epsilon_{si}qN_a(2\phi_f)/C_{ox}]^{1/2} \quad (4.8)$$

where Q_B is the charge induced in the depletion layer beneath the gate, V_{FB} the flatband voltage, $2\phi_f$ the Fermi potential, q the electron charge, N_a the substrate doping, ϵ_{si} the dielectric constant of silicon, and C_{ox} the capacitance of the oxide under the gate. The flatband voltage is related to the surface state density Q_{ss}, the oxide thickness t_{ox}, and the work function difference between the gate metal and the semiconductor ϕ_{ms} by

$$V_{FB} = \phi_{ms} - (Q_{ss}t_{ox}/\epsilon_{ox}) \quad (4.9)$$

and

$$\phi_f = (kT/q) \ln(N_a/N_i) \quad (4.10)$$

where N_i represents the intrinsic carrier concentration ($\sim 10^{10}$ in Si). None of these factors has any dependence on lateral geometry. However, Yau (1975) argued that some of the field lines emanating from the charge in the channel depletion region terminate on the source and drains, so that the effective value of Q_B is reduced. His corrected formula was

$$V_T - V_{FB} = 2\phi_f - \frac{Q_B}{C_{ox}}\left(1 + \frac{r_j}{L}\right)^{1/2} \qquad (4.11)$$

where r_j is the radius of the diffusion for the junctions forming the source and drains. Figure 4.15 shows the general agreement between experiment and the simplified theory.

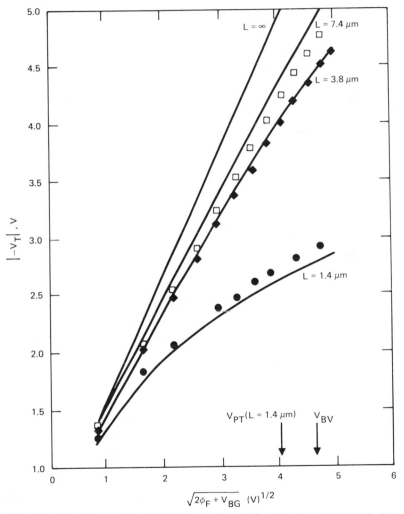

FIG. 4.15   Plot of threshold voltage versus $(2\phi_f + V_{BG})^{1/2}$ showing the decrease in V_T with smaller gate lengths. $V_{FB} = 0.30$ V; ———, theory; experiment: □, $L = 7.4$ μm ± 0.4; ◆, $L = 3.8$ μm ± 0.4; ●, $L = 1.4$ μm $+ 0.2$.

Pickar and Thibault (1973) observed that the transistor-to-transistor distribution of gate voltages required to induce a specified current was extremely tight for gates defined with electron-beam lithography. Since the current I_D depends upon the width W and the length L for MOS transistor via the relationship

$$I_D = \frac{W}{L} \mu_n C_{ox}\left(V_g - V_{FB} - 2\phi_f - \frac{V_D}{2}\right) V_D, \qquad V_D > 2\phi_f \quad (4.12)$$

it is seen that their observation was the result of careful control of the transistor geometry. As discussed in Section II, improved geometry control will be necessary for making advanced high resolution devices. Moreover, since the threshold voltage is gate length dependent in the regime ≤ 1 μm, a gate-to-gate dimensional variation will lead to different electrical characteristics, i.e., variation over a wafer, therefore to low yield.

Several reports have appeared describing the characteristics of various MOS structures made with electron-beam lithography. These include aluminum, polysilicon and tungsten gate devices, n-channel and p-channel versions, depletion mode and enhancement mode, CMOS, and CMOS/SOS. Speed was generally reported in terms of the propagation delay for multistage inverters or ring oscillators. Early work (Pease et al., 1973) with 4 μm gate lengths had delays of several nanoseconds, but 1 μm transistors gave 295 ps (Fang et al., 1973). A value of 170 ps was found for electron-beam ring oscillators with CMOS/SOS (Henderson et al., 1979). Transistors with gates as small as 0.50 μm have been reported (Elliot et al., 1977).

Several prototype integrated circuits have also been made with electron-beam lithography. Early work (Henderson et al., 1975) resulted in a 1024-bit RAM using p-channel enhancement mode, tungsten gate techniques. This device operated faster by a factor of two compared to the same circuit made photolithographically at twice the size. An even larger (8 kbit) RAM has also been made employing 1.25 μm minimum gate length transistors (Yu et al., 1975). This device showed a delay of 90 ns and required only 25 mW to operate.

Another prototype MOS circuit that has been made with electron-beam lithography is a 4096 bit charge coupled memory (Henderson et al., 1978). For this latter device, the ability of electron-beam lithography to make small contact holes and minimum geometry transistors was the key to being able to detect the small number of charges. And, the efficiency of charge transfer was reported to be as good as standard size devices despite the increase in the ratio of the cell periphery to storage area which is a typical cause of degraded performance for CCDs (Yau, 1976; Krambech et al., 1976). Other CCD shift register circuits have also been made with electron-beam lithography showing good charge transfer efficiency when appropriate care is taken in device design (Hashimoto and Saito, 1975; Chaterjee *et al.*, 1978).

E. Magnetic Bubble Devices

Magnetic bubble devices are another area of potential interest for high resolution lithography. Bubbles are small cylindrical magnetic domains whose polarity is opposite that of the surrounding material. The interest in these devices arises from the very low energy required to move the bubbles. Therefore, they would be ideal elements of large memories. Also, a bubble memory is not volatile, so that information is not lost if power is removed.

The general principles of a bubble memory may be seen in Fig. 4.16. In thin films of anisotropic crystals, the dipoles of magnetic domains will tend to line up either parallel or antiparallel with an applied bias field. Anisotropic materials are necessary in order to prevent the dipoles from rapidly switching due to random thermal energies. The size of the bubble will be determined by the minimum energy condition, balancing contributions from (a) the interaction of the applied field and the domain dipoles, (b) terms from the wall dipoles, and (c) the magnetostatic interaction. The latter term refers to the macroscopic field lowering with increasing subdivision of the magnetic material, whereby a lower energy condition occurs as opposing regions tend to cancel the field in space. For a bubble of radius r and height h, the total energy will be

$$\xi = H_A(2r^2hM_s) + (2rh)\sigma_w - \xi_m$$

  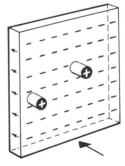

NO EXTERNAL   SMALL EXTERNAL   LARGER EXTERNAL
MAGNETIC FIELD   MAGNETIC FIELD   MAGNETIC FIELD

FIG. 4.16   Change of bubble domain character with increasing strength of applied bias magnetic field for thin films of anisotropic crystals. – – –, minus area; ■■, plus area.

where H_A is the applied field, M_s the magnetization of the bubble material, σ_w the wall energy, and ξ_m the magnetostatic energy. Expressions for ξ_m are complicated, but tend to diminish as r increases. Therefore, as shown schematically in Fig. 4.17 there will be a stable condition at some bubble radius, depending upon the material-dependent terms M_s and σ_w. A graph depicting the range of bubble size possible with different materials is shown in Fig. 4.18. Materials with small bubble size, but also low magnetization and anisotropy, are desirable for memories.

For device applications, there must be some mechanism to move bubbles. Moreover, bubbles must be detected, generated, or annihilated. Solutions to these problems have been found through forming suitable patterns in metallic thin films that are placed on the magnetic substrate.

When these pattern elements are themselves magnetic, such as permalloy ($NiFe_2$), bubble motion can be implemented through magnetic attraction. A common pattern is the T–I bar form shown in Fig. 4.19. These elements would be defined on the magnetic substrate that has been coated with a thin spacer layer, typically SiO_2. When an alternating field is applied perpendicular to the plane of the elements, plus and minus magnetic poles are induced. As the direction of the field rotates, the bubble is alternatively attracted to different elements. The gap separating the elements is typically one-quarter of the bubble diameter. Several other pattern designs, such as chevrons or Y–I, can be used.

Electron-beam lithography has been used to fabricate various designs of the metallization used to control the magnetic bubbles. Since the substrates are insulators, some means for discharging the beam must be employed. In early work, Henderson *et al.* (1972) used the lift-off technique

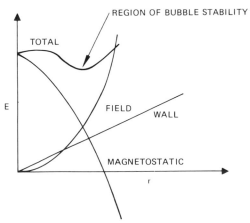

FIG. 4.17 Plot of total energy condition resulting from summing the three contribution terms represented in Eq. (4.13).

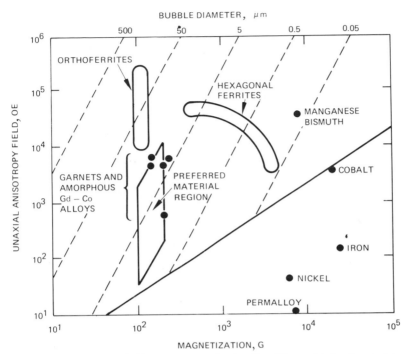

FIG. 4.18   Anisotropy field versus magnetization for different kinds of materials.

to fabricate permalloy elements. Circuit elements ~1 μm in dimension were made that showed successful bubble propagation up to 100 kHz. However, residual stress in the permalloy films made the fabrication technique difficult. Other studies such as those employing electroplating made basic pattern elements as small as 0.3 μm with separations 0.1 μm (Chang *et al.*, 1976).

Correcting for proximity effect and field stitching are two requirements in order to use electron-beam lithography for making bubble circuits. Correcting for proximity effect is necessary because the bubble detector elements usually have a tighter pattern density than propagation elements. Moreover, the desired chip size is very large for bubble devices, and can exceed the scan field size of the electron-beam machine. Hence, some solution is required that allows stitching together of adjacent electron-beam fields.

An 8 kbit bubble memory chip has been fabricated using electron-beam lithography (Kryder *et al.*, 1975), corresponding to a bit density of $10^7/in^2$. The minimum lithographic size was 0.75 μm for chevron shaped elements. One-micron-wide T–I bars, similar to Fig. 4.19, were used for propagation. Electric testing showed all functions of the chip were opera-

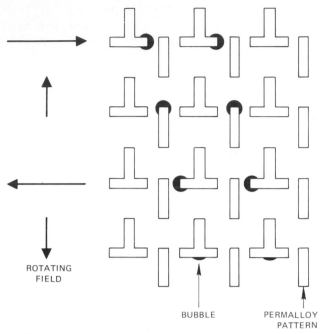

FIG. 4.19   Typical bubble device pattern used for propagating bubbles laterally.

tional. Either electroplating or lift-off methods could form the NiFe pattern elements for this circuit. Excellent bubble device operating characteristics were reported to be due to the uniformity achieved over the wafer due to the fabrication process.

V.   PROCESSING CONSTRAINTS ON ELECTRON-BEAM LITHOGRAPHY

As stressed in this chapter, device fabrication and lithography interact in many subtle ways. The exercise of prototype device fabrication emphasizes these complex interactions. In this section we will highlight some of these interactions.

A major concern of the device manufacturer is reproducibility. The ultimate resolution of the lithography tool is important, but linewidth control is critical. The importance of this parameter has already been discussed with respect to alignment yield (Fig. 4.2). However, performance yield should also be considered, because with modern integrated circuits thousands of interacting transistors, capacitors, and other components are constructed on a single chip. If the size of the structures is strongly varying, then the performance of the chip will not be controlled and the yield of circuits that operate within given specifications will be low. In fact, the circuit may not function at all if its components vary in size beyond a design tolerance.

This critical need for reproducibility is very demanding of the electron-beam machine capability. The magnitude of the control needed can be seen from the examples in Fig. 4.20, in which the effects on the resist profile due to 5% changes in the electron dose is shown. Relatively modest changes in dose lead to substantial changes in both the linewidth and the side wall angle. Note that the linewidth measures at the resist–air interface is relatively insensitive to dose; but most pattern transfer processes, such as etching, depend strongly on the resist–substrate interface. Consequently, the different resist profiles shown in Fig. 4.20 will lead to greatly variable linewidths upon etching the substrate.

There are several factors that can create linewidth excursions beyond the desired limits. Fluctuation in the beam current is one cause. Also, changes in the chemical properties of the developer solutions can lead to effects similar to that shown in Fig. 4.20. Moreover, with complicated structures there can be several pattern features separated by relatively short distances. Hence, the electron-beam writing of one feature may provide a background component to the exposure of adjacent features. Consequently, there has been considerable interest in computer algorithms that can selectively modify the pattern data to compensate for this proximity effect (Parikh, 1978; Chang, 1975; Nakata and Kato, 1978).

In order to control these variations, or to obtain real time feedback on achieved performance, it is common practice to expose test structures along with the device patterns. One structure proposed by Grobman and Speth (1978) consists of a rectangle over which the dose is varied mono-

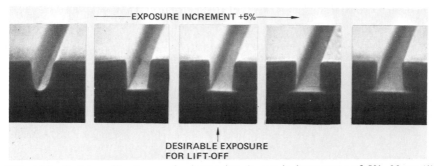

FIG. 4.20   Resist profile changes for increasing dosage in increments of 5%. Note: (1) change in side wall angle with relatively modest dose increments. (2) Backscatter component gives sharp undercut at resist–substrate interface. (3) Linewidth at resist surface insensitive to dose.

tonically along the length. In addition, the pattern has tick marks along the feature edge, thereby creating an image that is self-reading. The location along the edge of the fully developed resist that corresponds to a previously calibrated dose–development condition can be noted to determine the optimal dose.

Another self-reading structure due to Mayer (1978) is shown in Fig. 4.21. Here a programmed offset of separated rectangles is created. Again, simple microscopic inspection readily provides the linewidth control information because it is straightforward to observe the particular edges that line up. Consequently, the amount of over- or underdevelopment is determined by simple inspection without requiring calibrated linewidth measuring tools. Small fractions of a micron can be detected by this method. In fact, the structure shown in Fig. 4.21 serves as an under- or overetch monitor that remains permanently on the wafer. The photomicrograph on the right-hand side of Fig. 4.21 shows the results of etching a polycrystalline silicon thin film. The overetching in this case was 0.2 μm per edge.

Another often used test structure is a vernier offset pattern that provides a self-reading measure of alignment accuracy (Wilson *et al.*, 1978; Yau and Thibault, 1978). Accuracy of 0.1 μm can be obtained.

The control of line profile is often just as important in device fabrication as control of line size. For example, with integrated circuits the interconnect lines from one level typically cross over structures defined in a prior level. If the edge profile of the first structure is very steep, there will

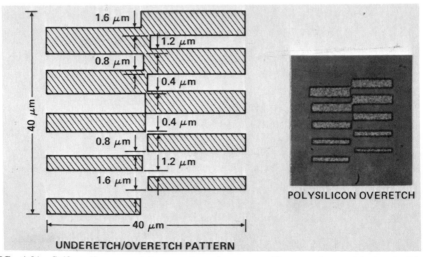

FIG. 4.21 Self-reading overetch or underetch pattern. Photograph on right-hand side shows overetching a polycrystalline silicon film by 0.2 μm.

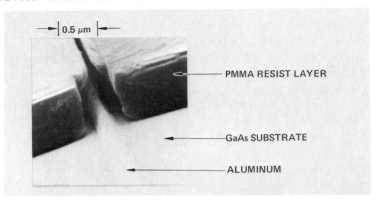

FIG. 4.22   Aluminum structure made by the lift-off process with positive resist. Note: (1) Edge shadowing from aluminum buildup on resist upper edge. (2) Eventual triangular metal line profile. (3) Reset undercut at substrate interface.

be step coverage problems and thus the yield of continuous lines will be affected.

As discussed in Section IV.C, the gate resistance is a limiting factor in FETs. Consequently, it is desirable to have as large a cross-sectional gate area as feasible. Figure 4.22 shows the difficulty of maximizing the cross-sectional area of a gate when using electron-beam lithography and the lift-off method. This figure shows a GaAs substrate on which a 0.5 μm gate structure has been exposed and aluminum deposited. The resulting structure has been scraped so that a view of the resist–metal profile is revealed. Note the triangular nature of the aluminum metal line which results from the buildup of an adhering layer to the resist surfaces. This buildup shadows the latter stages of the evaporation and results in a sloping profile for the gate line. Consequently, the maximum height as well as the cross-sectional area is limited compared with a rectangular structure.

Another constraint is wafer distortion. The thermal processing and film depositions should not unduly stress the sample so that plastic deformation of the wafers occurs. Here, electron-beam lithography offers unique flexibility because, compared to fixed mask replication, it is possible to adjust the exposed pattern, using the calculations discussed in Section III.B to compensate for wafer distortions.

A question remains whether distortion is random. Gegenworth and Laming (1977) reported random dislocation of surface images due to diffusion and high temperature annealing. On the other hand, Henderson (1977) and Yau (1978) measured symmetrical distortion for wafers processed to make MOSFET devices. In fact, Yau (1978) showed that the apparent in-plane distortion could be accounted for by the wafer bowing which he measured independently. It will be important to determine whether Yau's results for MOSFET processing remain valid for other techniques as well. For example, if in-plane distortion is truly dependent on wafer bow, which can be measured, then electron-beam patterns might be written accurately by using only three alignment marks on an entire wafer (Alles *et al.*, 1975). This conclusion would also mean that mechanical techniques could be used to hold the wafer flat, thereby allowing pattern exposure by fixed mask replication without misalignments due to bowing. On the other hand, if displacements are random, then repeated registrations on small subfields are necessary.

The limited scan field of electron-beam lithography is yet another constraint on device processing, particularly of integrated circuits. The problem is that the size of the chip can be substantially larger than the scan field size. Consequently, in the general case, adjacent scan fields require independent pattern data. Moreover, electron-optical distortion must be sufficiently controlled that it is possible to define reliably a continuous minimum size feature that crosses the scan field border, i.e., field stitching. This means that the pattern data to be exposed must be correlated with the work piece position, as well as demanding that adjacent low distortion scan fields be aligned with respect to each other.

Two methods have been demonstrated to solve this problem. In one case, registration on each field proceeds independently using on-chip alignment marks (Wilson *et al.*, 1975). The other solution is to use laser interferometers to control the stage motion so that together with electronic error correction the adjacent scan fields are precisely located. This latter result has been achieved successfully for 256 μm scan fields (Alles *et al.*, 1975) as well as 2000 μm scan fields (Wilson *et al.*, 1978). The laser control method is preferred because there is more available semiconductor area for active devices that otherwise would be used to define the alignment marks.

VI. SUMMARY

Clearly, electron-beam lithography cannot simply replace photolithography in existing wafer processing sequences; there are too many differences in chemistries, pattern transfer methods, and alignment techniques between photolithography and electron-beam lithography. Moreover, the typical modern application is satisfied better by smaller devices, which require the device structure to change. These factors all require changes in the procedure of device fabrication.

Furthermore, the demand for high resolution impacts the application of electron-beam lithography. For example, there are subtle edge factors associated with various etching techniques that must be controlled. This is a demanding task in view of the trend toward greater height-to-width ratios in etched features. Moreover, on a statistical yield basis, alignment and linewidth control must scale proportionally to the amount of size reduction. Yet modest fluctuations in the electron–resist dose–development can lead to variations in the resist side wall profile or linewidth.

However, good progress has been made to meet these requirements. Self-reading structures provide real time feedback with respect to resist exposure, over- or underetching, and alignment. Resists have been developed to be compatible with a number of pattern transfer methods. Several versions of electron-beam alignment marks are suitable for use in achieving accurate alignment. A variety of alignment strategies provides for process compatibility under many possible conditions. Pitfalls and procedure details have been documented regarding many pattern transfer steps.

This chapter also discussed some techniques with electron-beam lithography. Methods of generating pattern data was presented. The feasibility and methods of stitching electron-beam scan fields to make large area integrated circuits were discussed.

A review of prototype devices, fabricated with electron-beam lithography, showed a wide range of applications. Transistors (several varieties), SAW devices, bubble devices, and integrated circuits have all been demonstrated. Unique fabrication problems were encountered and solved. Interactions between the electron beam and the resulting device were found, but thermal treatment can eliminate these effects.

The overall result has been to demonstrate the feasibility of electron-beam lithography under a wide variety of conditions. The work has revealed new principles governing device behavior at small dimensions. And, in practically every case, the prototype devices have shown improvement in factors such as speed or power consumption. These benefits will continue to keep the interest in electron-beam lithography high, as is evident from the abundant literature published in the past several years.

REFERENCES

Aitken, J. M., Young, D. R., and Pan, K. (1978). *J. Appl. Phys.* **49**, 3386–3391.
Alles, D. S., Ashley, F. R., Johnson, A. M., and Townsend, R. L. (1975). *J. Vac. Sci. Technol.* **12**, 1252–1256.
Bobenrieth, A., Cohen, O., and Lyon-Caen, R. (1972). *Proc. Int. Conf. Electron Ion Beam Sci. Technol., 5th* p. 148. The Electrochemical Society, Princeton, New Jersey.
Broers, A. N., Leon, E. G., and Hatzakis, M. (1969). *Appl. Phys. Lett.* **15**, 98–101.
Butlin, R. S., Hughes, A. J., Bennett, R. H., Parker, D., and Turner, J. A. (1978). *Tech. Digest IEDM* 136–139.
Chang, T. H. P. (1975). *J. Vac. Sci. Technol.* **12**, 1271–1275.

Chang, T. H. P., Hatzakis, M., Wilson, A. D., Speth, A. J., Kern, A., and Luhn, H. (1976). *IBM J. Res. Dev.* **20,** 376–382.

Chatterjee, P. K., Fu, S. U., Tasch, A. F., Holloway, T. C., and Blocker, T. G. (1978). *J. Vac. Sci. Technol.* **15,** 957–959.

Churchill, R. V. (1960). "Complex Variables and Applications." McGraw-Hill, New York.

Darley, H. M., Houston, T. W., and Taylor, G. W. (1978). *Tech. Digest IEDM* 62–65.

Dennard, R. H., Gaensslen, F. H., Kuhn, L., and Yu, H. N. (1972). *Tech. Digest IEDM,* Abstr. No. 243.

El-Kareh, B., and Pattletz, A. F. (1978). *J. Vac. Sci. Technol.* **15,** 1047–1052.

Elliott, M. T., Splinter, M. R., Jones, A. B., and Reekstein, J. P. (1977). *Tech. Digest IEDM* 11.5–12.

Evans, S. A., Bartelt, J. L., Sloan, B. J., and Varnell, G. L. (1977). *IEEE Trans. Electron Devices* **ED-25,** 402–407.

Fang, F., Hatzakis, M., and Ting, C. H. (1973). *J. Vac. Sci. Technol.* **10,** 1082.

Friedrich, H., Zeitler, H. U., and Bierhenke, H. (1977). *J. Electrochem. Soc.* **124,** 627–629.

Furukawa, Y., Nahayama, N., Goto, Y., Igahi, S., and Tenagahi, T. (1978). *Proc. Int. Conf. Electron. Ion Beam Sci. Technol., 8th* pp. 63–67. The Electrochemical Society, Princeton, New Jersey.

Gegenworth, R. E., and Laming, F. P. (1972). *Proc. SPIE* **100,** 66–73.

Grobman, W. D., and Speth, A. J. (1978). *Proc. Int. Conf. Electron. Ion Beam Sci. Technol., 8th* pp. 276–284. The Electrochemical Society, Princeton, New Jersey.

Hashimoto, N., and Saito, N. (1975). *Thin Solid Films* **27,** 89–93.

Henderson, R. C. (1977). *Proc. SPIE* **100,** 151–160.

Henderson, R. C., Suiter, W. B., and Weber, T. A. (1972). *Proc. Int. Conf. Electron Ion Beam Sci. Technol., 5th* pp. 123–126. The Electrochemical Soc., Princeton, New Jersey.

Henderson, R. C., Pease, R. F. W., Voschenkov, R. M., Mallery, P., and Wadsack, R. L. (1975). *IEEE J. Solid State Cir.* **SC-10,** 92–98.

Henderson, R. C., Reiner, T., and Coppen, P. J. (1978). *IEEE Trans. Electron Devices* **ED-25,** 408–412.

Henderson, R. C., Mayer, D. M., and Nash, J. G. (1979). *J. Vac. Sci. Technol.* **16,** 260–268.

Krambeck, R. H., Retajczyk, T. E., and Yau, L. D. (1976). *IEEE J. Solid State Cir.* **SC-11,** 171.

Kruger, J. B., You, S. W., and Yuan, H. T. (1975). *J. Vac. Sci. Technol.* **12,** 301–303.

Krumm, C. F., Suyematsu, H. T., and Walsh, B. L. (1978). *IEEE MTT-S Digest* 383–386.

Kryder, M. H., Ahm, K. Y., and Paivers, J. V. (1975). *IEEE Trans. Magn.* **MAG-11,** 1145–1147.

Lynch, W. T. (1977). *Tech. Digest of IEDM* **7G.**

Magdo, S., Hatzakis, M., and Ting, C. (1971). *IBM J. Res. Dev.* **15,** 446.

Mayer, D. M. (1978). Unpublished.

Nakata, H., and Kato, T. (1978). *Proc. Int. Conf. Electron Ion Beam Sci. Technol., 8th* pp. 393–405. The Electrochem. Soc., Princeton, New Jersey.

Nuzillat, G., Arnodo, C., and Puron, J. P. (1976). *IEEE J. Solid State Cir.* **SC-11,** 386.

Ozdemir, F. S., Perkins, W. E., Yim, R., and Wolf, E. D. (1973). *J. Vac. Sci. Technol.* **6,** 1008.

Ozdemir, F. S., Ladd, G. O., Loper, D. D., Cleary, F. W., and Hirsch, N. (1976). *Proc. Int. Conf. Electron Ion Beam Sci. Technol., 7th* pp. 411–416. The Electrochem. Soc., Princeton, New Jersey.

Pankratz, J. M., Yuan, H. T., and Greagh, L. T. (1973). *Tech. Digest of IEDM* 44.

Parikh, M. (1978). *Proc. Int. Conf. Electron Ion Beam Sci. Technol., 8th* pp. 371–392. The Electrochem. Society, Princeton, New Jersey.

Pease, R. F. W., Henderson, R. C., Dalton, J. V. (1973). *J. Vac. Sci. Technol.* **10,** 1078–1081.
Pickar, K. A., and Thibault, L. R. (1973). *J. Vac. Sci. Technol.* **10,** 1074.
Spicer, D. F., Rodger, A. C., and Varnell, G. L. (1973). *J. Vac. Sci. Technol.* **10,** 1052–1055.
Stephani, D., and Froschle, E. (1978). *J. Vac. Sci. Technol.* **15,** 906–908.
Thibault, L. R., and Pickar, K. A. (1978). *Proc. Int. Conf. Electron Ion Beam Sci. Technol., 5th* pp. 148–152. The Electrochem. Society, Princeton, New Jersey.
Tsai, T. N., and Yau, L. D. (1976). *Tech. Digest of IEDM* 202–204.
Varnell, G. L., Spicer, D. F., and Roger, A. C. (1973). *J. Vac. Sci. Technol.* **10,** 1048–1051.
Wilson, A. D., Chang, T. H. P., and Kern, A. (1975). *J. Vac. Sci. Technol.* **12,** 1240–1245.
Wilson, A. D., Studwell, T. W., Folchi, G., Kern, A., and Voelker, H. (1978). *Proc. Int. Conf. Electron Ion Beam Sci. Technol., 8th* pp. 198–205. The Electrochemical Soc., Princeton, New Jersey.
Wolf, E. D., Ozdemir, F. S., and Weglein, R. D. (1973). *IEEE Ultrasonics Symp., Monterey, California* pp. 1–7.
Wolf, E. D., Coane, P. J., Ozdemir, F. S. (1975). *J. Vac. Sci. Technol.* **12,** 1266–1270.
Yau, L. D. (1975). *Electron Lett.* **11,** 44–45.
Yau, L. D. (1976). *IEEE J. Solid-State Cir.* **SC-11,** 214–219.
Yau, L. D. (1978). *Appl. Phys. Lett.* **33,** 756–758.
Yau, L. D., and Thibault, L. T. (1978). *J. Vac. Sci. Technol.* **ED-25,** 413–418.
Yu, H. N., Dennard, R. H., Chang, T. H. P., Osburn, C. M., Dilnardo, V., and Luhn, H. E. (1975). *J. Vac. Sci. Technol.* **12,** 1297–1300.

5

Mask fabrication by
electron-beam lithography

*J. P. BALLANTYNE**

BELL LABORATORIES MURRAY HILL, NEW JERSEY

* Present address: Bell Laboratories, 2525 N. 11th Street, Reading, Pennsylvania 19604.

259

I. INTRODUCTION

A major factor in the success of any microelectronic device is the ability of the manufacturing technology to produce the device reliably and economically. As shown in the previous chapters, these goals can be achieved successfully using electron-beam lithography for certain classes of devices. However, contemporary microelectronic manufacturing technology still relies almost exclusively on photolithographic processes for pattern delineation. Since the photolithographic process involves replication of patterns from masks, the quality of the original pattern delineated on the master mask is of crucial importance. Electron-beam lithography is finding growing application in the fabrication of photolithographic master masks because this new technology is capable of meeting the increasingly stringent requirements for mask fabrication more efficiently than alternative methods. This particular application of electron-beam lithography is the subject of this chapter. It is appropriate that the discussion begin with a closer look at photolithography and the role played by master masks in the fabrication of microelectronic devices.

In simplest terms, photolithography in device manufacture involves pattern transfer using ultraviolet light. A pattern of light is transmitted through a mask onto a device substrate coated with a photosensitive polymeric material called a photoresist. The molecular structure and therefore solubility of a photoresist are changed by irradiation with photons. Thus, the pattern of photon transmission through a mask determines the pattern that is chemically developed in the photoresist. The developed photoresist pattern is transferred, in turn, to an underlying material using a suitable etching agent. The etching agent removes those regions not protected by the photoresist. It is through this process in combination with a succession of masks that the patterns required for diffusions, metallizations, interconnections, etc., are delineated.

A master mask, as the name implies, is an original mask which contains a complete array of patterns at working size ready for photolithographic transfer. The master mask shown in Fig. 5.1 contains a variety of essential pattern information needed for one patterning step or level in the fabrication of a microelectronic device. This particular mask pattern is used to delineate the silicon gate level of a 1 kbit random access memory device. Since the device requires multilevel pattern delineation, this mask is one member of a set of master masks.

In addition to the actual device patterns, referred to as primary patterns, which will cover most of the area on a silicon wafer, there are usually test patterns dispersed throughout the primary array. These patterns define test structures which are used to measure important device

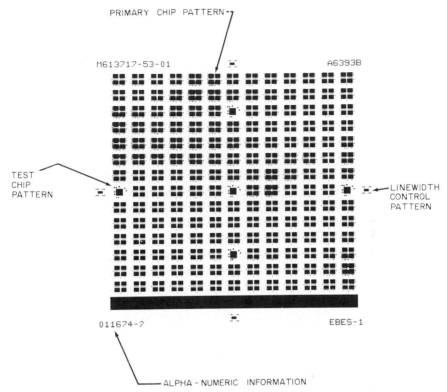

FIG. 5.1 Transmission photograph of a master mask showing a variety of pattern information required for one level in the fabrication of a 1-kbit random access memory device. The size of the patterned area on the master is approximately 6 cm × 6 cm.

parameters, such as oxide capacitance, doping density, sheet resistance, etc., at various stages of wafer processing. Ultimately, the silicon wafer is diced into individual chips, each, hopefully, containing a working device. Individual pattern areas on each mask level are thus frequently referred to as chips. As shown in Fig. 5.1, a typical master mask will also contain alphanumeric information for identification, as well as patterns used for linewidth control measurements.

Master mask pattern generation involves sophisticated, highly accurate, computer controlled hardware. The process is time consuming and expensive. A typical master mask costs several hundred dollars to fabricate, and the cost of a complete set of masters can easily total several thousand dollars.

Copies of a master can be made photolithographically for about one-tenth the cost of the original, with some deterioration in quality. In the past, economic pressures usually favored the use of copies as working masks on a production line, because of replacement costs for masks degraded in use by mask-to-wafer contact and other factors. With the recent trend to projection photolithography for mask-to-wafer pattern transfer, the leading cause of mask damage (i.e., mask-to-wafer contact) has been removed. High quality master masks can now be used economically on a production line with useful life limited only by design revisions and damage caused by mishandling.

II.   MASK FABRICATION REQUIREMENTS

A.   *Pattern Placement Accuracy*

The successful superposition of successive mask levels during device manufacture requires accurate pattern placement on the master mask. Each chip pattern on a particular mask in a set must align precisely with corresponding chip patterns on every other mask in the set.

The registration accuracy required between mask levels depends on the device design. Although a misalignment of 1 μm might be acceptable for 10 μm features, it will almost certainly be fatal for 2 μm features. With the trend in microelectronics toward larger scales of integration and higher packing densities, features sizes and alignment tolerances are being continually reduced. Submicron level-to-level alignment accuracy is becoming an increasingly common requirement for today's complex and high performance circuits. Therefore, pattern placement accuracy must generally be better than ± 0.5 μm.

Repeatable or systematic inaccuracies in pattern placement do not preclude level-to-level registration, but generally do prevent the mixing of masters fabricated on different pattern generation systems. This is because repeatable inaccuracies tend to be unique to a given system. Due to wear of mechanical parts and other forms of drift, repeatability of inaccuracies may only be short term on a particular system, necessitating the remaking of a complete mask set when an existing master is damaged or revised.

Pattern misregistration on the device can arise from factors other than pattern placement inaccuracies in mask fabrication. Good mask-to-wafer alignment, carried out by manual optical techniques, requires a high level of operator skill and alignment machine accuracy. Although manual registration accuracies of better than 1 μm appear to be achievable with newer 1:1 projection printers (Cuthbert, 1977), automatic registration methods are contributing to improvements in this area (Denning, 1976). Even under optimal alignment conditions, process-induced wafer warpage can cause registration as well as line size control problems. For these reasons care is taken in manufacturing operations, particularly at high temperature processing steps such as oxidations and diffusions to minimize process-induced warpage.

Temperature variations in the mask fabrication process can also cause misregistration. Thermal expansion of components in mask patterning systems, including the mask substrates, must be controlled to prevent registration problems. For example, a temperature variation of 1°C on the patterning system can result in a registration error between two mask levels as large as 0.7 μm over a 3-in.- (7.6-cm-) diameter pattern due to linear expansion of the glass substrate alone ($\alpha \approx 9 \times 10^{-6}°C^{-1}$). Similar considerations dictate that temperatures must be carefully controlled where the masks are used as well as where they are generated.

B. Resolution

The ultimate resolution which can be achieved in any mask fabrication process is limited by the smallest dimension that can be written or addressed on the mask pattern generator. The dimension of the smallest addressable unit on a pattern generator is commonly referred to as its address structure. Obviously, the finer the address structure, the higher will be the ultimate resolution capability of the pattern generator. Equally important is the fact that a finer address structure allows the designer to vary feature sizes in finer increments. However, system cost rises and throughput falls when the address structure is reduced; therefore, the choice of address structure is usually a compromise.

The resolution required in the master mask pattern ultimately depends upon limitations imposed by subsequent photolithographic processing. Minimum feature sizes in photolithography are limited by a combination of diffraction effects and exposure characteristics of photoresist materials (see Chapter 1). Under optimal conditions, involving intimate contact between two flat surfaces, submicron features can be delineated (Smith, 1974; Wada and Uehara, 1974). However, such conditions seldom prevail in device fabrication, and minimum feature sizes of 1–2 μm are widely accepted as the rule for general device fabrication using contact photolithography. A working minimum feature size for 1:1 projection systems using 3000–4000 Å exposure wavelengths is in the 2–3 μm range. Therefore, a resolution capability of about 500 line pairs per millimeter (1 μm lines and spaces) is adequate for the majority of masks intended for photolithographic use.

In order to meet this resolution requirement the address structure must be, at most, 1 μm. However, the increasingly common requirement of designers to vary feature sizes in submicron increments will generally impose an upper limit on address structure which is a fraction of this value.

C. Linewidth Control

The trend toward higher packing densities and smaller features in microelectronic devices has demanded tighter linewidth tolerances at critical patterning steps. When features are packed closer together the margin for error on feature size is obviously reduced. Furthermore, the successful performance of most devices depends upon control of the size of critical structures, such as gate electrodes in MOS devices, for example. Since the allowed size variation on such structures is generally a fixed proportion of the nominal feature size, reduced dimensions imply tighter tolerances. Good linewidth control over an entire wafer and from wafer to wafer is clearly a requirement for uniform device performance. Linewidth control of better than ± 0.5 μm from the design value is not an uncommon requirement for critical mask levels.

D. Defect Density

Defects in a master mask pattern which are large enough to be resolved by the photolithographic process will be transferred to the wafer and cause defects on the devices. Some of these defects will be fatal. Additional defects will be generated on the wafer by the photolithographic processing steps used to transfer the mask pattern. In the total sequence of processing steps needed to make a microelectronic device, the several photolithographic steps exhibit the lowest process yield. Taken together, these steps are dominant in determining chip yield. Mask defect density is thus an extremely important factor in the economics of microelectronic device production. Therefore, it is necessary to establish acceptance criteria for master masks which ensure an adequate yield of good device patterns at the end of the photolithographic patterning sequence. Various statistical estimates can be used for the purpose. Price (1970) proposed the following relation between device yield and defect density:

$$Y = \prod_{l=1}^{L} (1 + x_l)^{-1} \tag{5.1}$$

where Y is the potential yield of good devices or chips from the mask set, $x_l = D_l A$, A is the area of a chip, and D_l is the average density of fatal defects on the lth mask level. Another expression relating defect density and

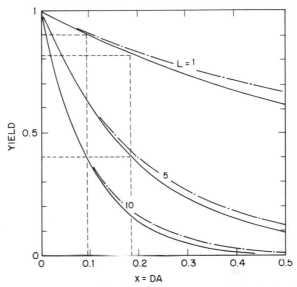

FIG. 5.2 Chip yield as a function of the defect parameter x, calculated using Eqs. (5.3) and (5.4): ———, $Y = (1 - e^{-x})^{2L}/x^{2L}$; —·—, $Y = (1 + x)^{-L}$.

device yield has been proposed by Murphy (1964) which can be modified to the form

$$Y = \prod_{l=1}^{L} \frac{(1 - e^{-x_l})^2}{x_l^2} \qquad (5.2)$$

to predict a cumulative yield for L mask levels. For the purpose of the present discussion, assume x_l is the same for all L mask levels. Equation (5.1) now becomes

$$Y = (1 + x)^{-L} \qquad (5.3)$$

and Eq. (5.2) reduces to

$$Y = (1 - e^{-x})^{2L}/x^{2L} \qquad (5.4)$$

Values of chip yield calculated using the above expressions are plotted in Fig. 5.2 for $L = 1$, 5, and 10. Price's and Murphy's estimators give comparable results out to $x = 0.5$. Note how rapidly yield decreases for a fixed value of x when the number of mask levels is increased. For most devices the number of mask levels ranges from $L = 5$ to $L = 10$.

In order to achieve a photolithographic yield potential of say at least 40%* from a mask set, the chip yield on each level in a five-level set must

* This somewhat arbitrary value was chosen for illustrative purposes only.

exceed 80%, while for a ten-level set the chip yield must exceed 90% per level. This condition requires $x < 0.2$ and $x < 0.1$, respectively (see Fig. 5.2). Large-scale integrated circuits such as 4-kbit random access memory devices have chip areas of about 0.2 cm². Therefore, the maximum allowable density of fatal defects per mask level for such a device ($L = 5$) is about 1 cm^{-2} if a chip yield of better than 80% per level is to be maintained.

Clearly, mask inspection criteria must be established by the mask maker and the circuit designer which will allow an inspector or inspection system to identify fatal defects. If the rejection criteria are too loose, measured D values will be too low, and masks having intolerably low chip yields may end up on the production line. Conversely, if the criteria are too stringent, inspected D values may be overly pessimistic, and potentially useful masks may be rejected. The defect density performance of a mask fabrication process can generally be specified adequately by a mean defect density value D_0 (cm^{-2}), and the standard deviation σ of the measured sample from the mean. A typical defect density distribution might follow the general shape of the normal distribution shown in Fig. 5.3a. If, from considerations similar to those outlined above, a new device requires a defect density of $D \leq D_l$ on each mask level, then the manufacturing yield Y_m for these new masks can be estimated from the normal law integral (Knowler *et al.*, 1969):

$$Y_m = \int_{-\infty}^{a} \frac{1}{\sqrt{2\pi}} e^{-z^2/2} \, dz \tag{5.5}$$

where

$$z = (D - D_0)/\sigma \tag{5.6}$$

and

$$a = (D_l - D_0)/\sigma \tag{5.7}$$

Values of Y_m can be estimated from the chart in Fig. 5.3b. For example, consider the previous case of a set of five masks for a 4-kbit memory circuit having a chip area of 0.2 cm². Assuming a 40% photolithographic yield is required from the set, the defect density must be better than 1 cm^{-2} on all mask levels. Now let us assume a mask fabrication process with normal defect density distribution characterized by $D_0 = 1.4$ cm^{-2} and $\sigma = 0.8$ cm^{-2}. Then $a = -0.5$, from Eq. (5.7), and, from Fig. 5.3b, $Y_m = 31\%$.* Thus, the statistical data predict that more than two-thirds of

---

* In a later section it will be shown that the values assumed here for illustrative purposes are reasonable for a conventional mask fabrication process.

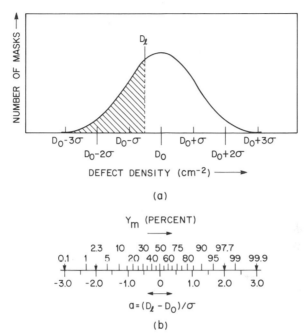

FIG. 5.3 (a) Defect density distribution which follows normal law. (b) Manufacturing yield associated with a given defect density D_l from the normal law integral [Eq. (5.5)].

the masks started for this mask set will be rejected at inspection. Such calculations can be used to estimate the potential economic returns of process improvements for existing device designs. They can also be useful in predicting the process performance required for new mask sets having larger chip dimensions.

E. Maximum Chip Size

The basic building block for a master mask array is the chip pattern. Achievement of larger scales of integration has required larger chip sizes because processing technology has not been able to cope with the full scaling of feature sizes that would be necessary to place more devices on a given size chip. MOS memory chips with 5 mm dimensions are common today, and occasionally the need arises for much larger chips. Magnetic bubble memory circuits and area-imaging charge-coupled device circuits are two cases where chip dimensions can reach 20 mm or more.

Increasing chip size without process improvement results in lower chip yields as shown in the previous section (larger value of x in Fig. 5.2). The decrease in the percentage of good devices per wafer due to increasing chip size is compounded further by the fact that there are fewer of the larger chips on a wafer. Larger chip sizes, therefore, can result in more costly devices since a major cost in integrated circuit manufacture arises from processing operations performed on the complete silicon wafer. One solution is to process larger wafers. Judging by past performance, the microelectronics industry will continue the trend to larger wafer diameters as economic pressures dictate and materials technology allows. Future mask making systems must be capable of writing pattern arrays exceeding the current industry standard of 3 in. (7.6 cm).

Even if chip areas can be held constant for larger scales of integration, the problem of lower chip yield has not been completely solved. Without process improvements in both mask fabrication and device processing, chip yields can be expected to drop as device features are made smaller due to the increase in fatal defect density as smaller defects become significant.

F.   Turnaround Time and Flexibility

The fabrication of a conventional working mask involves a number of time consuming steps, including conceptual circuit design, circuit layout, exposure of 10× reticle, photographic reduction, step-and-repeat over the master mask, and replication of working masks. Depending on the complexity of the circuit, the backlog in the mask shop, and the priority assigned to a particular job, the turnaround time from layout to working mask in a typical mask shop can vary from several weeks to several months. This elapsed time can be much more costly to an urgent device development program than the actual mask fabrication cost.

Therefore, rapid turnaround is essential for the timely introduction of a new device, and this is as important in mask making as it is in every other area of device fabrication. The requirement is particularly acute during the development phase where design changes may be frequent.

Flexibility, too, is important in any mask fabrication process. For example, it is often desirable to investigate a range of device parameters during the development of a new device. If several different chip designs could be incorporated economically on each mask, these various designs could then be evaluated under the same processing conditions, allowing the designer to optimize his circuit for the prevailing process.

G.   Cost

The success of a mask fabrication method is measured ultimately in economic terms. A straightforward relation between mask cost and the key economic parameters in a mask fabrication process is given in the following expression:

$$\text{mask cost} = \left[\frac{(S + O + P)}{T} + M \right] \frac{1}{Y_\text{m}} \tag{5.8}$$

where S is the hourly system cost,

$$S = \frac{\text{total system cost}}{\text{expected service lifetime (years)} \times \text{yearly service (hours)}}$$

O = hourly operating costs including operator and overhead expenses, P = hourly processing and inspection costs including operator and overhead expenses, T = mask throughput (masks/hour), M = materials cost per mask, Y_m = manufacturing yield (Section II.D).

This expression will be used in subsequent discussions to provide a first-order estimate of mask cost for conventional and electron-beam mask fabrication methods.

III. MASK FABRICATION METHODS

A. Photolithographic Methods

Photolithographic methods of mask fabrication can involve several patterning steps. The number of lithographic steps associated with a given method depends on the amount of image reduction required to reduce the output of the pattern generator to final working size. The resolution capability and pattern placement accuracy of the pattern generator determine the amount of image reduction required (Horne, 1973; Rottmann, 1974; O'Malley, 1975; Tobey, 1975).

The basic process, which is illustrated schematically in Fig. 5.4a, begins with a circuit or chip layout by the designer for each mask level. This step frequently is accomplished with the help of computer-aided design routines. The chip layout is then converted to an appropriate input code to control a pattern generator which draws the chip pattern in a recording medium at 10–20× final size. In the most advanced commercially available optical pattern generators, patterning is done at 10× final size with light exposure through a variable geometry aperture. The recording medium is usually high resolution photographic emulsion.

A 10× chip pattern is generally referred to as a reticle. The reticle is used in a step-and-repeat camera to produce an array of chip patterns at final size on the master mask substrate. Each different chip pattern on the master requires a reticle, which must be first aligned in the camera and then arrayed at the proper locations.

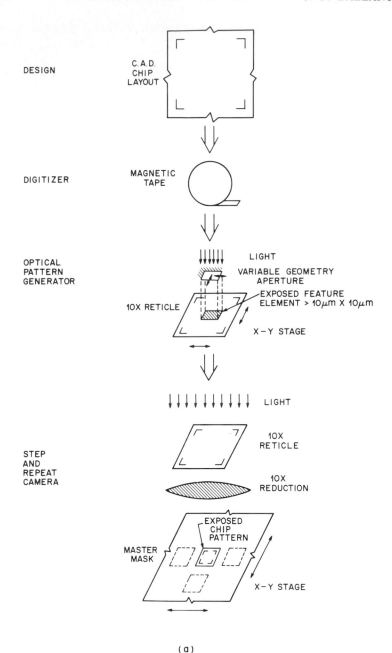

DESIGN   C.A.D.
                CHIP
                LAYOUT

DIGITIZER   MAGNETIC
                TAPE

OPTICAL   LIGHT
PATTERN   VARIABLE GEOMETRY
GENERATOR   APERTURE
                EXPOSED FEATURE
10X RETICLE   ELEMENT > 10μm X 10μm
                X-Y STAGE

                LIGHT

STEP   10X
AND   RETICLE
REPEAT
CAMERA   10X
                REDUCTION

                EXPOSED
                CHIP
                PATTERN
MASTER
MASK

                X-Y STAGE

(a)

FIG. 5.4   Schematic representation of two master mask fabrication methods: (a) photolithographic; (b), electron beam.

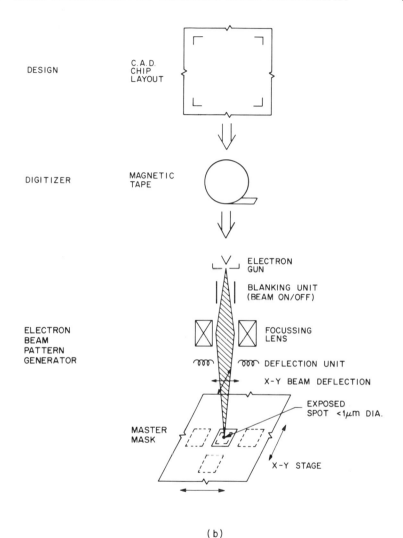

(b)

FIG. 5.4b   See legend for Fig. 5.4.

The master pattern is usually delineated either photographically in high resolution emulsion on glass substrates or photolithographically in chromium films on glass substrates. The latter approach involves longer writing times due to the lower light sensitivity of photoresists. In spite of a considerable sensitivity advantage, emulsion masters are becoming less popular. Emulsion film thicknesses generally range from 4 to 6 μm. Developed images are grainy and prone to defects arising from inhomogeneities in the emulsion. Chromium films, on the other hand, are typically less than 0.1 μm in thickness and are conducive to high resolution and good edge definition. Chromium also appears to be a more durable mask material than emulsion in most applications.

The writing times for reticle generation on advanced optical pattern generators vary considerably from one type of system to another and tend to be dependent on pattern complexity. Writing times on conventional systems can vary from tens of minutes to several hours. The most advanced step-and-repeat cameras have a writing rate of about 50 cm^2/min in emulsion and 5 cm^2/min in photoresist. Since several reticles must be generated, aligned, and arrayed for a typical master mask, total writing times of several hours are common.

For an estimate of mask cost, consider the case of a conventional optical mask fabrication system consisting of a pattern generator and step-and-repeat camera costing, say, $600,000 with an expected service life of 7 yr and a yearly service of 4000 hr. The hourly system cost would be about $20. Assuming the following values for 4 in. (10.2 cm) masks and 3 in. (7.6 cm) pattern arrays: $O = \$30$, $P = \$40$, $T = 0.7$, $M = \$20$, and $Y_m = 0.5$, Eq. (5.8) yields

$$\text{mask cost} = \left[\frac{(20 + 30 + 40)}{0.7} + 20 \right] \frac{1}{0.5} \approx \$300$$

It is clear from this example that throughput and manufacturing yield are dominant factors in mask fabrication cost. It is important to note that the cost of system amortization in the above example contributes only about one-fifth of the final mask cost, over the reasonably long service life (30,000 hr) chosen.

B. Electron-Beam Methods

Electron-beam mask fabrication methods are becoming increasingly popular because they offer the potential for significant improvements in several critical performance areas. The inherently higher resolution capability of electron-beam lithography allows the master mask to be patterned directly at final working size without the photoreduction operations required in photolithographic methods (Fig. 5.4). The advantages that can be expected from the reduced number of lithographic steps and higher resolution capability include faster turnaround, better linewidth control, lower defect densities, and smaller minimum features. The extent to which these advantages are realized in practice depends greatly on system performance.

1. Types of Systems

Electron-beam systems presently used for mask fabrication fall basically into two classes distinguished by the writing strategy. The oldest approach, which is illustrated schematically in Fig. 5.5a, involves step-and-repeat exposure of each chip pattern (Cahen *et al.*, 1972; Saitou and Nonogaki, 1972; Friedmann *et al.*, 1973; Piwczyk and McQuhae, 1973; Livesay, 1974; Varnell *et al.*, 1974; Beasley and Squire, 1975). In order to minimize the total time spent stepping and settling between scan fields, the field size should be as large as possible. For this reason, most systems of this type are designed to expose each complete chip pattern, and scan fields as large as 6 mm × 6 mm are used. Deflection systems must be carefully designed and fabricated to keep pattern distortions within acceptable limits over such large areas (refer to Chapter 3). All of these systems utilize a vector-scan exposure method whereby the electron beam is directed to expose sequentially each feature element in the scan field.

The second approach, which is represented in Fig. 5.5b, involves very small deflections of an electron beam in a raster scan mode combined with a continuously moving $X-Y$ table. In the first system of this type described by Herriott *et al.* (1975) the length of the beam scan was 128 μm, or 256 addresses each 0.5-μm long. The maximum deflection field, which accommodated deflections to compensate for table errors as well as the line scan deflection was 140 μm × 140 μm. Distortion within such a limited scan field is negligible.

This system was superceded in performance by an improved version which featured an enlarged beam scan of 256 μm and a choice of either 0.5 or 0.25 μm address structure (Alles *et al.*, 1975b). Commercial versions of this second generation system are being marketed by two U.S. companies.

Reports in the literature indicate that both the step-and-repeat and the continuous table motion approaches have proven satisfactory for mask fabrication. Performance data will be reviewed in a later section. For the present discussion we will concentrate on those system aspects which are most important in mask fabrication applications. A detailed description of operating principles for these systems is given in Chapter 3.

Early step-and-repeat systems such as those described by Friedmann *et al.* (1973) and by Beasley and Squire (1975) require patterning of fiducial marks on the mask substrate prior to electron-beam exposure. These marks have to be located within each scan field for registration purposes. In practice this method would be costly and tend to increase the number of defects in the starting material.

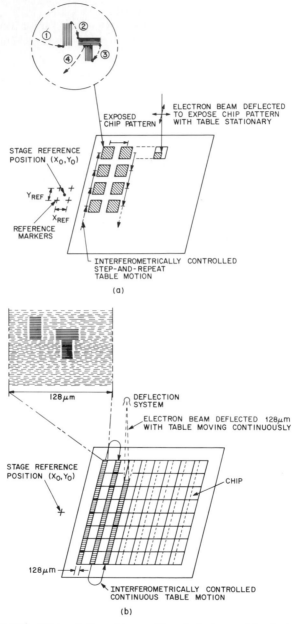

FIG. 5.5 Schematic representation of two writing strategies used in electron-beam mask fabrication systems. Stage mounted reference markers are used for pattern registration. (a) Large scan field with step-and-repeat table motion. (b) Small scan field with continuous table motion.

In later systems, laser interferometric control methods were developed which provide the pattern placement accuracy required for mask fabrication without the use of alignment markers on the mask substrate. Reference markers, located in the image plane and permanently fixed to the stage, are used to determine X and Y gain, rotation, and orthogonality at the beginning of each mask run (see Chapter 3). The positional accuracy of the mask substrate relative to the fixed stage reference position can be controlled within acceptable limits using mechanical means. A typical alignment procedure for mask fabrication is as follows:

(1) The mask substrate is loaded manually onto the stage or into a transfer cassette and secured against X, Y, and Z reference surfaces located on the stage.

(2) The stage is moved to a stage reference marker located at X_0, Y_0 under computer control.

(3) X and Y gain, rotation, and orthogonality are checked together with beam current and focus.

(4) The stage is then moved, again under laser interferometer control, to the starting position of the mask pattern using X_0 and Y_0 as the reference position.

(5) Checks for drift are made by periodically returning to the reference position X_0, Y_0.

Because of the method used in building up chip patterns in the small scan field, continuous-motion type of system, there is essentially no fundamental limit to the chip size which can be handled. In the step-and-repeat type of machine, however, the maximum field size is limited by the resolution and nonlinearity of the deflection system. For example, in a system having a nonlinearity of 0.05%, which is a reasonable value to choose (Varnell et al., 1974), the pattern distortion is 0.5 μm/mm. For 6 mm × 6 mm scan fields, pattern distortions can be as large as 3 μm. Such distortions can be tolerated if they are repeatable. However, as discussed in Section II.A, inaccuracies which are system specific lead to compatibility problems. Furthermore, if chip sizes exceed the maximum scan field, individual scan fields must be butted together. This is only possible as long as pattern distortions are kept small enough to allow adequate registration between scan fields. In the example given above, chip patterns larger than the maximum scan field would probably have to be built up of scan fields no larger than 2 mm × 2 mm.

Pattern distortion within the scan field can be reduced by periodically calibrating deflection system errors and applying appropriate corrections to the beam deflection signals. Such a strategy has been employed successfully on a direct wafer exposure system described by Weber and

Yourke (1977). The details of this system were discussed in Chapter 3. Deflection errors are reportedly kept within 0.003% (0.03 μm/mm) of ideal by scanning a calibration grid on a special target and then compensating for sensed errors. Registration errors are reported to be less than 0.5 μm (3σ) for 5 mm scan fields. In principle, the same correction method could be employed on mask fabrication systems to build up large chips from 5 mm or larger scan fields.

Unlike systems used for direct wafer exposure, mask fabrication systems do not require a realignment capability. In principle, all that is required is a registration scheme which is capable of measuring the position of reference markers located on the stage. However, as shown by Alles *et al.* (1975a), it is desirable to extend this capability to include provision for checking the true writing performance of the machine by measuring special patterns written on test masks. In this mode the system is used as a computer-controlled coordinate measuring machine.

The minimum feature size required for most master masks intended for photolithographic use is about 1 μm. This requirement allows the use of a relatively coarse address structure and large beam diameter for mask fabrication compared to specialized device applications where submicron feature sizes and even smaller placement accuracies are required. All other factors being equal, coarser address structures and larger beam diameters generally result in more rapid exposure of a given area and thus higher throughput.

The mask fabrication system described by Varnell *et al.* (1974) has an average writing rate of about 1 cm²/min for 50% area exposure over a 6.35 mm × 6.35 mm (maximum) scan field with a beam diameter of 1 μm and an address structure of 0.25 μm. Since this system uses the vector scan method of pattern exposure, the average area writing rate for a given chip array will decrease as the exposed pattern area increases. Field size, beam diameter, and address structure are all variable on this system.

The continuous-table-motion system described by Alles *et al.* (1975b) has a writing rate of 2 cm²/min for a 0.5-μm address structure and 0.5 μm beam diameter. The stepping rate along the beam scan direction is 20 MHz, which corresponds to an exposure time of 50 ns per address. The system can also be operated with a 0.25 μm address structure with a writing rate of 0.5 cm²/min. The table moves continuously at a velocity of 2 cm/s under the control of laser interferometers (*X* and *Y* axes) which can measure table position to within 0.03 μm. Normal exposure time for a 3 in. (7.6 cm) pattern array on a 4 in. (10.2 cm) mask is 40 min in the 0.5-μm address structure mode.

Exposure times on both the step-and-repeat and continuous table motion systems compare very favorably with the total time required to pattern a master mask using photolithographic methods, where 5–10 hr may be consumed by the larger number of exposing, processing, reticle alignment, and inspection steps. In addition to faster turnaround, the reduced number of lithographic and handling steps in electron-beam mask fabrication should result in lower defect densities and better linewidth control. As will be shown later, evidence to support this hypothesis is emerging in production reports from electron-beam mask fabrication facilities.

A further justification for electron-beam mask fabrication is the elimination of critical operations such as reticle alignment in the step-and-repeat camera and the suitability of the method to complete automatic control. With the elimination of the reticle, it is possible to consider incorporating a variety of chip designs on a single mask. This increased flexibility can be particularly valuable during the development stage of device fabrication.

2. Cost Analysis

Consider the case of an electron-beam system costing, say, $1,500,000 with an expected service life of 30,000 hr. Using Eq. (5.8) and the following assumed values for 4 in. (10.2 cm) masks and 3 in. (7.6 cm) pattern arrays: $O = \$30$, $P = \$40$, $T = 1.3$, $M = \$20$, and $Y_m = 0.8$,

$$\text{mask cost} = \left[\frac{50 + 30 + 40}{1.3} + 20 \right] \frac{1}{0.8} \approx \$140$$

Mask cost is about 53% lower in this example than in the case of the optical system considered in Section III.A. The lower mask cost results, in spite of a 170% increase in system cost, from increases in throughput and manufacturing yield. In the example above the assumed operator and processing costs are the same as those used in Section III.A for the optical mask fabrication method. However, additional cost savings will be realized with electron-beam mask fabrication through the elimination of reticle processing, inspection, and alignment. The available performance data on electron-beam mask fabrication suggest that the assumed values of T and Y_m are reasonable (Section VI). The service life and overhead costs assumed for both systems may be overly optimistic. They are used here only for comparison.

IV. CHOICE OF MATERIALS

The electron-beam mask fabrication process is illustrated schematically in Fig. 5.6 (refer also to Chapter 2). Electrons in the beam penetrate the resist, causing a chemical change in the irradiated region. The exposed pattern is developed by applying organic solvents over the surface of the resist. Negative resists become less soluble in the developer where

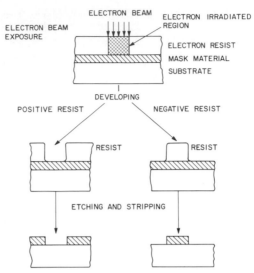

FIG. 5.6   Schematic representation of the electron-beam mask fabrication process.

irradiation has taken place, while positive resists are rendered more soluble in the irradiated region. After the resist has been developed the mask pattern is etched in the mask material. Once the resist has been removed the mask is ready for use. Thus, in one lithographic step a mask pattern is generated at final working size. As illustrated in Fig. 5.6, the mask fabrication process involves a three-component materials system consisting of the electron resist, the mask material and the substrate.

A.   Electron Resists

Electron resists are generally compared on the basis of required exposure dose, resolution capabilities, and processing characteristics. It is useful, therefore, to review the meaning and significance of these parameters as they relate to mask fabrication.

The required exposure dose is expressed in units of electronic charge per unit area (C/cm^2), and is the dose required to achieve the necessary level of chemical response in the resist. In a negative resist a certain amount of electron-induced molecular cross-linking must take place for a sufficient portion of the irradiated region to become insoluble. In a positive resist a certain exposure dose is required to break up a number of large molecules in the irradiated region sufficient to produce the necessary increase in solubility. If I (A) is the beam current required for time t (s) to produce the necessary response in an exposed area A (cm^2), then the exposure dose $D(C/cm^2)$ can be calculated from the following expression:

$$D = (It/A) \qquad (C/cm^2) \qquad (5.9)$$

The required dose for a particular resist is referred to as the sensitivity of the resist S. The energy of the exposing electrons has a direct influence on the required dose; consequently, accelerating voltage must be specified when S values are quoted.

As shown in Chapter 2, resolution capability is dependent on the electron scattering distribution within the resist layer, and is influenced, therefore, by a variety of factors, including resist thickness, accelerating voltage, substrate atomic number, and beam diameter. However, the response characteristics of the resist are also critical in determining resolution. The key parameter is resist contrast. The meaning of this parameter is illustrated in Fig. 5.7, which shows the response curve for a typical negative electron resist. The response curve is a plot of resist thickness remaining after developing as a function of the logarithm of the incident dose. Resist contrast γ is defined by the relation [after Thompson (1974)]

$$\gamma = [\log(D_g^0/D_g^i)]^{-1} \qquad (5.10)$$

where D_g^i is the dose required for incipient film formation and D_g^0 the dose required for extrapolated 100% film remaining. High contrast values are desirable. In high contrast resists, response falls off very rapidly with decreasing electron dose, thus minimizing the effects of electron scattering and promoting high resolution (see Thompson, 1974). Contrast values for positive resists can be obtained in a similar manner with appropriate reversal in notation (refer also to Chapter 2).

Since pattern delineation in mask processing involves rather elemen-

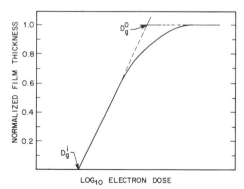

FIG. 5.7 Typical shape of the response curve for a negative electron resist. The thickness of the resist film remaining after developing is normalized to the original film thickness and plotted as a function of the logarithm of the incident electron dose.

tary etching procedures, the processing requirements of a resist used for mask fabrication are generally less stringent than those for device fabrication. The principal requirements are good adhesion, good thermal stability, cleanliness, and adequate shelf life. The precise requirements will become clear in the ensuing discussion on processing procedures used for mask fabrication.

Some of the more commonly used electron resist materials are listed in Table 5.1. The required resist sensitivity will, of course, depend on the design of the electron-beam pattern generator. Systems described by Varnell et al. (1974) and Herriott et al. (1975) require S values of about 10^{-6} C/cm² or less at 10 kV.

B.   Mask Materials

Mask materials must meet the requirements of low defect density in the blank plates, adequate resolution capability, durability, and good contrast characteristics for subsequent photolithographic printing. The properties of some commonly used mask materials are listed in Table 5.2. Since the substrate is usually an insulator, the thin film of mask material must also be capable of dissipating electronic charge at a rate sufficient to avoid charging problems during electron-beam exposure.

Chromium is used, almost exclusively at the present time, as the mask material for electron-beam mask fabrication because it meets all of these requirements. Chromium is a well-established mask material in the

TABLE 5.1

Electron Resists

Resist	Type	Commonly used abbreviation	Required dose @ 10 kV (C cm⁻²)	Reference
Poly(methyl methacrylate)	Positive	PMMA	6×10^{-5}	Haller et al. (1968)
Cross-linked Poly (methyl methacrylate)	Positive	X-PMMA	1×10^{-5}	Roberts (1975)
Poly(butene-1 sulfone)	Positive	PBS	8×10^{-7}	Bowden et al. (1975b)
Epoxidized poly(butadiene)	Negative	EPB	1×10^{-7}	Hirai et al. (1971)
Poly(butadiene)	Negative	PB	3×10^{-6}	Brewer (1974)
Poly(diallyl orthophthalate)	Negative	PDOP	1×10^{-6}	Bartelt (1974)
Poly(glycidyl methacrylate -co-ethyl acrylate)	Negative	P(GMA-co-EA)	2×10^{-7}	Thompson et al. (1974)

TABLE 5.2

Mask Materials

Material	Film thickness (Å)	Reflectivity at 0.4 μm (%)	See through capability
Chromium	600–800	70	No
Chromium and antireflection layer	800	<5	No
Iron oxide (chemical vapor deposited)	3000–3500	25	Yes
Iron oxide (sputtered)	1200	25	Yes
Silicon	700	60	Yes

microelectronics industry, and high quality chromium mask plates are readily available from a number of suppliers. The chromium films, which have an established record of durability in mask applications, are generally sputter deposited to a thickness of 600–800 Å. This thickness results in an optical density typically greater than 2.5, where optical density is defined by the relation:

$$OD = \log_{10}\left(\frac{\text{incident light intensity}}{\text{transmitted light intensity}}\right) \qquad (5.11)$$

Optical density is measured at the light wavelength used for photolithographic copying of the master, which is usually about 0.4 μm. An optical density of 2.0 is sufficient for the production of well-defined photoresist patterns (Glang and Gregor, 1970).

Since visual mask alignment is not required in making working copies from a master mask, the fact that the chromium film is opaque in the visible portion of the spectrum is usually not a disadvantage. However, there may be circumstances under which it is desirable to use the master directly for wafer exposure. Under such conditions the see-through capability afforded by iron oxide and silicon, for example, may be an advantage although charge dissipation in these materials is poor compared to chromium. However, the growing use of automatic alignment and new alignment strategies is reducing the need for see-through capability.

Reflectivity may pose a more serious problem for chromium masters used directly for wafer exposure. Multiple light reflections between the chromium mask and a highly reflective metal layer on the wafer may cause spurious exposure patterns in the photoresist and thus limit resolution and image quality. This problem can be overcome, without compromising the advantages of chromium, by using chromium blanks which have been treated during manufacture to form an antireflective surface layer of chromium oxide. Although the total film thickness is essentially unchanged, the 200–300-Å-thick antireflective layer reduces the reflectivity at the 0.4 μm wavelength from 80% to well below 5%. Working plates with the antireflection coating are becoming increasingly popular and are available commercially from a number of established chromium suppliers. Antireflection plates are processed in a manner identical to that used for normal chromium plates.

C. Substrates

The principal requirements of photomask substrates are adequate transparency at the 0.4 μm exposing wavelength used in the copying process, adequate flatness, and chemical compatibility with the mask fabrication process.

Transmission requirements for conventional photolithographic applications are met with glass substrates which transmit about 92% of incident light at the 0.4 μm wavelength. Optical mask fabrication systems require very flat substrates due to the limited depth of focus inherent in high resolution optical systems. Commercially available 0.06-in.- (1.52-mm-) thick master grade glass substrates typically have a maximum bow of 200 μin. (5 μm) for substrate sizes up to 4 in. × 4 in. (10.2 cm × 10.2 cm). This degree of flatness is more than adequate to ensure proper focus in electron-beam exposure systems since the depth of focus is comparatively large. For example, the system described by Herriott *et al.* (1975) has a depth of focus of about 25 μm.

In electron-beam pattern generators the pattern distortion caused by substrate nonflatness can be more significant than beam defocusing. Consider the case of two adjacent scan fields, each S cm × S cm, as shown in Fig. 5.8. The two scan fields should butt at point O in the image plane (the

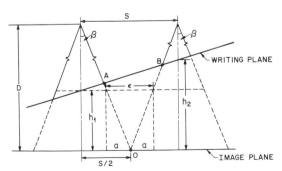

FIG. 5.8   Pattern distortion caused by departure of the writing plane from the image plane in electron-beam mask fabrication.

desired writing plane). However, due to a departure h of the writing plane from the image plane, the edges of the two scan fields will be at A and B, respectively, in the writing plane. The misregistration AB between scan fields is approximated by ϵ in the figure. It is mathematically convenient, and justifiable in practice, to assume that $h_1 \approx h_2 = h$. Then

$$\epsilon = 2a = 2h \tan \beta$$

Noting that $\tan \beta = S/2D$, where D is the distance from the final lens of the electron-optical column to the substrate,

$$\epsilon = hS/D \tag{5.12}$$

Maximum pattern distortion within a scan field is $\pm \epsilon/2$, which can lead to maximum level-to-level registration errors of ϵ. For example, the system described by Varnell $et\ al.$ (1974) has $S \approx 0.6$ cm and $D \approx 7.5$ cm, from which $\epsilon = 0.08h$. Thus, for this particular case, if level-to-level misregistration or misregistration between scan fields is to be kept below 0.5 μm, departures from the image plane must be held to less than about 6 μm. This discussion, of course, takes no account of imperfections in the electron-optical system.

Subsequent photolithographic processing using electron-beam fabricated masks may place even more stringent flatness requirements on the substrate. For example, projection aligners similar to the system described by Markle (1974) hold the promise of higher yields due to the elimination of mask-to-wafer contact and concomitant mask and wafer damage. Although the depth of focus for 3 μm geometries is claimed to be about ± 12.5 μm, the major portion of the flatness budget is consumed by wafer variations, so that a premium will be placed on mask flatness. For such applications it may be necessary to specify the more expensive, flatter grades of glass (down to about 35 μin./in. flatness) available from a limited number of glass suppliers.

The type of glass selected as the substrate material must be compatible with every step in the mask fabrication process, from deposition of the mask material to final stripping of the electron resist. An example of the problems that can be encountered as a result of substrate incompatibility is the well-known intrusion defect in chromium mask fabrication. Chromium patterns displaying this defect are shown in Fig. 5.9.

Studies by Izumitani $et\ al.$ (1975) and Padden and Ballantyne (1976) have shown that intrusion defects in the chromium–glass system can result from mobile sodium ions in the glass substrate. The number of defects formed during etching was found to correlate with the amount of sodium in the substrate and the baking temperature used in processing. Unacceptable defect levels were observed when baking temperatures exceeded

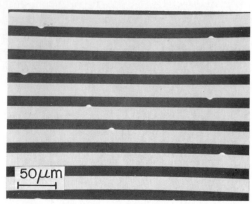

FIG. 5.9   Photomicrograph (in transmission) showing intrusion defects in a chromium mask pattern. The intrusion defects are observed as notches in the dark chromium features. [After Padden and Ballantyne (1976).]

120°C with some conventional soda–lime glass substrates containing about 15% Na_2O. Since baking temperatures for some electron resists exceed 120°C, alternative substrates must be used which have a sufficiently low sodium concentration at the chromium–glass interface. Suitable glass types exist and others are almost certainly being developed. Recently introduced substrate types show that glass compositions are being tailored to meet the needs of the mask industry. Borosilicate glass substrates, for example, not only have low sodium concentrations but also have a thermal expansion coefficient which is about half that of conventional soda–lime glass substrates.

V.   PROCESSING

A.   Resist Coating and Prebake

Electron resists are applied to mask substrates using conventional spin coating methods which obey the relation

$$T = KC^2/\sqrt{S} \qquad (5.13)$$

where T is the resist film thickness, C the concentration of the resist solution (% solids), S the spinning speed (rpm), and K the constant of proportionality, which varies with the intrinsic viscosity of the polymeric material and thus is a function of the molecular weight of the polymer. This relation is discussed more fully by Thompson and Kerwin (1976).

Resist thicknesses required for mask fabrication are generally less than those required for device processing mainly because step coverage is not necessary. If the resist solution has been carefully filtered, and the mask substrate is clean, satisfactory performance can be achieved using relatively thin resist layers. As a rule of thumb, the thickness of the resist layer should exceed the diameter of the largest particles likely to be passed through the final filtration process. In photolithographic mask processing, resist thicknesses of about 0.5 μm are common.

In electron-beam mask fabrication, the resist thickness should be a minimum for highest resolution, due to lateral electron scattering effects in the resist layer (see Chapter 2). However, since the difficulty of preparing defect-free thin films generally varies inversely with film thickness, the choice of resist thickness involves a compromise. This compromise, between resolution on one hand and defect density on the other, is usually reached through trial and error. With state-of-the-art filtration methods, resist thicknesses used in electron-beam mask processing typically range from 0.2 to 0.6 μm.

Following spin coating, mask substrates are usually given a preexposure baking treatment, frequently referred to as a prebake, for the purpose of drying the resist film. Proper prebaking avoids contamination of the vacuum system by the coating solvent and generally is considered conducive to good adhesion. The limits on prebake temperature will vary from one resist to another. The lower limit is usually set by the glass transition temperature of the polymer. Above the glass transition temperature a polymer undergoes a glass-to-rubber transition which is accompanied by the release of internal stresses which may be formed during coating. For example, the glass transition temperatures of PMMA, PBS, and P(GMA-co-EA) are 100–110°C (Harris, 1973), 95°C (Bowden *et al.*, 1975a) and 20°C (Feit, 1976), respectively. The upper limit to prebake temperature is generally set by the thermal stability of the resist. Since negative resists can cross link thermally and positive resists can be degraded by thermal effects, care must be taken to avoid these reactions.

B. Electron-Beam Exposure

The correct exposure condition is simply that which results in masks having feature sizes equal to the designer's specifications. The exposure condition chosen must allow, therefore, for any systematic feature size variation between the developed resist pattern and the completed mask. Thus, in some situations, the exposure condition may be chosen deliberately to bias the feature size in the developed resist pattern with respect to the design value. For example, a particular etching process might give a systematic bias on etched features of, say, -0.1 μm with respect to the resist features. In this case, the exposure level would be set to give resist features biassed $+0.1$ μm with respect to the design or nominal value. Feature size bias in the master copying process can also be compensated for by fabricating masters biased with respect to the design value. However, such practices must be administered carefully when more than one copying process is in use or when some masters are used directly for device lithography. Feature size bias in the mask making process may also be accounted for by the designer, who can shrink or grow coded feature sizes to the mask maker's specifications. This method is desirable when feature size bias exceeds two address units on the pattern generator. Feature symmetry is preserved when feature sizes are reduced by eliminating an equal number of address units from each edge of the feature.

The correct exposure condition is achieved with the appropriate choice of accelerating voltage (kV) and electron dose (C/cm²).

1. Accelerating Voltage

The choice of accelerating voltage is influenced by resist thickness, resolution, and sensitivity requirements. The relevant effects of accelerating voltage on electron penetration, lateral scattering, and energy loss were discussed in detail in Chapter 2 and are considered only briefly here.

The voltage chosen must, of course, be great enough to achieve electron penetration of the resist layer. The minimum voltage required can be estimated from the Grün relation (see Chapter 2):

$$R_G = (0.046/\rho)V_a^{1.75} \qquad (5.14)$$

where R_G is the Grün range in microns, which must be at least as great as the thickness of the resist layer, V_a is the accelerating voltage (kV), ρ is the density of the resist material (g/cm³) which is generally taken as 1.0.

Theoretical and experimental results show that lateral scattering can be reduced at the expense of resist sensitivity with increasing accelerating voltage (see Chapter 2). An example of how quickly resist sensitivity falls off with increasing voltage is shown in Fig. 5.10. The decrease in sensitivity with increasing accelerating voltage can be offset somewhat by the linear increase in brightness of the electron beam (see Chapter 3). However, for the resist whose response is shown in Fig. 5.10, the gain in brightness is not sufficient to compensate for reduced sensitivity when accelerating voltages exceed about 20 kV. The electron-beam mask fabrication systems described in Section III normally operate in the 10–20 kV range.

2. Negative Resist Exposure

The amount of cross linking or gel formation which takes place in the irradiated regions of a negative resist (see Fig. 5.6) depends on the amount

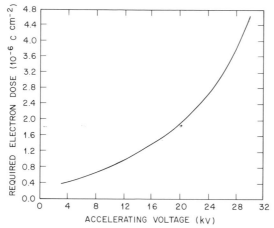

FIG. 5.10   Observed variation of the required electron dose with changes in accelerating voltage for 1.0 μm of PDOP on chromium.

of energy absorbed in the resist layer. For a given initial resist thickness and accelerating voltage, the amount of gel formed, and hence the thickness remaining after developing, is directly proportional to the electron dose (see Fig. 5.7). Since the volume of gel formed increases with increasing electron dose, the irradiated region can be expected to grow laterally as well as vertically. A typical plot of developed resist linewidth as a function of electron dose is shown in Fig. 5.11a. The nominal value of linewidth called for in the pattern design was 10.0 μm. For this particular batch of P(GMA-co-EA) the nominal feature size is achieved in the developed resist pattern at a dose of 1.8×10^{-7} C/cm² at 10 kV. Note that the nominal feature size is achieved on the steepest portion of the curve, where linewidths are varying by about 0.1 μm for each 10% change in exposure. Therefore, a beam current stability of better than 10% is required to maintain ±0.1 μm linewidth control in this region.

The fractional film thickness remaining after developing, normalized to the initial resist thickness, is plotted in Fig. 5.11b as a function of electron dose for the same batch of P(GMA-co-EA). The data reveal that the dose required for nominal feature size in the developed resist pattern results in a developed resist thickness which is about 35% of the original resist thickness. Similar behavior has been observed for both P(GMA-co-EA) and PDOP over a range of resist thicknesses and accelerating voltages (Ballantyne, 1975). The effect has been explained by Heidenreich *et al.* (1975).

The linear portion of Fig. 5.11b can be approximated by the equation

$$T = \gamma \log_{10}(D_g^t/D_g^i) = 0.434\gamma \ln(D_g^t/D_g^i) \qquad (5.15)$$

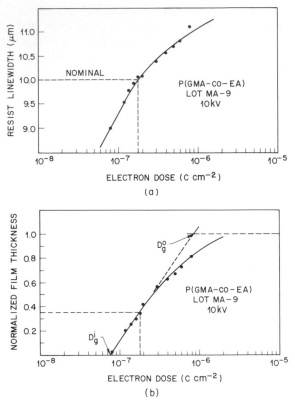

FIG. 5.11   (a) Measured variation of developed resist feature size with electron dose for P(GMA-co-EA). The nominal feature size is achieved with an electron dose of 1.8×10^{-7} C/cm^{-2} for Lot MA-9. The initial resist thickness was 0.6 μm and the accelerating voltage was 10 kV. (b) Measured variation of the fractional film thickness remaining after developing normalized to the initial resist thickness. The electron dose required for nominal feature size in (a) results in a normalized film thickness of 0.35 after development.

where T is the fractional resist film thickness remaining after developing normalized to the initial resist thickness t/t_i and D_g^t is the electron dose (C/cm^2) required to yield a developed resist thickness t. D_g^i and γ are the dose required for incipient film formation and the contrast, respectively, as defined in Eq. (5.10). From Heidenreich *et al.* (1975), the dose required for nominal feature size in a developed negative resist pattern is

$$D = 2.4 D_g^i \tag{5.16}$$

This relation was derived from a Gaussian scattering theory for the case of features exposed by line scans separated by a distance equal to the Gaussian beam diameter. The theory assumes that electrons lose less than about 10% of their initial energy in passing through the resist layer. At 10 kV the theory can be applied to film thicknesses up to about $0.5-0.6$ μm. The theory is evidently in good agreement with the data shown in Fig. 5.11 for the case of a 0.6 μm film and an accelerating voltage of 10 kV. The beam diameter and separation between line scans were 0.5 μm.

Substituting the required value of dose into Eq. (5.15) yields

$$T = 0.434\gamma \ln(2.4D_g^i/D_g^i)$$

which reduces to

$$T = 0.38\gamma \tag{5.17}$$

From Eq. (5.10) and Fig. 5.11b the value of contrast γ for this particular batch of P(GMA-co-EA) is 0.95. Substitution of this value of γ into Eq. (5.17) yields $T = 0.36$, which is in very good agreement with the value of 0.35 found experimentally.

In systems having a fine enough address structure it may be desirable to "overexpose" the resist to achieve thicker resist films and compensate for enlarged features by reducing the coded feature size. Such compensation methods can be handled easily by software provided that resist response is adequately characterized.

3. Positive Resist Exposure

In a positive electron resist, electron irradiation causes the fracture of long molecular chains into shorter chains, thereby decreasing the average molecular weight. The amount of chain scission which takes place, and hence the decrease in molecular weight, is generally directly proportional to the electron dose. Since the solubility rate of the exposed region is a function of molecular weight (Harris, 1973; Hatzakis et al., 1974), the developing time can be expected to vary with electron dose. Also, the solubility rate for any molecular weight depends on the strength of the developing solvent. The dependence of developing time on electron dose and developing solvent is illustrated in Fig. 5.12 for the case of PMMA. The figure clearly shows that a wide range of dose values can be chosen depending on developer strength and developing time. These extra degrees of freedom in the case of positive resists allow more latitude in setting the correct exposure level than is possible with negative resists, since the latter are generally less sensitive to developing conditions. This, in turn, implies the need for tighter control of developing conditions for a positive resist in a production environment.

The correct exposure condition for positive resists is usually established by trial-and-error adjustment of developing time, developer strength, and electron dose. The electron dose is chosen to satisfy certain

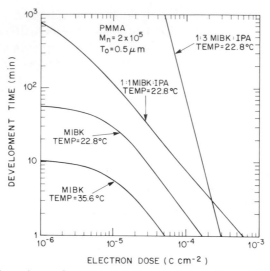

FIG. 5.12   The dependence of development time on electron dose at 20 kV under various developing conditions for PMMA: M_n, number average molecular weight; MIBK, methyl iso butyl ketone; IPA, iso propyl alcohol. [After Greeneich (1975).]

minimum requirements involving separation of molecular weight distributions in the irradiated and unirradiated regions, thereby permitting selective dissolution of the irradiated material (Bowden, 1975; also refer to Chapter 2). The separation condition is illustrated in Fig. 5.13. Increasing electron dose causes further separation of the two distributions and generally allows less critical developing conditions since there is greater differential solubility between the irradiated and unirradiated regions. Bowden (1975) found that approximately 3 Mrad of γ irradiation produced separation of the two distributions in samples of PBS having appropriate

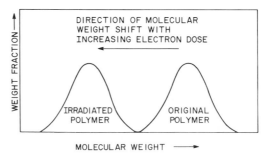

FIG. 5.13   Separation of molecular weight distributions caused by electron irradiation of positive resists.

molecular parameters. Conversion of this radiation dose to an equivalent electron dose, using the depth–dose theory of Heidenreich *et al.* (1973), resulted in a required dose of about 8×10^{-7} C/cm^2 at 10 kV. In practice, this exposure condition proved to be adequate for PBS on chromium mask substrates with careful selection of the developing solvent (Bowden *et al.*, 1975).

C. Developing and Postbake

Exposed mask patterns are developed into resist images using appropriate solvents. Dissolution of unwanted areas of the resist film is achieved either by spray or bath developing. Following the developing step, masks are usually baked to remove the developing solvent and promote resist adhesion. Since developing and postbaking conditions are considerably different for negative and positive resists, each case is discussed separately.

1. Negative Resists

The role of the developing solvent in the case of a negative resist is to provide complete dissolution of the unexposed regions of the mask pattern, leaving the exposed regions behind. In more precise terms, the developing solvent should dissolve those regions not cross linked (gelled) by electron irradiation and cause a minimum of swelling and distortion in gelled regions. Unfortunately, the selection of appropriate solvents for a particular resist is more of an art than a science at the present time.

The amount of gel formed in the irradiated regions of a negative resist is generally a well-behaved function of electron dose and molecular parameters (Thompson *et al.*, 1975). Developing conditions have little effect on the amount of gel remaining but can have a pronounced effect upon the shape of the developed resist profiles. The quality of the developed resist image, particularly in the case of submicron features, is strongly influenced by the response of the gel to the developing solvent (Heidenreich *et al.*, 1975).

The shape of developed resist profiles is less critical in photomask processing than in device fabrication because only a relatively thin layer of mask material has to be etched. The specific resist profiles required for the ion milling and lift-off processes which are frequently used for pattern delineation in thick films are not required for photomask processing. The required resolution and feature quality can generally be achieved in thin masking layers using conventional wet etching methods.

Postbake temperatures are usually selected to provide adequate resist adhesion to the mask material and thus avoid undercutting during the etching step. The postbake temperature must not be too high or it will cause flowing of the resist or deleterious chemical reactions between the resist, mask material, and glass substrate. Since baking temperatures for negative resists frequently exceed 120°C, care must be taken in selecting an appropriate glass type for the substrate material (see Section IV.C).

2. Positive Resists

The developing step, as discussed previously, is critical in positive resist processing. Developing and exposure conditions must be carefully matched to achieve correct feature size and good image quality. In the case of a positive resist, one can develop for any dose down to a threshold defined by Bowden et al. (1975) as the dose at which separation of the irradiated and unirradiated molecular weight distributions is achieved (see Fig. 5.13). Further irradiation shifts the distribution in the direction of lower molecular weight; hence one can choose a developer according to the desired exposure level. As the desired exposure level moves closer to the threshold value, development becomes increasingly critical since the solubility difference between the exposed and unexposed regions decreases. In principle, it should be possible to develop for doses less than the threshold value (i.e., where the distributions overlap) providing that some thinning of the unexposed region can be tolerated.

Additional consideration must be given to exposure and developing conditions when resist profiles having a specific shape are required (Greeneich, 1974; Hatzakis, 1975). For the reasons outlined previously, profile shapes are generally not critical in mask processing. Feature size control and reproducibility are far more important.

As in the case of negative resists, postbake conditions are chosen to promote adhesion. The upper limit of postbake temperature tends to be lower for positive resists than for negative resists for several reasons. Developed PMMA patterns begin to flow at about 130°C while PBS maintains its shape at this temperature but begins to degrade thermally at about 140°C (Bowden et al., 1975a).

D. Etching

Etching methods in electron-beam mask fabrication have tended to follow conventional photolithographic practice, particularly in the case of the most popular mask material, chromium. Chromium is generally etched in a ceric ammonium nitrate solution. A typical formulation is as follows: 164.5 g ceric ammonium nitrate, 43 mliter of concentrated (70%) perchloric acid and water to make 1 liter (Glang and Gregor, 1970). Since the chromium layer is typically only about 800 Å in thickness, submicron feature sizes can be etched with little difficulty once the resist pattern has been successfully delineated (Section VI).

Although wet etching methods have provided acceptable linewidth control and defect densities when used with compatible materials and processing, alternative methods hold the promise of improved performance. Plasma etching has found some application to mask fabrication but few performance data have been published. Among the potential advantages of the method are elimination of undercutting due to poor resist adhesion, more uniform etching and hence better linewidth control, and, perhaps, lower pinhole and intrusion densities. Plasma etching is also attractive because it is well suited to automated processing.

Following etching, the resist is removed by a suitable stripping agent. Specially developed stripping solutions or an appropriate plasma treatment can be used for the purpose. The mask is then rinsed and dried as necessary prior to inspection.

E.   Inspection

Inspection is obviously an important part of any mask fabrication process. Linewidth measurements and defect density data provide the information required either to accept or reject a given mask. They also provide the process engineer with vital statistical data on process performance.

Linewidths are measured using transmitted light either automatically with television techniques or manually with filar or image shearing eyepieces (Engle, 1975). The precision of the measurement technique is generally given as the standard deviation σ of a set of n measurements X_i on the same feature, where

$$\sigma = \left(\sum_{i=1}^{n} (X_i - \bar{X})^2/n \right)^{1/2} \tag{5.18}$$

and $\bar{X}$ is the average of the measured values. For optical linewidth measurement techniques precision values typically range from about 0.1 to 0.3 μm with chromium masks (Engle, 1975). Precision generally deteriorates when the number of observers increases, particularly when measurements must be performed at several locations using different equipment. For this reason, the use of automated linewidth measuring equipment is becoming popular. Linewidths on photomasks are typically controlled to within ± 0.5 μm, so that a precision better than 0.25 μm (1σ) is required among all observers in order to achieve the desired control limits 95% of the time.

The types of defects encountered in mask fabrication are illustrated in

Fig. 5.14. The relationship between mask defect density and device yield as well as the importance of adequate mask inspection were discussed in Section II.D. The task of mask inspection is usually performed by trained operators equipped with optical microscopes. Human capabilities in this area have been reviewed by Bruning *et al.* (1975), Schoonard *et al.* (1970) and Garland (1964). Their findings are summarized below.

Human eyesight is capable of resolving object diameters of 0.1 mm over a field of view of about 17 mm at the minimum comfortable viewing distance of about 250 mm. Outside this field, resolution decreases rapidly. Accordingly, defects down to 2 μm in size can be detected over a 0.34 mm field using a microscope at a 50× magnification. At this magnification the complete viewing field is about 2 mm × 2 mm, which the eye can cover in about 35 separate glances. The rate of eye movement is limited by the blurring frequency of about 10 Hz, beyond which the retinal receptors cannot follow. Therefore, thorough inspection of a 2 mm × 2 mm field takes at least 3 s. A 50 mm × 50 mm chip array on a mask would require in excess of half an hour for complete inspection.

Unfortunately, even trained inspectors cannot do such tasks very well. Generally more than 20% of inspected fields containing at least one defect are falsely passed as good although false rejects tend to stay below 2%.

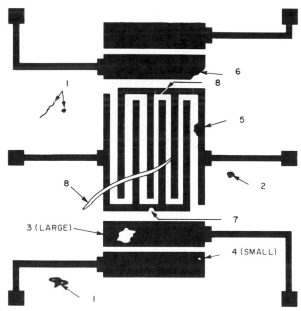

FIG. 5.14   Types of defects encountered in mask fabrication. (1) Contamination, (2) opaque spot, (3) large hole, (4) small hole, (5) excess material, (6) lack of adhesion, (7) intrusion, (8) scratch.

Performance deteriorates throughout the day as the strain and tedium of visual inspection wear upon the operators. Fortunately, automated inspection methods are being developed which greatly reduce operator strain and inspection time (Bruning *et al.*, 1975; Skinner, 1977, Sandland, 1977). Automated systems, however, are presently not capable of complete defect classification. This important task, which is the key to control and improvement of any mask fabrication process, must be performed by human inspectors until more sophisticated inspection systems are developed.

VI. PERFORMANCE

Available performance data indicate that mask fabrication systems based on both the vector scan and the continuous-table-motion exposure strategies have been successful in meeting the mask making requirements discussed in Section II. Growing acceptance of electron-beam mask making through the expanding commercial exploitation of this technology suggests that the advantages cited previously for the method are being realized. Published data for the vector-scan system described by Varnell *et al.* (1974) and the continuous-table-motion system described by Herriott *et al.* (1975) will be used to represent the two approaches.

Varnell *et al.* (1974) report that, with proper temperature and flatness control of the substrate, the combination of registration system accuracy, laser interferometer accuracy, stage shift correction accuracy, and beam placement accuracy limits pattern stackability of mask sets (overlay accuracy) to ± 0.5 μm. The authors add that this error is approximately the same magnitude as the measuring errors of the overlay comparator used for mask stacking accuracy measurements. Figure 5.15 shows two typical levels measured. Overlay measurements were made on random chips (bars) over a 5.5×5.5 cm array. The writing time for each chip (bar) is shown in the figure. Pease *et al.* (1975) report a pattern placement accuracy of better than 0.5 μm on the system described by Herriott *et al.* (1975). Measurements showed that the overlay accuracy of masks fabricated on this system was better than the 1 μm measurement accuracy of the particular overlay comparator used.

The resolution and linewidth control achieved in a production environment appear to be adequate for photomask fabrication. Varnell *et al.* (1974) and Ballantyne (1975) report that 1 μm feature sizes are obtained routinely (Fig. 5.16). Linewidth control better than ± 0.5 μm (3σ limits) has been achieved with the system described by Herriott *et al.* (1975) using the negative resist P(GMA-co-EA) on chromium (Ballantyne, 1975).

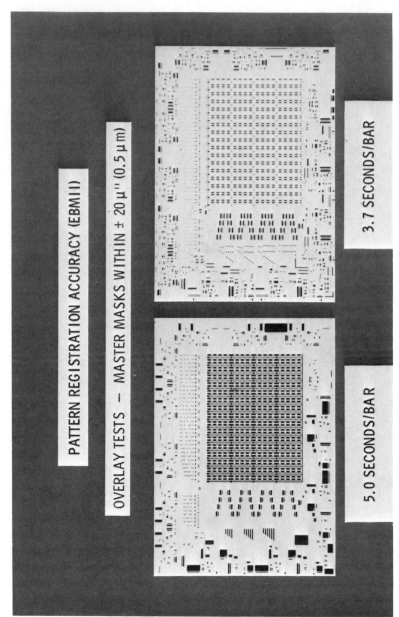

FIG. 5.15   Pattern registration accuracy. [After Varnell *et al.* (1974).]

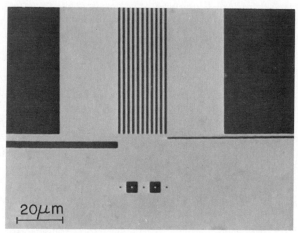

FIG. 5.16 Photomicrograph (in transmission) of 1 μm lines on 2 μm centers on a chromium mask fabricated with the system described by Herriott *et al.* (1975) using the negative resist P(GMA-co-EA).

Monthly linewidth control data from the Bell Laboratories Murray Hill mask laboratory are shown in Fig. 5.17 (Skinner, 1976). The measured control feature is a 5 μm (nominal) isolated opaque line which is located (see Fig. 5.1) at the top and the bottom of each 2.5 and 4 in. mask written on the system described by Herriott *et al.* (1975). The acceptance tolerance is ± 0.3 μm, as shown by the dashed lines. Linewidths are measured on an in-house developed video-optical system. The standard deviation of the measured daily error of this system is about 0.05 μm.

Defect density performance is a difficult subject to deal with quantitatively because mask inspection methods and defect classification criteria

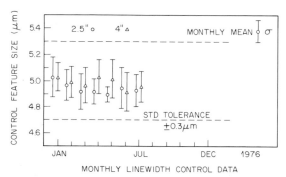

FIG. 5.17 Monthly linewidth control data for 2.5 and 4 in. chromium master masks fabricated in a production environment using the system described by Herriott *et al.* (1975). [After Skinner (1976).]

vary widely from one mask shop to another. In the absence of adequate standardization codes for inspection methods and defect classification, each case must be treated individually; defect density figures, when quoted, must be accompanied by elaborate qualification. Rather than attempt to deal superficially with a subject rendered virtually intractable by a lack of data, it is more appropriate to the purpose of the present discussion to consider a particular case history.

Electron-beam mask fabrication was introduced into the Bell Laboratories Murray Hill mask laboratory in August 1974. Previously, mask fabrication was accomplished with a three-step optical procedure consisting of artwork generation at 35× final size in the primary pattern generator (Poole *et al.*, 1970), 3.5× reduction of the artwork to a 10× reticle (Rawson *et al.*, 1970), and, finally, step-and-repeat onto the master mask (Alles *et al.*, 1970). All patterning was done in emulsion. The typical manufacturing yield (masks accepted/masks started) for the optical process was about 30%.* Following the transition to electron-beam mask fabrication with the system described by Herriott *et al.* (1975), the manufacturing yield increased to about 60%. The transition was made under the same management, with the same processing and inspection personnel using essentially the same criteria for mask acceptance as before the change. With further system and process refinement the manufacturing yield reached 80–90% in 1975 (see Fig. 5.18). System malfunctions and operational errors account for about 50% of the rejections.

During this interval, acceptance criteria were tightened somewhat, as larger, more complicated chip patterns assumed a greater share of mask production. Therefore, in this particular case, manufacturing yield im-

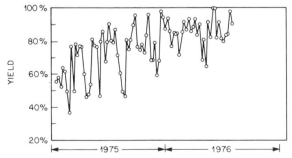

FIG. 5.18 Weekly manufacturing yield 1975–1976 for chromium master masks fabricated in a production environment using the system described by Herriott *et al.* (1975). Rejects caused by system malfunctions and operational errors are included in the yield data. [After Skinner (1976).]

* This yield value was used in an illustrative example in Section II.D.

proved by about a factor of three with the transition to electron-beam mask fabrication and subsequent process development. As a result, mask cost and turnaround time were significantly reduced (Skinner, 1976).

The typical writing time on the system described by Varnell *et al.* (1974) for a 50 mm × 50 mm array of chip patterns, having a complexity similar to those shown in Fig. 5.15, is less than 1 hr. The 2.5 in. (64 mm) mask shown in Fig. 5.1 was written in about 45 min on the system described by Herriott *et al.* (1975). The total processing time for this mask, excluding inspection, was about 2 hr (Ballantyne, 1975).

Pattern nonlinearity on the system described by Varnell *et al.* (1974) is less than 0.05% of the field size. For a 6 mm field, the distortion at the edges of the field can presumably approach 3 μm, which would preclude field butting with this field size to form larger chips. The scan field would have to be reduced until the distortion at the edge of the field was small enough to allow adequate registration between scan fields (see Section III.B). On the system described by Herriott *et al.*, there is no fundamental limit, imposed by pattern distortion, to the size of chip which can be written. An example of the large chip capability of this system is shown in Fig. 5.19. The dimensions of the two area-imaging CCD chips shown in the figure are 16 mm × 20 mm. The chips are so large that only two can be

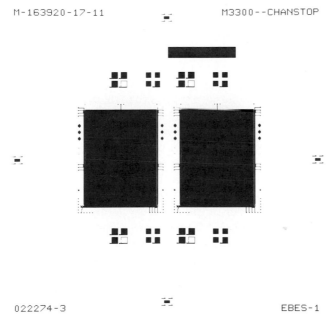

FIG. 5.19   A 2.5 in. (6.35 cm) chromium master mask showing one level used in the manufacture of an area imaging CCD.

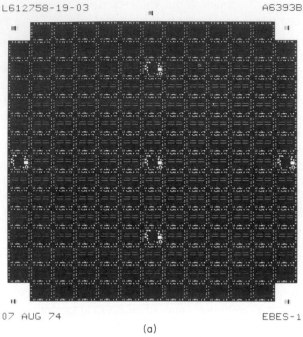

(a)

FIG. 5.20   (a) A 2.5 in. (6.35 cm) chromium master mask fabricated using the negative resist P(GMA-co-EA) showing tone reversal by the control computer. (b) A 2.5 in. (6.35 cm) chromium master mask fabricated using the positive resist PBS.

accommodated on a 2.5 in. mask. The total writing time for this mask was about 1 hr.

For some applications masks are required which are opposite in tone to the coded pattern. Tone reversal can be achieved on electron-beam systems by using either a software routine or a positive resist. Figure 5.20a shows an example of a pattern which has been reversed in tone by the control computer. Note that the opaque regions of the mask extend only to the edge of the pattern area. Figure 5.20b shows an example of tone reversal using a positive resist. In this case, only the exposed areas are clear and the remainder of the mask is opaque. The writing times for the two cases shown in Fig. 5.20 were not significantly different on the raster scanning system described by Herriott *et al.* (1975) since the entire pattern area is scanned whatever the pattern density. The writing times for the same cases on a vector scanning system of the type described by Varnell *et al.* (1974) would be substantially different, however, because writing times on such systems are directly proportional to the area exposed (see Chapter 3). With such systems, then, there may be important economic advantages in choosing the appropriate resist type for a particu-

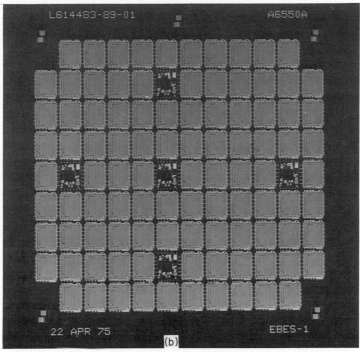

FIG. 5.20b   See legend for Fig. 5.20.

lar mask. That is, in a machine using vector scan pattern generation the type (positive or negative) of resist should be chosen to minimize written area (therefore writing time), if both resists are equivalent in other characteristics.

Other factors must also be considered in selecting the type of resist used. For example, pinholes may be the major defect in negative resist processing and large exposed (opaque) areas may result in lower yields and hence higher mask costs, quite apart from exposure time considerations. A positive resist process, however, may give a lower pinhole density but a higher density of opaque spots. Thus, the positive resist process would be most suitable for masks having a small exposed (clear) area. Under the hypothetical conditions assumed above, the two processes would be complementary and the resist type could be chosen which would minimize mask cost. At the present time there are insufficient data on positive and negative electron–resist processing to say whether the conditions assumed above will prevail in practice. However, the example given serves to illustrate the type of tradeoff which a mask maker must recognize and exploit if he wishes to improve the efficiency of his process.

Resolution capabilities are a further consideration in selecting a resist material. When very high resolution is required positive resists may have the advantage. Reports in the literature consistently show that the resolution capabilities of the positive resist PMMA are superior to those of any known negative resist. The 450 Å features reported by Wolf *et al.* (1971) were delineated using PMMA. Experience with the system described by Herriott *et al.* (1975) has shown that the positive resist PBS consistently outperforms the negative resist P(GMA-co-EA) in the area of resolution. The differences between the two resists becomes apparent in the submicron region. The lines shown in Fig. 5.21 are nominally 0.5 μm. The lines were delineated in chromium using a 0.25-μm-thick PBS film and wet etching. This level of resolution has not been achieved with an equivalent developed thickness of the negative resist P(GMA-co-EA) on the same system. Experience has shown that the resolution limit for a developed 0.25-μm-thick film of P(GMA-co-EA) lies in the region of 0.5–1.0 μm on the system described by Herriott *et al.* (1975).

There are several reasons for the observed differences in resolution capability. First, it will be recalled from Section V.B that the resist thickness remaining after developing in the case of P(GMA-co-EA) is about 40% of the initial resist thickness when the exposure level is set to produce the coded feature size in the developed resist pattern. With a positive resist such as PBS or PMMA, the developed thickness is generally the same as the initial thickness. Therefore, in the case of a negative resist with a contrast of about 1.0, the thickness of the electron scattering resist layer is about twice that of the positive resist for the same final resist thickness. The thicker resist film allows more lateral spread of electrons and hence results in wider lines. The effects of lateral electron scattering are further reduced in PBS because it appears to have a significantly

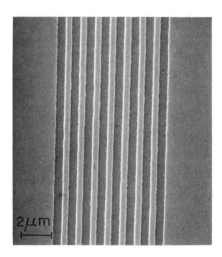

FIG. 5.21   SEM micrograph of 0.5 μm lines on a chromium mask fabricated with the system described by Herriott *et al.* (1975) using the positive resist PBS. The brighter regions are chromium.

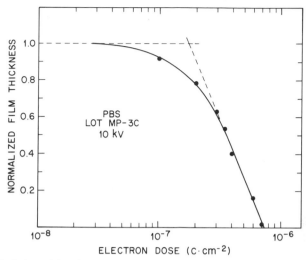

FIG. 5.22   Variation of developed resist thickness with electron dose for the positive resist PBS. The initial film thickness was 0.25 μm.

higher contrast than P(GMA-co-EA). For example, Fig. 5.22 shows the response curve for PBS under the same processing conditions used to delineate the lines shown in Fig. 5.21. The contrast value calculated from Eq. (5.10) is 1.7, which is about a factor of 2 greater than the contrast of P(GMA-co-EA) (Fig. 5.11b).

As pointed out earlier, a resolution capability of 1 μm should be adequate for photomask fabrication and both negative and positive resists are available that appear equal to the task. However, as discussed in the following chapter, electron-beam mask fabrication may soon move into a new realm of higher resolution to meet the needs of advancing high resolution lithographic technologies involving x rays and projected electron beams. For such applications the choice of resists may be determined in large measure by submicron resolution capabilities.

VII.   OUTLOOK

Looking to the future it would appear that the use of scanned electron beams for mask fabrication is assured. The successful development of several greatly different prototype systems serves to confirm the basic feasibility of the method. An example of a production electron-beam exposure system is shown in Fig. 5.23.

The 256 μm scan length in the system described by Alles et al. (1975b) appears overly conservative from the electron-optical viewpoint, while

FIG. 5.23 A production electron-beam exposure system used to fabricate chromium
master masks (Alles *et al.*, 1975b). The electron-optical column, the interferometrically controlled $X-Y$ drive assembly, and the vacuum system are situated on the right of the photograph. The operator's console is shown on the left. (Photograph courtesy of Western Electric Company.)

the nonlinearity of 0.05% in the 6 mm scan field described by Varnell *et al.*
(1974) can lead to system compatibility difficulties and registration
problems in butting scan fields. Masks fabricated on different systems
may be incompatible due to different linearity characteristics, and
problems may arise when chip sizes exceed the 6.35×6.35 mm maximum. In the period of rapid system development, which almost certainly
lies ahead in this technology, a compromise approach appears likely.

In addition to system improvements, developments are likely in the
processing area. Larger scales of integration with larger chip sizes and
smaller features will motivate continued improvement in process performance. Very clean and well-characterized resist solutions will contribute to this improvement as will the development of glass substrates designed specifically for photomask applications. Chromium is likely to remain the principal mask material for some time and, combined with the

correct glass types, should provide starting mask blanks of excellent quality.

Recent growth in the use of projection printing suggests that many electron-beam-fabricated master masks will be used directly for pattern delineation in wafer processing. The scanning projection printing approach described by Markle (1974) involves an out-of-contact 1:1 image transfer of an arc-shaped area of the mask onto the corresponding part of the wafer. The mask and the wafer are scanned in synchronism until the entire mask pattern has been transferred. The method has two significant advantages from the mask maker's point of view. First, the master mask can be used directly since there is no damaging mask-to-wafer contact, thereby obviating the need for inferior working copies of the master. Second, since the mask can, in principle, be used indefinitely, provided that adequate handling precautions are observed, it is worth the effort to produce a mask of optimal quality.

Developments in optical lithographic systems appear likely to continue in the quest for ever smaller feature sizes. Step-and-repeat reduction projection systems and the use of deep uv exposure wavelengths are two approaches which show promise. Electron-beam mask fabrication methods are compatible with both approaches.

Further into the future, it appears inevitable that the inexorable demands for smaller feature sizes in the microelectronics industry will exceed the capabilities of photolithography. Development of high resolution replication technologies involving x rays and electron beams is already well underway, as will be seen in the following chapter. Mask fabrication for 1:1 projection systems will almost certainly require the delineation of features well below 1 μm in size. Development of pattern generation systems with submicron resolution capabilities over 3-in.-(7.6-cm-) diameter or larger pattern areas will be accompanied by a variety of new processes involving new mask materials, substrates, and resists.

It is probably fair to say that, with the routine use of electron beams for mask fabrication, device lithography has entered a new and exciting era.

REFERENCES

Alles, D. S. et al. (1970). Bell Syst. Tech. J. **49**, 2145–2178.
Alles, D. S., Ashley, F. R., Johnson, A. M., and Townsend, R. L. (1975a). J. Vac. Sci. Technol. **12**, 1252–1256.
Alles, D. S. et al. (1975b). Late news paper Supplement to Int. Electron Devices Meeting Proc. IEEE Catalog No. 75CH1023-1ED, p. 1.
Ballantyne, J. P. (1975). J. Vac. Sci. Technol. **12**, 1257–1260.
Bartelt, J. L. (1974). J. Polym. Sci. Symp. No. 23, 139–145.

Beasley, J. P., and Squire, D. G. (1975). *IEEE Trans. Electron. Devices* **ED-22**, 376–384.
Bowden, M. J. (1975). *J. Polym. Sci.* Symposium No. 49, 221–226.
Bowden, M. J., Robinson, W., and Biolsi, M. (1975a). Paper presented at the *North Am. Chem. Congr., 1st, Mexico City, December.*
Bowden, M. J., Thompson, L. F., and Ballantyne, J. P. (1975b). *J. Vac. Sci. Technol.* **12**, 1294–1296.
Brewer, T. L. (1974). *Proc. Int. Conf. Electron Ion Beam Sci. Technol., San Francisco, California* (R. Bakish, ed.), pp. 71–80. Electrochemical Society, Princeton, New Jersey.
Bruning, J. H., Feldman, M., Kinsel, T. S., Sittig, E. K., and Townsend, R. L. (1975). *IEEE Trans. Electron. Dev.* **ED-22**, 487–495.
Cahen, O., Sigelle, R., and Trotel, J. (1972). *Proc. Int. Conf. Electron Ion Beam Sci. Technol., Houston, Texas* (R. Bakish, ed.), pp. 92–101. Electrochemical Society, Princeton, New Jersey.
Cuthbert, J. D. (1977). *Solid-State Technol.* August, 59–69.
Denning, P. A. (1976). *Solid-State Technol.* May, 43–47.
Engle, P. R. Jr. (1975). *Proc. Kodak Microelectron. Seminar, Monterey.*
Feit, E. D. (1976). Private communication.
Friedmann, E. B., Livesay, W. R., and Rubiales, A. L. (1973). *J. Vac. Sci. Technol.* **10**, 1020–1024.
Garland, L. H. (1964). *Am. J. Roentgen.* 1950.
Glang, R., and Gregor, L. V. (1970). *In* "Handbook of Thin Film Technology" (L. I. Maissel and R. Glang, eds.), Chapter 7. McGraw-Hill, New York.
Greeneich, J. S. (1974). *J. Appl. Phys.* **45**, 5264–5268.
Greeneich, J. S. (1975). *J. Electrochem. Soc.* **122**, 970–976.
Haller, I., Hatzakis, M., and Srinivasan,R. (1968). *IBM J. Res. Dev.* **12**, 251.
Harris, R. A. (1973). *J. Electrochem. Soc.* **120**, 270–274.
Hatzakis, M. (1975). *J. Vac. Sci. Technol.* **12**, 1276–1279.
Hatzakis, M., Ting, C. H., and Viswanathan, N. (1974). *Proc. Int. Conf. Electron Ion Beam Sci. Technol., San Francisco, California* (R. Bakish, ed.), pp. 542–579. Ellectrochemical Society, Princeton, New Jersey.
Heidenreich, R. D., Thompson, L. F., Feit, E. D., and Melliar-Smith, C. M. (1973). *J. Appl. Phys.* **44**, 4039–4047.
Heidenreich, R. D., Ballantyne, J. P., and Thompson, L. F. (1975). *J. Vac. Sci. Technol.* **12**, 1284–1288.
Herriott, D. R., Collier, R. J., Alles, D. S., and Stafford, J. W. (1975). *IEEE Trans. Electron Dev.* **ED-22**, 385–392.
Hirai, T., Hatano, Y., and Nonogaki, S. (1971). *J. Electrochem. Soc.* **118**, 669.
Horne, D. F. (1973). *Opt. Acta* **20**, 939–957.
Izumitani, T., Nakajima, Y., Miyada, E., and Segawa, D. K. (1975). *Proc. Kodak Microelectron. Seminar, Monterey.*
Knowler, L., Howell, J., Gold, B., Coleman, E., Moan, O., and Knowler, W. (1969). "Quality Control by Statistical Methods." McGraw-Hill, New York.
Livesay, W. R. (1974). *Solid-State Technol.* **17**, 37–42.
Markle, D. A. (1974). *Solid-State Technol.* **17**, 50–53.
Murphy, B. T. (1964). *Proc. IEEE* **52**, 1537–1545.
O'Malley, A. J. (1975). *Solid-State Technol.* **18**, 40–45.
Padden, F. J., Jr., and Ballantyne, J. P. (1976). Unpublished work.
Pease, R. F. W., Ballantyne, J. P., Henderson, R. C., Voschenkov, A. M., and Yau, L. D. (1975). *IEEE Trans. Electron Devices* **ED-22**, 393–399.
Piwczyk, B. P., and McQuhae, K. G. (1973). *J. Vac. Sci. Technol.* **10**, 1016–1019.

Poole, K. M. *et al.* (1970). *Bell Syst. Tech. J.* **49**, 2031–2075.
Price, J. E. (1970). *Proc. IEEE* **58**, 1290–1291.
Rawson, E. G., Poulsen, M. E., and Stafford, J. W. (1970). *Bell Syst. Tech. J.* **49**, 2117–2143.
Roberts, E. D. (1975). Am. Chem. Soc. Div. Org. Coat. Plast. Chem. Pap. 35 (2) 281.
Rottmann, H. R. (1974). *IBM J. Res. Dev.* **18**, 1074.
Saitou, N., and Nonogaki, S. (1972). *Proc. Int. Conf. Electron Ion Beam Sci. Technol., 5th, Houston, Texas* (R. Bakish ed.), pp. 68–79. Electrochemical Society, Princeton, New Jersey.
Sandland, P. (1977). *SPIE Semicond. Microlithogr. II* **100**, 26–35.
Schoonard, J. W., Gould, J. D., and Miller, L. A. (1970). IBM Res. Rep. RC 3085.
Scott, J. P. (1975). *IEEE Trans. Electron Dev.* **ED-22**, 409–413.
Skinner, J. G. (1976). *Proc. Kodak Microelectron. Seminar, Monterey.*
Skinner, J. G. (1977). *SPIE Semicond. Microlithogr. II* **100**, 20–25.
Smith, H. I. (1974). *Proc. IEEE* **62**, 1361–1387.
Thompson, L. F. (1974). *Solid State Technol.* **17**, 27–30.
Thompson, L. F., and Kerwin, R. E. (1976). *Ann. Rev. Mater. Sci.* **6**, 267–301.
Thompson, L. F., Ballantyne, J. P., and Feit, E. D. (1975). *J. Vac. Sci. Technol.* **12**, 1280–1283.
Tobey, A. C. (1975). *Ind. Res.* September, 66–70.
Varnell, G. L., Spicer, D. F., Rodger, A. C., and Holland, R. D. (1974). *Proc. Int. Conf. Electron Ion Beam Sci. Technology, 6th, San Francisco, California* (R. Bakish, ed.), pp. 97–110. Electrochemical Society, Princeton, New Jersey.
Wada, Y., and Uehara, K. (1974). *Jpn. J. Appl. Phys.* **13**, 2014–2018.
Weber, E. V., and Yourke, H. S. (1977). *Electronics* November 10, 96–101.
Wolf, E. D., Ozdemir, F. S., Perkins, W. E., and Coane, P. J. (1971). *Record Symp. Electron, Ion Laser Beam Technol., 11th* (R. F. M. Thornley, ed.), p. 331. San Francisco Press, San Francisco, California.

6

Replication techniques

JACQUES TROTEL and BERNARD FAY

SERVICE DE MICROLITHOGRAPHIE
THOMSON-CSF
ORSAY, FRANCE

I. INTRODUCTION

A. *The Need for a Batch Process*

The words "batch process" imply a type of production in which a large number of samples are treated simultaneously. For example, diffusion of impurities into semiconductors is a batch process because about 100

309

wafers are put together into the diffusion oven. Interest in the batch process as a means of production of microelectronic devices arises because of the economy of scale that is afforded vis-a-vis serial or one-at-a-time processes. However, there are limitations to the value of a batch process. For example, the throughput of a particular process step must be matched to the rest of the production line, and the marketing possibilities of the product to the risk of failure of an entire batch and to the possibility of a breakdown of the process equipment on the production of the factory.

In the case of lithography, the important consideration is the resolution point or pixel; a batch process is one in which a large number of points in a pattern are drawn at the same time. A measure of the "batchness" of the process can be given by an evaluation of the number of points that are processed simultaneously. Table 6.1 gives this evaluation for several of the lithographic processes. The dimension of the pixel is assumed to be equal to one-fifth of the minimum linewidth which can be controlled. It is seen, for example, that the Gaussian spot electron beam can expose only one pixel at a time; this is a serial process. However, a shaped electron beam can expose perhaps a thousand or so minimum resolution elements at one time; this is an elementary batch process. At the other end of the scale, a high resolution x-ray replication process can expose up to 10^{11} pixels (if an entire wafer can be printed simultaneously).

B.   Replication Techniques: Definition

Table 6.1 shows that, except for the gaussian electron beam, all of the lithographic processes are batch processes to some degree. However, we will differentiate between those processes that can draw a pattern from data in a computer memory and all the other techniques, which can only reproduce an image that already exists in a material form. The former are called composition processes, namely, the gaussian electron beam, the fixed shaped beam, the variable shaped electron beam, and the variable slit optical pattern generator. The latter processes are called replication techniques.

The several replication techniques in Table 6.1 can be divided into two generic classes, viz.:

(1) *True imaging systems.* In this class an optical system forms a stigmatic image of the mask on the sample. Systems of this type include the photorepeater, the 1:1 optical projector, the 1:1 electron-image projector, and the electron-demagnifying projection system.

(2) *Shadow casting systems.* The sample is exposed in areas not

TABLE 6.1

Comparison of Batchness Factor of Various Lithographic Processes

	Minimum controlled linewidth (μm)	Dimension of "batch" image	Number of points "batch image"
Gaussian electron beam[a]	0.5	0.1 μm	1
Fixed shaped electron beam[a]	2.5	2.5 μm $\times$ 2.5 μm	25
Variable shaped electron beam[a]	1	10 μm $\times$ 10 μm	2.5×10^3
Variable slit optical pattern generator[a]	5	3 mm $\times$ 3 mm	9×10^6
Photorepeater[b]	1	10 mm $\times$ 10 mm	2.5×10^9
Optical 1 : 1 Projection[b]	3	ϕ 75 mm[c]	1.2×10^{10}
Optical proximity printing[b]	4	ϕ 75 mm	6.9×10^9
Optical contact printing (conformable wafer–mask)[b]	1	ϕ 75 mm	1.1×10^{11}
1 : 1 Electron-image projection[b]	1	ϕ 75 mm	1.1×10^{11}
Electron shadow image[b]	2	ϕ 75 mm	2.8×10^{10}
Electron-reduction image projection[b]	0.5	3 mm $\times$ 3 mm	9×10^8
X-ray shadow image[b]	0.5	ϕ 50 mm	2.5×10^{11}

[a] Composition processes.
[b] Replication processes.
[c] ϕ indicates diameter.

shadowed by the mask. Systems of this type include the optical contact and proximity, the electron-shadow image, and the x-ray shadow image systems.

C. *The Registration Problem: Mask and Substrate Geometrical Stability*

In most cases, the fabrication of a real device requires several sequential mask levels to register together.

The registration precision and the pattern delineation precision must be on the same order of magnitude; specifically, registration precision of one-fifth of the minimum pattern linewidth is generally acceptable. Registration is not possible if the geometry of the mask and/or the wafer is not reproducible from one mask level to the other. The geometry can change for several reasons:

(1)   Thermal expansion.

(2)   Modification of the materials: for example, some organic membrane x-ray masks can swell due to moisture absorption from the air or the structure of the material can change when exposed to x-ray radiation.

(3)   Modification of internal stresses in the wafer due to the fabrication processes. For example, silicon wafers can distort both laterally and vertically when they undergo high temperature processes.

To illustrate the latter point, consider the growing of a thermal silicon dioxide layer on a silicon wafer. The oxide is grown at high temperature. When the wafer is cooled, the silicon shrinks more than the oxide because the temperature coefficients are different. As a result, the wafer is bowed so that the oxidized surface is convex. If the wafer is flattened, its diameter is increased; this expansion will be approximately $\Delta d/d = 1.5 \times 10^{-5}$, depending on the oxide thickness and growth temperature. In general the mask and substrate stability is in the range of 10^{-4}–10^{-5}. When several masks levels must be registered, this stability limits the number of points in the image to about 10^9.

Referring to Table 6.1 it is seen that several lithography processes exceed this limit, and in fact these large capacity replication processes often cannot be used to their full limits, even when very accurate alignment means are provided, because registration errors can occur over the whole image field as a result of substrate deformation. Therefore submicrometer replication processes are virtually forced to employ step-and-repeat of sub images over the wafer, rather than whole wafer exposure. These sub-image fields will be limited to between 10^4 and 10^5 resolution elements on a side.

II.   PHYSICS OF REPLICATION SYSTEMS

A.   *Relation between Resolution and Radiation Energy*

Ultraviolet photons, electrons, or x-ray photons can be used as sources of energizing radiation. However, there is a definite relation between the energy per photon of the radiation emitted by the source and the ultimate resolution of the replication system. The ultimate resolution of a replication system can be limited as much by the resolution of the radiation pattern projected by the mask as by the ability of the resist layer to record faithfully this radiation pattern.

Furthermore, diffraction is one of the most important factors limiting the resolution of the radiation pattern projected by a mask, and the effect of diffraction is slightly different in true imaging systems than in shadow casting systems.

It can be shown that diffraction in true imaging systems results in a limit of controllable linewidth of

$$d_1 = \lambda/(NA) \tag{6.1}$$

(Binder and Lacombat, 1979), where λ is the wavelength of the radiation and NA is the numerical aperture of the optical system. Light optical imaging systems frequently use lenses with numerical apertures ranging from 0.2 to 0.5, giving a value for d_1 of roughly 1 μm for visible light ($\lambda \approx 0.4\ \mu$m).

In optical and x-ray shadow casting systems, the effect of diffraction can be described by considering Fresnel diffraction of a plane wave at an opaque straight edge. The intensity distribution behind the edge varies as shown in Fig. 6.1. It may be regarded as the result of interference from the incoming plane wave, cut off sharply at the edge, and a cylindrical wave diverging from the edge (Sommerfeld, 1954). We may define the distance over which the normalized intensity distribution varies between 0.5 and 1 as the line edge definition that will be produced in a resist layer of reasonably good contrast. The minimum reproducible linewidth, which is taken as five times the line edge definition, can therefore be written as

$$d_2 = (2\lambda g)^{1/2} \qquad \text{(with } g \gg \lambda) \tag{6.2}$$

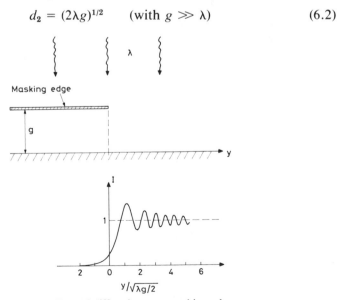

FIG. 6.1 Fresnel diffraction at a masking edge.

Thus diffraction results in a resolution limit proportional to λ in the case of true imaging systems and to the square root of λg in the case of shadow casting systems. The increase in resolution achieved by halving the wavelength of radiation is therefore greater for a true imaging system than for a shadow casting system, unless the gap spacing value is reduced accordingly. A typical value of d_2 with a proximity gap of 20 μm might be 4 μm at optical wavelength ($\lambda = 0.4$ μm) and only 0.2 μm at x-ray wavelength ($\lambda = 10$ Å). Electron energies in electron-beam systems are usually in the 10–20 keV range, resulting in an associated wavelength for the electrons of roughly 1 Å, so that for electrons of this energy diffraction effects are truly negligible.

The resolution of the image developed in the resist layer is limited by scattering effects occurring within the resist layer upon absorption of the energizing radiation. This effect has been discussed in Chapter 2 for the case of electron-beam radiation. Electron-backscatter effects increase with electron-beam energy as well as with substrate atomic number and thickness. The effect of this electron backscatter is an exposed line in resist that is much larger than the exposing beam width.

In the case of x-ray radiation, x-ray absorption in the resist layer occurs by the photoelectric effect. Photoelectrons are released upon absorption of an x-ray photon, with an initial kinetic energy that can at most be equal to the full photon energy. These photoelectrons expose the resist either by breaking or by cross-linking molecules, in the same manner as electron-beam radiation. However, in the electron-beam case the maximum electron energy is in the 10–20 keV range, while in the x-ray case it is only in the 0.3–3 keV range. Therefore scattering effects are much less serious in x-ray systems than in electron-beam systems.

The effect of photoelectron scattering may be expressed by a photoelectron range that is a function of electron-beam energy. A convenient expression for the electron range may be obtained from the depth–dose universal curve obtained by Gruen (1957) for energy dissipation versus penetration distance. Letting E_B denote the beam energy in kilo-electron-volts the Gruen range R_G is given (in centimeters) by

$$R_G = (4.6 \times 10^{-6}/\rho)E_B^{1.75} \qquad (6.3)$$

where ρ is the resist density (in grams per cubic centimeter).

An electron range value of $0.5R_G$ may be taken as a first approximation to the lateral spreading due to electron scattering. Furthermore, the minimum linewidth as limited by photoelectron scattering effects in the resist layer may be taken as five times the lateral spreading just defined, that is,

$$d_{SC} \simeq 0.096E_B^{1.75} \quad (\mu\text{m}) \qquad (6.4)$$

assuming a resist density $\rho = 1.2$ g cm^{-3}, corresponding to PMMA resist.

In the case of uv radiation, with radiation energy only of the order of a few electron volts, scattering effects involving photoelectrons are negligibly small.

Another type of scattering is called Rayleigh scattering, which refers to the interaction of photons with particles of diameter small in comparison with the wavelength. This effect is a limiting factor in the resolution of large grain size high speed silver salt photographic emulsions (Stevens, 1957). The amount of scattering is proportional to D^6/λ^4 where D is the diameter of the scattering particle. However, this type of scattering appears to be of negligible importance with modern photoresists and x-ray resists, which show a smooth nongrainy structure.

The minimum linewidth in a replication system as a function of the radiation energy is plotted in Fig. 6.2 using the relations (6.1)–(6.3) and typical values of some important system parameters. The limit curve for electron-beam lithography is due to backscattering of primary electrons from the substrate as discussed in Chapter 2. This graph shows that replication systems are resolution limited by diffraction and electron-beam systems by scattering, and that x-ray systems can be limited in resolution either by diffraction or by scattering. It also shows that x-ray replication systems offer the highest resolution, with minimum replicated linewidth well into the submicron domain.

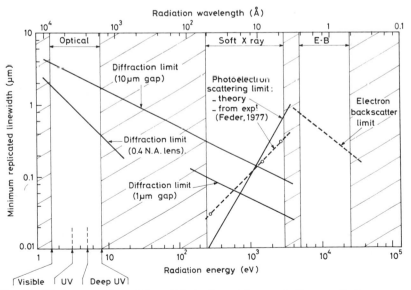

FIG. 6.2   Minimum replicated linewidth (= 5× minimum pixel) vs. radiation energy or wavelength.

B. Physical Effects of Ultraviolet and X-Ray Radiation on a Resist Layer

The first step in a lithographic process is to open windows in a resist layer.

The effects of electrons on resist have been studied in Chapter 2; the effects of photon beams on resist will be discussed in this chapter. While detailed analyses of this subject have been given by Dill (1975) and by Brochet and Dubroeucq (1977), the fundamental process can be described as follows. Photons dissipate their energy in the material, and if the resist has appropriate characteristics, the energy is not entirely used to heat the material but, rather, it induces some change in the structure.

The photon–resist interaction can be analyzed by using the following simplifying assuptions: the substrate is not reflecting; the absorption of the resist does not change throughout the exposure; and the photons are in the form of an infinite parallel beam perpendicular to the surface. Then, after exposure, the absorbed energy density is expressed by $E_V(z) = E_V(0)e^{-\mu(\lambda)z}$, where $E_V(z)$ denotes the energy density at depth z in the resist, and $\mu(\lambda)$ the absorption coefficient at wavelength λ.

The energy density $E_V(z)$ can be related to the measurable surface energy density E_S by integrating through the resist:

$$E_S = \int_0^\infty E_V(z) \, dz = E_V(0)/\mu(\lambda) \tag{6.5}$$

from which

$$E_V(z) = \mu(\lambda)E_S e^{-\mu(\lambda)z} \tag{6.6}$$

In order that the entire thickness t_R of the resist be adequately exposed, the inequality $E_V(t_R) > D_V$ must hold, from which $\mu(\lambda)E_S \, e^{-\mu(\lambda)t_R} > D_V$. Here D_V denotes the resist sensitivity, assumed independent of λ, which is valid over a limited range of wavelength.

The minimum value of E_S necessary to fully expose the resist is called the surface resist sensitivity D_S.* Therefore, D_S is a function of λ through the relation

$$D_S = [D_V/\mu(\lambda)]e^{\mu(\lambda)t_R} \tag{6.7}$$

This equation is plotted versus the penetration depth $1/\mu$ in Fig. 6.3 (curve A). It is seen that the resist can be exposed with the minimum irradiation dose by choosing a wavelength for which the penetration depth μ^{-1} is equal to the resist thickness t_R.

Another criterion for choosing the wavelength is to have the energy ab-

---

* For reference, this quantity is denoted by the symbol S in others chapters.

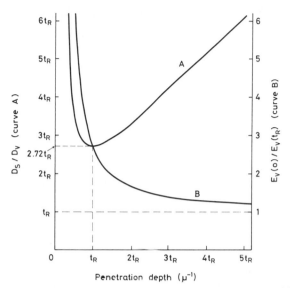

FIG. 6.3   Dependence upon penetration depth of the ratio of surface sensitivity to volume sensitivity D_S/D_V (curve A) and of exposure homogeneity $E_V(0)/E_V(t_R)$ (curve B).

sorbed as uniformly as possible throughout the thickness of the resist. The inhomogeneity in absorption can be measured by the equation

$$[E_V(0)/E_V(t_R)] = e^{\mu(\lambda)t_R} \qquad (6.8)$$

This quantity is plotted as curve B in Fig. 6.3. It is noted that energy is still being absorbed at penetration depths greater than t_R.

Based on this idealized case, the optimal wavelength for minimum irradiation dose corresponds to a penetration depth close to the thickness of the resist. However, to obtain a more even absorption through the resist, μ^{-1} must be larger than t_R. But this choice has a deleterious effect on the surface sensitivity of the resist, so that μ^{-1} should not be chosen larger than about $3t_R$. A reasonable compromise would be to choose t_R such that $t_R < \mu^{-1} < 3t_R$. The analyses above assumed a nonreflecting substrate. In some types of lithography the substrate does reflect a portion of the incident radiation. We shall not analyze this situation here. As can be expected, standing waves appear in the thickness of the resist which result in the familiar periodic (with depth) pattern in thick resist exposed with visible radiation.

We can see now the methods for getting the best results from photolithography:

(1)   Choice of wavelength so that the reflectivity of the substrate is low. Most materials have a low reflectivity for deep uv and the reflectivity

is practically zero for x rays. The reflectivity can also be lowered by a special coating (Van den Berg, 1978).

(2) Use of a resist with a long penetration depth compared to its thickness. This condition implies a waste of precious radiant energy which will be lost in the substrate.

(3) Use of a nonlinear resist, i.e., a resist in which the penetration depth changes during exposure. AZ 1350, a widely used positive resist, exhibits this property and gives good results for near uv (Brochet and Dubroeucq, 1977; Smith, 1974).

The mechanism of the molecular alteration by exposure of some of the more popular uv and x-ray resists can now be discussed briefly. Those resists which have been used for submicrometer lithography in this wavelength range include

(1) AZ 1350 for near uv,
(2) methacrylates for deep uv (near 2000 Å) (Mimura, 1978; Lin, 1975),
(3) electroresists, or electroresists with additives to increase x-ray absorption, for x rays (Brault, 1974; Taylor *et al.*, 1977).

AZ 1350 is composed of two parts (Deforest, 1972): a base resist and a photosensitive compound (PSC). The base polymer is not active by itself. With the PSC it is nearly insoluble in an alkaline solution. However, the PSC absorbs light from the near uv to the beginning of the visible range. This absorption causes the PSC to transform into a carboxylic acid, which makes the base resist soluble in an alkaline solution. Methacrylates, when exposed to deep uv, are altered by main chain scission induced by side group elimination (Hiraoka, 1977), which is also the mechanism when exposed to an electron beam. Electroresists exposed to x rays are altered by photoelectrons (Spears and Smith, 1972) which are generated in the bulk by photon absorption.

III. DESCRIPTION OF REPLICATION SYSTEMS

There are many possible approaches to the replication of high resolution patterns, each one characterized by the particular choice of elements making up a replication system. In general, the elements of any replication system are the following:

(1) a source of energizing radiation with accompanying optics;
(2) the mask, in which the pattern to be replicated is defined as an absorber pattern for the energizing radiation;

(3) a resist layer, sensitive to the energizing radiation, covering the substrate;

(4) means of registration to allow accurate alignment of the replicated mask with any previous levels carried by the replication substrate.

Each approach is characterized by a specific set of properties that are fundamental to every replication system, viz., ultimate resolution, source and resist properties, mask and substrate requirements, alignment accuracy, distortion of replicated pattern, exposure time, and throughput.

A. Ultraviolet Shadow Casting Systems

These systems are conceptually the simplest. They require a source of uv radiation, some kind of collimating optics to provide a parallel beam of radiation, a mask with regions transparent and opaque to this radiation, and a resist covered substrate in close proximity to the mask (see Fig. 6.4). It is seen that a shadow image of the absorber pattern on the mask is formed on the resist layer.

Systems of this type using a 4000 Å radiation source, either contact or proximity (10–20 μm gap), with exposure through chrome or emulsion on glass masks, are the workhorse replication systems used in the semiconductor industry. However, the resolution is limited to minimum linewidth—about 1 μm in the contact mode and 4 μm in the proximity mode. Improvements in resolution can be obtained in such systems by reducing the spacing between mask and wafer and by reducing the wavelength of the radiation source.

Shadow printing with conformable masks or with conformable substrates is one way to reduce the gap spacing effectively to zero. A conformable photomask typically consists of a thin (600 Å) chromium pattern

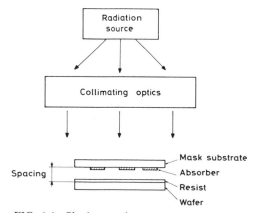

FIG. 6.4   Shadow casting system configuration.

on a glass substrate assembly in a vacuum mount as shown in Fig. 6.5. In this way intimate contact between the mask pattern and the photoresist layer is achieved and diffraction occurs only within the thickness of the resist where the index of refraction is high (e.g., $n = 1.612$ for AZ 1350 resist) and the nonlinear behavior of photoresist reduces the diffraction broadening. This technique allowed Smith to replicate gratings of 8000 Å period with sharp vertical walls in a micron-thick AZ 1350 resist layer, using 4000 Å radiation, as shown on Fig. 6.6 (Smith, 1974). However, this method is not suitable for multilevel masking because the alignment accuracy is very poor due to the large deformation occurring in the mask when the vacuum is applied.

Deep uv lithography uses radiation in the 2000–2500 Å range. Resolution is better because of the shorter wavelength, but also because of excellent resist behavior in this wavelength range. Electron resists, particularly PMMA, are sensitive to deep uv radiation and show a low value of optical absorption coefficient, which allows deep penetration of the radia-

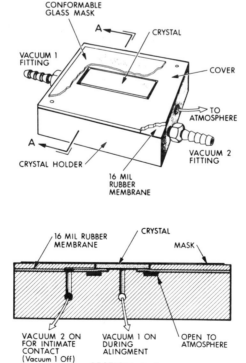

FIG. 6.5 Vacuum frame which permits a conformable photomask to be aligned with respect to a substrate and then pulled into intimate contact. [From Smith (1974).]

FIG. 6.6 Scanning electron micrograph of the cross section of a grating pattern exposed in AZ 1350 H, 9800 Å thick, using a high pressure mercury arc lamp and the conformable photomask intimate contact technique. [From Smith (1974).]

tion into the resist layer and therefore very high height-to-width aspect ratio of the developed resist pattern.

Quartz photomask substrates must be used instead of regular glass. A 500–800 Å chromium or aluminium layer is adequate as the opaque layer, allowing the use of conventional mask fabrication processes. Extremely high resolution can be achieved when deep uv radiation and intimate contact are used together. With this technique Lin (1975) has replicated 0.5 μm Y–I bars separated by 0.25 μm gaps in PMMA resist 1.78-μm thick, as shown in Fig. 6.7. In the proximity mode, it is possible to replicate 2 μm linewidths with a 20 μm spacing and 1 μm lines with a 5 μm spacing, using PMMA resist. With the available deep uv sources the exposure time with PMMA resist is in the range of 1–10 min (Lin, 1975; Mimura et al., 1978). Mask alignment can be provided as in conventional contact or proximity mask aligners.

B. Electron Shadow Casting System

Figure 6.8 shows the schematic of an electron shadow casting system (Lischke et al., 1977a). In this technique, the beam emerging from an elec-

FIG. 6.7   0.5 μm Y–I bars separated by 0.25 μm gaps, printed in PMMA 2041 resist, 1.78-μm thick with a deep uv source. [From Lin (1975).]

tron source is converted into a parallel beam by two electromagnetic condenser lenses. The electrons then pass through a stencil mask which is separated from the resist-coated sample by a relatively large distance (about 100 μm). Compared to uv shadow casting and x-ray shadow casting, the main advantage of electrons is the large gap that can be tolerated because electrons do not suffer from diffraction and the beam can be collimated so that there is no conical distortion. The maximum value of this gap is limited by the source diameter and scattering of electrons by the mask, both giving an angular dispersion of the beam.

The exposure time is still given by the formula derived in Chapter 3,[*] viz.,

$$T = D_S/(B\pi\alpha^2) \tag{6.9}$$

where α is the semiangle of dispersion of the beam. For example, with an angle of dispersion of 10^{-5} rad, a brightness of 5.10^4 A cm^{-2} sr^{-1}, and a resist sensitivity of 10^{-4} C cm^{-2}, the exposure time would be about 15 s. Registration of mask levels is achieved by operating the system as a scanning electron microscope, as indicated in Fig. 6.8c.

Therefore, electron shadow casting is a replication technique that is diffraction free, relatively distortion free and rather fast. The real problem

[*] Refer to Eqs. (3.7) and (1.2).

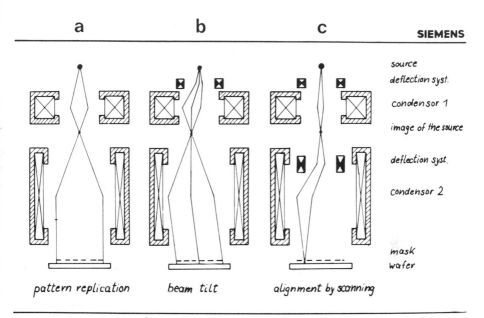

E - Beam Shadow - Printing 1:1

FIG. 6.8 Electron shadow casting system. [From Lischke *et al.* (1977a).]

with this method is the need for a stencil type mask (a mask for which the absorber is self-supporting) because no material is transparent enough to electrons to serve as a mask substrate. To circumvent this problem, it has been proposed that the mask be made on a fine grid; the bars of the grid do not appear on the image if that image is blurred by tilting the beam as indicated in Fig. 6.8b.

C. Optical Imaging Systems

Light optics systems are practically the only lithographic tools currently used in production, and very few such systems have been described that can really control submicron linewidth (Lacombat *et al.*, 1977).

Submicron lithography has been demonstrated with visible radiation. Lacombat *et al.* (1977) showed 0.6-μm-wide lines printed in 0.36-μm-thick AZ 1350 resist using a projection optical system. However, this demonstration represents a laboratory result that probably cannot be adapted to production use. As shown earlier, submicron images are only possible with a high numerical aperture lens, which results in an extremely short depth of focus. In order to obtain more practical systems, the wavelength must be reduced. However, a limiting difficulty in making a uv refracting system is the availability of transparent material in that wavelength range.

In contrast to refracting systems, reflecting systems present no material problems. Aluminium coatings, for example, show a good reflection coefficient in the uv range. Also there is no chromatic aberration, so the system is not limited to monochromatic sources. However, there are problems in correction or field aberrations; in fact, simple solutions can be found only for 1:1 magnification between object and image.

Figure 6.9 is a schematic of the optical part of a commercial reflecting system (Moller, 1975). Systems of this type have been used to print 2-μm-wide lines with good step coverage. No effects of standing waves in the resist are obtained, because of the polychromatic light source.

In most optical imaging systems, registration is done manually. The operator looks through a microscope at the mask. If the sample is properly illuminated, the image of the sample is formed through the main optical system on the plane of the mask, so the operator sees the superposed images of mask and wafer and can align them by mechanical displacements. Usually the illumination wavelength during registration is not the

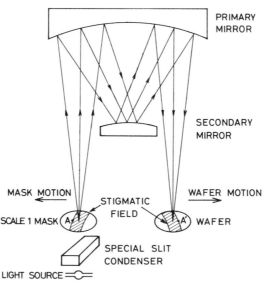

FIG. 6.9   Reflecting uv exposure system. No contact resolution = 2 μm.

same as during exposure, so the registration wavelength is chosen so that the resist is not exposed and visual observation is more comfortable. Therefore, the main optical system must be corrected for both the exposure and registration wavelengths. Usually this double correction is avoided by the use of an additional optical system which is removed during exposure. Visual observation is rather subjective and most operators can achieve only about ± 1 μm registration. Submicron registration is achieved practically only by an automatic process. In one such automatic alignment system for a photorepeater, the image of a mark on the wafer is projected on the reticle and a correlation signal is measured by light detectors. The image of the mark can also be projected on a vidicon target (Lacombat and Dubroeucq, 1978). The precision that can be achieved depends strongly on the contrast of the image of the mark on the wafer, which can vary over a large range with machine and wafer parameters.

D.   Electron-Imaging Systems

One of the greatest advantages of using electron beams in lithography is the flexibility provided by the ease of deflection of electrons, which has been fully implemented in electron-beam pattern generators as described in Chapter 3. The high resolution capability of electron beams in lithography is another great advantage but it is somewhat less obvious, particularly when speaking of submicron lithography with linewidths of the order of 0.5 m or less. Electron backscattering effects are such that for this application electron-beam processes are very critical, requiring careful electron-dose control to reduce the proximity effect described in Chapter 2. One fundamental limitation of parallel exposure systems using electron beams is the difficulty of achieving the degree of dose control necessary to obtain the highest resolution. Also, with a parallel exposure system, the flexibility asset is lost. This is why, in view of the continuing writing speed improvements of electron-beam pattern generators, electron-beam parallel exposure methods have lost some of their attractiveness. Nevertheless, the two imaging type electron-beam replication systems, namely the 1:1 photocathode projection system and the demagnifying electron-projection system, should not be neglected, because they can show a decisive edge over pattern generators in terms of exposure speed and cost.

1.   One-to-One Electron-Image Projection System
(ELIPS)

The ELIPS system was first proposed by O'Keefe et al. (1969) as a means of combining the high resolution capability of electron-beam lithography with the throughput of parallel exposure systems. The principle involves a photocathode mask with localized photoemissive regions defined by an absorber pattern on the mask (see Fig. 6.10). The photocathode mask emits photoelectrons with an initial kinetic energy V_0 with $V_0 = \phi_c - h\nu$, where ϕ_c is the electron work function for the photoemissive layer of the mask and $h\nu$ the photon energy of the uv radiation.

a. Focus conditions and depth of field. The photocathode and wafer anode planes are parallel and separated by a gap L of the order of several millimeters. A voltage V applied between these electrodes results in a uniform electric field $E = V/L$ in the interelectrode space. Because of the initial kinetic energy of the photoelectrons a uniform magnetic field B, collinear with E, must be used so that the projected image will be focused.

A photoelectron emitted with a transverse velocity component will move along a helical trajectory and will land in focus provided that the following condition is respected:

$$B_k = \frac{k}{L} \sqrt{\frac{2mV}{q}} \left(1 - \sqrt{\frac{V_z}{V}}\right)^{-1}, \qquad k = 1, 2 \qquad (6.10)$$

where B_k denotes the value of magnetic field necessary to achieve focus for the kth multiple of the cyclotron period, m is the electron mass, q the electron charge, and V_z the most probable longitudinal component of initial kinetic energy.

In practice $V_z \ll V$ and $k = 1$ so that Eq. (6.10) can be written

$$B = 1.06 \times 10^{-5} \sqrt{V}/L \qquad \text{(in MKSA units)} \qquad (6.11)$$

A simple calculation shows that the image of a point on the mask is a spot of maximum diameter given by

$$d = 2L\left[\frac{V_0}{V} + \sqrt{\frac{2V_0}{V}}\left(\frac{\Delta V}{2V} + \frac{\Delta B}{B} + \frac{\Delta L}{L}\right)\right] \qquad (6.12)$$

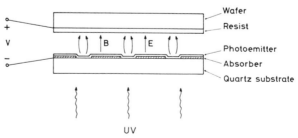

FIG. 6.10   One-to-one photocathode projection system principle.

where ΔV, ΔB, and ΔL correspond to the uncertainty in the values of V, B, and L and V_0 is the total initial kinetic energy. The term ΔL may be taken as the depth of field of the imaging system. Figure 6.11 shows the maximum spot diameter as a function of gap spacing L and accelerating voltage V for the case of a 20 μm (± 10 μm) depth of field assuming

$$\Delta V/V = \Delta B/B = 10^{-4} \quad \text{and} \quad V_0 = 0.1 \quad V$$

This curve shows that for maximum resolution, high accelerating voltage and small interelectrode spacing L should be used. From Eq. (6.11), this condition also means that a high focusing magnetic field must be applied.

b. Image distortion. In practice the electric and magnetic fields are not perfectly uniform, resulting in image distortion (Scott, 1975a; Wardly, 1975a). Magnetic distortion can occur due to inhomogeneities in the magnetic field and in the deflection coils, if any. Great care must be taken to avoid locating parts with residual magnetism near the interelectrode region. Magnetic distortion problems can be solved by careful design of the magnet and deflection coils. Field homogeneity of 10^{-4} can be achieved quite easily over a large volume by using a magnet

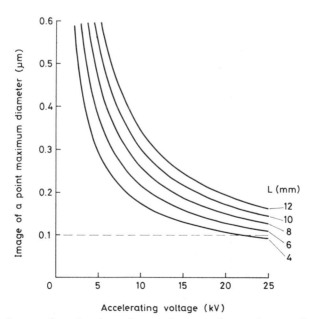

FIG. 6.11 Influence of accelerating voltage and gap spacing on the spot diameter corresponding to an emitting point on the mask (assumed depth of field $\Delta L = \pm 10$ μm, electron excess energy $V_0 = 0.1$ eV, and 10^{-4} stability of V and B supplies).

328   JACQUES TROTEL AND BERNARD FAY

with shaped iron pole pieces (Fay, 1974) or notched solenoid coils (Scott, 1974). Electric distortion may arise from geometrical causes such as mask and wafer holder configuration as well as flatness departures in mask and wafer resulting in electric field inhomogeneities. It may also arise from charging effects in the resist or on dust particles.

The first type of electric field induced distortion is only important in the outer edge regions of both mask and wafer (Fig. 6.12a), where the two electrode planes must present some kind of discontinuity due to the holding fixtures. This results in transverse electric field components as defined by Laplace's equation, of exponential decay toward the center with a characteristic length of the order of the gap spacing value. These transverse electric fields when combined with the principal E and B fields result in image displacements that are maximum near the edge of the wafer and decay rapidly with the radial distance measured from the wafer edge. It is always possible therefore to define on the wafer a working zone diameter where this type of distortion can be neglected. A typical working diameter for a 50 mm wafer and 0.1 μm maximum nonreproducible distortion would be 35 mm.

The second type of electric field induced distortion is more serious because flatness variations of the wafer can occur any place on the wafer (Fig. 6.12b). The effect of wafer warpage was analyzed by Wardly (1975b), who showed that lateral image displacements can occur with a magnitude that can be as high one-seventh of the ripple amplitude on the wafer. This effect represents a serious disadvantage of the 1:1 electron-image projection system in submicrometer applications that require several masks to be registered accurately.

In this case, the only solution is to limit the wafer warpage by avoiding high temperature processing steps that are the main cause of warpage, and

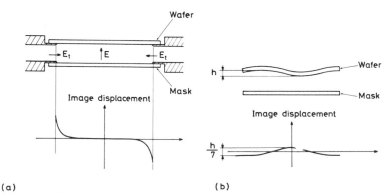

(a) (b)

FIG. 6.12   Electric-field induced distortion in a 1:1 electron-projection system. (a) Effect of mask and wafer holder geometry. (b) Effect of water ripple.

to flatten the wafer in a reproducible way using an electrostatic holddown chuck such as described by Wardly (1973), or by flattening and gluing the wafer against a flat holder as the conventional vacuum chuck will not operate in a vacuum environment. An interesting design for an electro-static chuck is taken from Livesay (1978) and shown in Fig. 6.13. The elec-trostatic wafer holder eliminates any mechanical lip surrounding the wafer. Furthermore, by adjusting the voltage on the wafer, it is possible to achieve a uniform electric field in the interelectrode space. In this way, pattern distortion is electrically controlled by adjusting the wafer clamping volt-age. The last type of electric field induced distortion (resist charging) can be avoided if necessary by coating the resist with a thin metallic layer such as 200 Å of aluminium and by careful dust control.

   c. Effect of backscattered electrons.   Backscattered electrons in a 1:1 electron-projection system have a twofold effect. First, the prox-imity effect is just as important as in direct electron-beam writing. However electron-dose control procedures are much more difficult to achieve in this case than with scanning systems. One approach de-veloped by Scott (1978) uses two-tone masks for which the large window areas are less transparent than small window areas. Another approach pursued by Livesay (1978) is to lower the accelerating voltage from 10–20 kV to 5 kV so that the electrons lose most of their energy in the resist layer and consequently suffer little backscattering from the un-derlying substrate. Reducing the electron energy, however, results in some loss of resolution as shown by Fig. 6.11.

   The second effect produced by backscattered electrons is specific to the 1:1 electron-projection systems. High energy electrons backscattered from the wafer are reflected back toward the wafer by the electric field. This results in a loss of contrast in the electronic image as the reimpacting electrons cause a background exposure. The importance of this effect is dependent on the degree of transparency of the mask, which affects the magnitude of the background exposure. Lowering the electron energy is one solution to this problem. Otherwise, it may require the constraint that

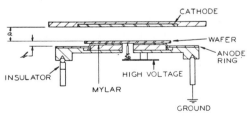

FIG. 6.13   Distortion correcting electrostatic wafer holder. [From Livesay (1973).]

the average mask transparency should not exceed a given level of the order of 30% (Scott, 1978).

   d.   Photocathode mask.   In the initial work on this subject (O'Keefe *et al.*, 1969), photosensitive layers of palladium, 40-Å thick, with a photoelectric threshold of 4.6–5 eV were used in conjunction with uv illumination of energy 4.90 eV, corresponding to the 2537 Å mercury resonance line. Quartz or fused silica mask substrates are required for uv transparency. The uv blocking layer consisted of a 1000-Å-thick titanium dioxide layer obtained by oxidizing in air at 400°C a patterned layer of titanium 400-Å thick. It has been reported that the photoelectric threshold of palladium can be lowered by tungsten contamination (Yu and Spicer, 1968), which can occur if the palladium layer is evaporated from a tungsten filament. The result is then a greater energy spread of the emitted photoelectrons with decreased image resolution, but allowing current densities in excess of 20 μA/cm^2 to be extracted from the photocathode with proper uv illumination (high pressure, high power mercury discharge lamps). With PMMA resist of sensitivity $\sim 10^{-5}$ C/cm^2, this would correspond to an exposure time of less than a second. For maximum resolution, pure palladium or gold layers deposited by dc sputtering must be used (Fay, 1977). Emission current densities obtainable with low power, low pressure mercury discharge lamps are then in the 10^{-7}-A/cm^2 range, corresponding to exposure times of the order of a minute.

   Another approach for obtaining high image resolution is to use a cesium iodide (CsI) photoemissive layer with a work function of 6.25 eV coupled with uv illumination by the 1849-Å line (energy 6.7 eV) produced in low pressure mercury discharge lamps (Scott, 1975b). Emission current densities obtainable in this way are in the 10^{-6}A/cm^2 range. The main problems with cesium iodide are that it is very hygroscopic and that it is an insulator, requiring an additional conducting layer that will absorb some of the uv radiation.

   Titanium dioxide can be replaced advantageously by chromium, 600-Å thick, in making the uv blocking layer, so that standard chrome on glass mask fabrication processes can be used, the only change being that a quartz blank instead of glass must be used.

   Whatever the nature of the photocathode material, aging effects occur after prolonged use. The emission current density decreases with time, so that the photoemissive layer must be refreshed after typically 100 exposures. To do this, it is only necessary to dissolve the previous layer by chemical etching in the case of gold or by water rinse in the case of CsI, without affecting the patterned chromium layer, and to redeposit a uniform coating of photoemissive material.

e. Registration. In order to register the mask pattern over a previous mask level carried by the wafer, it is necessary to have at least two alignment marks of given geometry on the mask and matching alignment marks of the wafer surface. Registration is achieved when the electronic image of the alignment marks on the mask are made to coincide with the alignment marks on the wafer. The marks on the wafer must be such that they yield an alignment signal of magnitude proportional to the overlapping of two corresponding marks (Fig. 6.14).

Accurate alignment is only possible if the alignment marks are located sufficiently far from the wafer edge in a region where edge distortion effects are negligible. Early experiments with ELIPS systems used active alignment marks on the wafer based on beam induced conductivity in an oxide layer (O'Keefe, 1970) and required electrical contact to the wafer. The x-ray emitting alignment marks (Fay, 1974) and the hole type alignment mark (Livesay, 1973) are preferred alignment methods because they do not require electric contact with the wafer.

X-ray alignment with tantalum pentoxide (Ta_2O_5) markers on the wafer requires high accelerating voltages, in the 15–20 kV range, to produce high energy Bremsstrahlung x rays that can be detected after transmission through the silicon wafer. For lower accelerating voltages, it is possible to thin the wafer locally in the area of the registration marks to improve

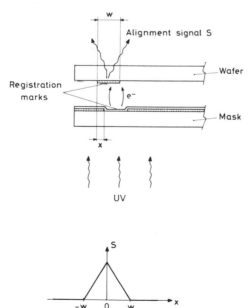

FIG. 6.14   Registration in a 1:1 electron-projection system.

x-ray transmission. Automatic alignment operation with 0.2 μm accuracy has been reported by Scott (1975c). Alignment with hole type markers on the wafer has been described by Livesay (1973). This method is compatible with low voltage operation (5 kV) of the system. Computer controlled automatic alignment with 0.2 μm accuracy has been reported by Livesay (1978).

  f.   State of the art in one-to-one electron-projection systems.   The few existing 1:1 electron-image projection systems have all demonstrated submicron linewidth capability and at least 0.2 μm alignment accuracy. Figure 6.15 shows some narrow lines of 0.6 μm periodicity printed in PMMA resist with a system operating at 16 kV, with 6.25-mm gap spacing using a 50-Å-thick sputtered gold photolayer (Fay, 1977).

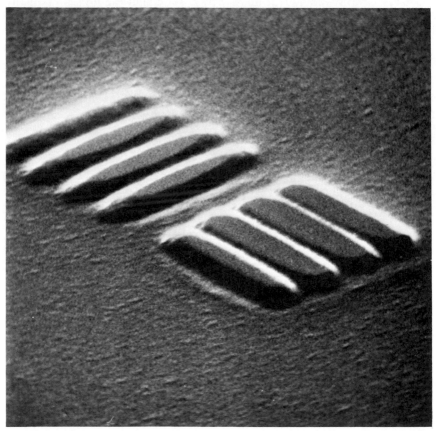

FIG. 6.15   Replication of small geometries with a 1:1 electron-projection system (0.6 μm periodicity) in PMMA resist 2000-Å thick.

These systems are designed for 2 or 3 in. wafer size. Exposure time is of the order of a minute with PMMA resist.

Registration using either the x-ray or the hole alignment method can be achieved either by mechanical displacement of the mask or wafer or by magnetic translation of the projected image by means of deflection coils. In this latter case only $X - Y$ image translation is allowed since large distortion effects are associated with magnetic image rotation which requires a magnetic field gradient. The rotation must then be achieved by mechanical means.

Fabrication of Schottky gates, ion implanted FET transistors requiring four masking levels, was reported by Fay (1974), demonstrating the possibilities of the x-ray alignment method using tantalum oxide alignment marks. Another result of multimask circuit fabrication was reported by Fuller (1977) using the system developed by Scott (1975c).

2. Demagnified Electron-Image Projection System

The goal of demagnified electron-image projection systems is to offer the advantages of optical image projection systems, viz., a large number of points in the image, stability and reproducibility, and the low cost of a simple system, but to have the resolution associated with electron-optical systems. Early electron-beam microlithography was performed with such systems (Koops et al., 1968–1969). While scanning electron-beam systems were started later, they are now at a point where they are used in production, which is not the case for electron-image projection. The reason for this slow development is the technical difficulties, which will be examinated in this section, and the fact that the advantage of flexibility of scanning electron-beam systems overcomes at the present time the advantage of potential speed of electron-image projection systems. The electron-image projection technique should be considered when mass production of submicrometer devices becomes economically feasible, and then it will have to compete with the other submicron replication techniques that have been described.

As a result of their efforts to design a system of the highest possible number of resolution points in the image, several research efforts resulted in very similar systems (Heritage, 1975; Koops and Bernhard, 1975; Lischke et al., 1977b). A schematic of the system by Heritage (1975) is shown in Fig. 6.16a. In this system the electron source is demagnified by two condenser lenses, while a third condenser lens collimates the beam into parallel rays that flood a mask. The image of this mask is then demagnified and projected onto the wafer by a system of two lenses.

If m is the desired demagnification, the first projection lens is an m-time scaleup of the second projection lens. The number of ampere turns in both

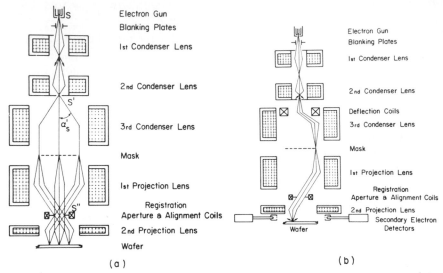

FIG. 6.16   Demagnified electron-image projection principle: (a) Exposure mode; (b) Registration mode [From Heritage (1975).]

lenses is equal but the magnetic fields of the two lenses are in opposite directions. The mask is in the object focal place of the first projector lens; the image focal plane of the first projector lens is the same as the object focal plane of the second projector lens. The image focal plane of the second projector lens is on the wafer.

This column configuration eliminates some aberrations and errors. Anisotropic aberrations and errors, i.e., aberrations and errors associated with image rotation in a magnetic lens (described in Chapter 3), vanish because the image rotation on the first projector lens is opposite to the rotation of the second projector lens. There is no magnification error because the magnification is fixed by mechanical positions of the lenses. Isotropic distorsion of the first projector lens is compensated by the distorsion of the second lens because the two lenses are similar in geometry and excitation. The other aberrations can be reduced by properly choosing the system parameters; a dominant remaining error is field curvature, which can be reduced by choosing a moderate demagnification factor—a value of 10 is common.

Characteristics of such a system are as follows (Heritage, 1975):

minimum linewidth	$0.25\ \mu m$
defined to	$0.05\ \mu m$
field size	3×3 mm
mask size	30×30 mm

depth of focus   1 mm
registration accuracy   0.05 μm
maximum distortion   0.05 μm
exposure time per field   0.1 s

Registration is performed by using the system as a scanning electron-beam system, as shown on Fig. 6.16b. In this mode, the third condenser lens is made more convergent so as to form an image of the source on the mask, and that image is scanned by deflection coils. The system is then operated as a scanning electron microscope and displays on the screen both the image of the mask and of a mark on the wafer; these images can then be focused and registered.

Mask technology is a dominant problem in this technique. The mask must be self-supporting; transparent regions are holes in a thin metal foil 5-μm thick. Obviously this mask technology places severe constraints on the topology of the pattern. To circumvent this problem it has been proposed (Lischke et al., 1977a) to support the mask on a fine grid, where the bars of the grid are very narrow (about 1 μm) so that their image does not appear in the resist.

Heritage proposed to solve the stencil problem by synthesizing the image by multiple deflection and exposure of the mask (Heritage, 1975). It has also been proposed (Speidel, 1976) to use a photocathode mask as in 1:1 electron-image projection, but the brightness of such a photocathode is not high enough to make the system competitive with scanning electron-beam systems for speed.

Another difficulty that could be encountered is the sensitivity to spurious electric and magnetic fields. To obtain small aberrations the system must have a small aperture angle and the electrons must travel long distances, over which they may be deflected by spurious fields.

Figure 6.17 (Heritage, 1975) shows some examples of structures realized by demagnified electron-image projection showing real submicrometer capability.

E. X-Ray Shadow Casting Systems*

X-ray lithography uses as the source of radiation soft xrays of wavelength between 4 and 50 Å. The choice of this wavelength domain is dictated by the x-ray absorption properties of material composing the x-ray mask and the x-ray resist as will be shown later.

In the absence of suitable x-ray optical components, x-ray lithography is limited to a shadow casting system configuration as shown in Fig. 6.18.

---

* For a more extended coverage of this subject, the reader is referred to a recently published review paper by Spiller and Feder (1977).

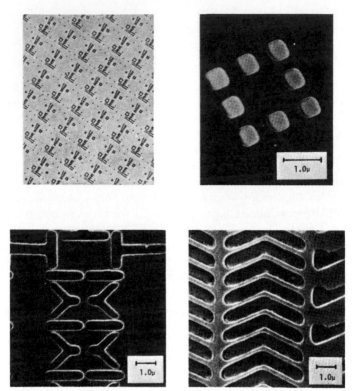

FIG. 6.17   0.5 μm structures in a 3 mm field fabricated by the 10× electron-beam projection system. [From Heritage (1975).]

The x-ray source shown is of the electron bombardment type, as in all conventional x-ray tubes. Electrons of energy 10–20 keV (typically) are focused on a metallic target so as to produce a source of x rays of effective diameter ϕ.

Since x-ray lenses are not available at these wavelengths, a diverging beam must be accepted. This condition means that the mask and wafer must be placed far enough from the source so as to limit the geometrical effects of penumbral blurring and radial shift distortion. Geometrical errors in such a shadow casting system are illustrated in Fig. 6.18.

In this figure A' is the image of point A, w the radial distance of point A on the mask, ϕ the diameter of the irradiating source, D the source to object distance, and g the spacing between object and image planes. Because of the finite diameter of the source, the image of point A is a penumbral spot of diameter

$$d = \phi g/D \tag{6.13}$$

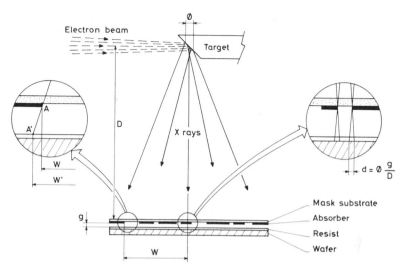

FIG. 6.18 X-ray shadow casting system configuration. Geometrical errors.

Because of the finite mask–image spacing, the replication is not an exact
1:1 reproduction of the object since

$$W'/W = (D + g)/D \qquad (6.14)$$

where w' is the radial distance of A' on the shadow image. Moreover, if
there is an uncertainty Δg in the spacing value, due, for example, to
out-of-plane wafer or mask warpage, there is an uncertainty $\Delta w'$ in the position of A', given by

$$\Delta w' = w\, \Delta g/D \qquad (6.15)$$

From these expressions it can be seen that the errors can be reduced by
using a large source to mask distance D, but the radiation power density
at the resist varies as D^{-2}.

Therefore, there is a resolution–exposure time tradeoff inherent in the
use of this type of x-ray source. Even with the newly developed high
power x-ray sources and with sensitive resists, the exposure time necessary with an x-ray lithography system will be on the order of several
minutes. This time is much longer than of other replication systems, except perhaps deep uv systems in which source problems are also quite
severe.

Among the several high resolution replication techniques, x-ray replication offers the greatest potential for very high resolution lithography.
This conclusion follows from the several important advantages associated
with x-ray lithography, viz.:

(1)   the short wavelength of x rays reduces the effect of diffraction and allows high resolution and noncontact exposure to be achieved simultaneously;

(2)   the low energy of soft x rays reduces the scattering effects associated with x-ray absorption within the resist layer;

(3)   the low absorption of x rays in the resist material results in uniform, deep exposure and thereby vertical resist profiles;

(4)   x rays are insensitive to dust particles of low atomic number as well as to electrical charging;

(5)   the replicated linewidth is independent of the substrate material and resist thickness because of the limited scattering, absence of reflection, and the uniform (in depth) exposure.

However, one must also be well aware of the difficulties associated with this technique:

(1)   the intensity of conventional soft x-ray sources is low, resulting in exposure times on the same order as attainable with advanced direct writing electron-beam systems;

(2)   mask fabrication is complex because it requires the use of mask substrates with thickness in the micron range;

(3)   the low absorption of x rays in most resists favors sharp image profiles but at the same time results in low resist sensitivity;

(4)   vacuum exposure is needed if x-ray wavelengths above 10 Å are used to achieve very high resolution;

(5)   registration methods capable of achieving 0.05 μm registration accuracy are required if the full high resolution capability of the technique is to be exploited. Mask and wafer dimensional stability then become critical and a step and repeat mode of operation will probably be necessary.

X-ray lithography, in the absence of suitable x-ray optical components, is limited to a shadow casting process. This means that the x-ray mask must be full scale, which in the highest resolution case may contain pattern linewidths as small as 0.1 μm. Within the allowed wavelength range of x-ray lithography, i.e., between about 4 and 50 Å, the choice of a particular x-ray wavelength can be dictated strictly by the resolution requirement as determined from the resolution limit curves of Fig. 6.2, which include the effect of the particular gap spacing selected.

However, there are many conflicting factors which must also be considered, such as mask contrast, which for a given absorber layer thickness increases with wavelength; resist sensitivity, which also increases with wavelength; and intensity available from conventional x-ray sources, which varies with wavelength. Therefore selection of a particular x-ray wavelength is necessarily a compromise that depends strongly on the application intended.

The fundamental components of an x-ray replication system, namely, the source, the mask, the resist, and the registration method, are discussed in the next sections. This will be followed by a description of practical embodiments of x-ray systems that have been built.

1. X-Ray Source

X-ray sources can be classified as conventional and nonconventional. Conventional sources are based on electron bombardment of a suitable target. Nonconventional sources exploit other mechanism for producing x rays. Among these the synchrotron radiation sources are very attractive for x-ray lithography (Doniach et al., 1975).

Other nonconventional sources of soft x rays are those relying on the phenomenon of x-ray emission from high temperature laboratory plasmas (Nagel et al., 1978).

a. Conventional electron-bombardment source. All commercial x-ray sources for medical or industrial radiography applications are of the type in which x-ray radiation is produced by electron bombardment of a target material. In operation of this source, electrons in the kiloelectron volt energy range are focused onto a metallic target where they excite a spectrum of x-ray radiation consisting of a discrete line spectrum, characteristic of the target material, superimposed on a continuous spectrum (Bremsstrahlung spectrum) extending, in terms of energy, from zero to a cutoff energy of value equal to the bombarding energy. The characteristic radiation is produced when inner shell electron vacancies produced by the bombarding electrons are filled with electrons from outer shells.

The rate of production of x rays increases with electron energy but so does the penetration depth of the electrons into the target. X rays generated inside the target can be reabsorbed on their way out of the target. Because of this target reabsorption there is an optimal voltage for each target material and source angular parameters (incidence angle of electrons and x-ray takeoff angle).

The continuous x-ray spectrum intensity is proportional to the atomic number of the target element. This radiation provides a background of unwanted high energy x rays which tends to reduce the contrast of the x-ray exposure and should therefore be kept as low as possible by using low accelerating voltages and low Z target materials. However, the choice of target materials is limited in the x-ray range between 4 and 50 Å to a few materials producing K and L lines, listed in Table 6.2. Power conversion efficiency is typically of the order of 50 $\mu W/W/sr$.

TABLE 6.2

Target Materials and Their Characteristics Wavelengths

Material	Atomic no.	Type of line	Wavelength (A)	Energy (keV)
Pd	46	L	4.4	2.83
Rh	45	L	4.6	2.69
Mo	42	L	5.4	2.29
Si	14	K	7.1	1.74
Al	13	K	8.3	1.49
Cu	29	L	13.3	0.93
C	6	K	44.7	0.28

The power rating of a conventional x-ray source is generally limited by the ability of the anode to dissipate power. Rotating (several thousand revolutions per minute) water cooled anodes can withstand power dissipation densities of the order of 1 kW/mm² for target materials such as Cu or Al (Wardly *et al.*, 1977), corresponding to an x-ray source brightness of the order of 50 mW/mm²/sr.

b. Synchrotron radiation source. Synchrotron radiation refers to the electromagnetic radiation emitted by electrons in response to the radial acceleration that keeps them in orbit in an electron synchrotron or storage ring.

The properties of synchrotron resolution that are most interesting for x-ray lithography are

(1) high intensity (total radiated x-ray output in the kilowatt power range),

(2) continuous spectrum extending from x ray to infrared,

(3) high collimation (beam divergence between 10^{-3} and 10^{-4} rad in the plane normal to the orbit).

Figure 6.19 shows the spectrum radiated by the ACO storage ring of the University of Orsay (France) for two values of the electron energy: 540 and 400 MeV. It can be seen that this spectrum is peaked in the wavelength range between 10 and 50 Å, which is near ideal for high resolution x-ray lithography (Fay *et al.*, 1976). The continuous, tunable spectrum of synchrotron radiation allows the wavelengths that effectively expose the resist to be selected by varying the electron energy and by proper choice of mask substrate material and thickness since the mask substrate acts as an x-ray selective filter.

Examples of patterns replicated in thick PMMA resist (1.6 μm) using the 540 MeV synchrotron radiation of ACO are given in Fig. 6.20. In both cases the gold absorber thickness of the x-ray mask is only 1000-Å thick and exposure time is about a minute. Similar experiments with the synchrotron radiation produced by the 7.5-GeV DESY synchrotron in Hamburg (Germany) and by the 1.3 GeV INS-ES synchrotron of the University of Tokyo (Japan) have also been reported (Spiller *et al.*, 1976; Aritome *et al.*, 1978).

Despite the attractive intensity and thereby throughput with this source, the cost of building and running a synchrotron radiation source is unfortunately very high; estimates for such a facility are approximately $10–15 million for the capital acquisition cost. To circumvent this cost it has been proposed that the x-ray radiation from a storage ring that is part of an existing high energy particle facility be used as a production x-ray lithography source.

  c. Other x-ray sources. These sources are of several types: laser focus, plasma focus, vacuum spark, and exploding wire. In all cases a high temperature, dense plasma must be generated in a small volume of

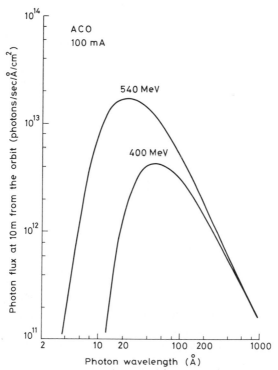

FIG. 6.19 Synchrotron radiation spectrum of the ACO storage ring (University of Orsay, Paris, France) for a 100 mA stored current at 540 and 400 MeV.

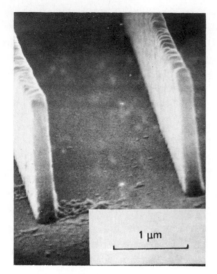

FIG. 6.20   Replication of small structures using the synchrotron radiation from ACO (540 MeV spectrum) in PMMA resist 1.6-μm thick.

space during a short time interval. The x-ray spectra produced from these sources is usually a mixture of continuous spectrum on which are superimposed discrete emission lines from the plasma ions. These sources can radiate a large amount of soft x rays with high efficiency (Nagel *et al.*, 1978; McCorkle, 1977).

2.   X-Ray Mask

The desirable properties of an x-ray mask are

(1)   low x-ray attenuation of the mask substrate,
(2)   high x-ray attenuation of the opaque layer, i.e., high contrast ratio of the x-ray mask,
(3)   good dimensional stability of the substrate.

For lithography in the near- or submicrometer range the absorbing layer of a mask must be less than 1-μm thick. The absorption of x rays in matter is a rapidly varying function of wavelength. Below 4 Å, the absorption is very weak, so that there is no material suitable for use as the absorber layer. Above 50 Å, material absorption is very high and there is no material with sufficient transmission suitable for use as a mask substrate. These points are illustrated in Fig. 6.21, in which x-ray absorption is plotted versus wavelength for several common absorbers and substrates. The important characteristic here is the contrast that is achievable, i.e., the attenuation of the absorber. Even below 50 Å wavelength, the strong

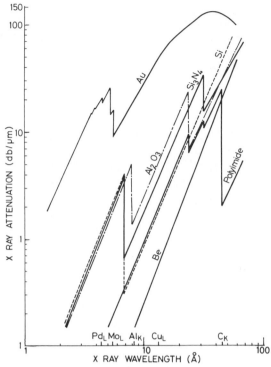

FIG. 6.21 X-ray attenuation of various materials vs. x-ray wavelength.

absorption of soft x rays means that mask substrates must be very thin (typically 1–10 μm) to provide adequate transmission.

Gold is the universally adopted absorber material because the technology of deposition is well known and the x-ray attenuation of all high absorption heavy elements is similar to that of gold in this wavelength range. The thickness of the gold layer must be adjusted to provide adequate mask contrast ratio for the x-ray resist and wavelength used. This dependence of the thickness of the gold layer on the x-ray wavelength affects the resolution of the mask because the minimum linewidth defined in the gold absorber layer cannot be smaller than the gold thickness for this would lead to an aspect ratio larger than one, which is both difficult to achieve and mechanically unstable. Therefore, the resolution of the mask is limited by the x-ray wavelength and by the contrast ratio required for the resist being used. Both longer wavelengths and higher contrast resists will improve the mask resolution by reducing the required gold absorber thickness.

The engraving of the pattern on the gold layer of the mask may be achieved in different ways depending upon the thickness of the gold layer.

Commonly used techniques are the additive method of liftoff for small thickness (less than 2500 Å) and electrolytic plating, and the substractive methods of ion beam and plasma etching. The pattern in resist is defined by the use of electron-beam lithography.

The attenuation for the mask substrate materials is seen (Fig. 6.21) to vary from approximately 0.1 to 10 dB/μm in the wavelength range of x-ray lithography with corresponding substrate thickness of several microns to a fraction of a micron. Table 6.3 lists various mask substrates that have been used in x-ray lithography with their main characteristics. The polyimide membranes can be used throughout the whole wavelength range of x-ray lithography by varying the thickness according to the wavelength.

The dimensional stability of 25-μm polyimide membranes has been measured by Maydan et al. (1977) and found to be better than 0.25 μm on a 2-in.-diameter mask. Flanders and Smith (1978) have presented some distortion measurement on thin polyimide membranes (0.9 μm) bearing on the possible distortion arising from stresses induced by the deposited absorber pattern with very favourable results. However, the long term stability and resistance to x-ray exposure of thin polyimide membranes has not yet been demonstrated.

The ultrathin membranes Si_3N_4 (Bassous et al., 1976), Al_2O_3 (Sullivan and McCoy, 1976), and polyimide (Flanders and Smith, 1978) are particularly important for applications requiring the utmost resolution. Very high resolution patterns can be defined by electron-beam masking on these membranes because the backscattering of electrons is very much reduced on such thin light element substrates (Sedgwick et al., 1972). These high resolution patterns can readily be transferred into a thin gold layer pattern

TABLE 6.3

X-Ray Mask Substrate

Substrate material	Thickness (μm)	Supporting structure	Window diameter	For x-ray wavelength (Å)
Si	2–4	Etched Si	Up to 5–8 cm	8.3
Be	12	Metal ring	2.5–5 cm	4–8.3
Si_3N_4	0.2–0.5	Etched Si	Few mm	8.3–13.3
Al_2O_3	0.2	Etched Al	Few cm	8.3–13.3
Polymer	25	} Glass or Metal ring (etched Si)	} Up to 5–8 cm	4–5
Mylar Or	3–6			8.3–45
Polyimide	0.5		Few cm	13.3

and the resulting mask can be replicated at long x-ray wavelengths (13.3 Å) on thick substrates, where they could not have been obtained by direct electron-beam masking because of the backscattering effect.

Figure 6.22 shows the fabrication steps involved in the preparation of silicon nitride membranes on a silicon wafer for use as an x-ray mask substrate (Dubée, 1978).

3. X-Ray Resist

The desirable properties of an x-ray resist are

(1) high sensitivity to x-ray radiation of selected wavelength,
(2) high contrast, i.e., high difference in dissolution rate between masked and unmasked regions during the development stage,
(3) high resolution,
(4) good resistance to etching agents (chemical, ion, plasma).

The sensitivity of an x-ray resist is generally expressed in terms of the energy absorbed per unit area (joules per squared centimeter) since the incident x-ray flux is a measurable quantity. However the dissolution rate

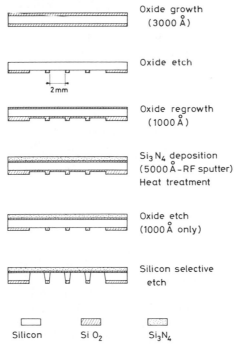

Oxide growth
(3000 Å)

Oxide etch
2 mm

Oxide regrowth
(1000 Å)

Si_3N_4 deposition
(5000 Å – RF sputter)
Heat treatment

Oxide etch
(1000 Å only)

Silicon selective
etch

Silicon   Si O_2 Si_3N_4

FIG. 6.22   Fabrication steps of silicon nitride membrane windows on a silicon wafer, for use as the x-ray mask substrate.

TABLE 6.4

X-Ray Resists

Resist	Type	Sensitivity	Minimum linewidth (μm)	Contrast
PMMA	Pos.	1–2 J/cm² (at 8.3 Å)	0.1	High
PBS	Pos.	100 mJ/cm² (at 8.3 Å)	1	Low
FBM (F)	Pos.	50 mJ/cm² (at 5.4 Å)	0.3	High
PGMA-co-EA	Neg.	50 mJ/cm² (at 8.3 Å)	2	Low
DCl PA	Neg.	10 mJ/cm² (at 4.37 Å)	1	Low

of the resist during development is determined by the energy absorbed per unit volume (joules per cubic centimeter), which depends upon the x-ray absorption of the resist and, for weak absorption, is given by the incident energy flux times the x-ray linear absorption coefficient (per centimeter). Thus, because of the higher x-ray absorption, the sensitivity of a resist is greater at the longer x-ray wavelengths. Increase in resist sensitivity, particularly at the shorter x-ray wavelength, can be achieved by doping the resist with suitable highly absorbing impurities. This was successfully demonstrated by Taylor *et al.* (1977) with a chlorine doped negative resist with a very high sensitivity (10 mJ/cm²) to Pd_L x rays (4.4 A) (Pd_L: L x-ray line of palladium spectrum).

Positive resists generally exhibit higher contrast and resolution than negative resists, although negative resists are usually more sensitive. The resolution of negative resist is impaired by swelling effects occurring during the development process. Table 6.4 lists the characteristics of some resists that have been used in x-ray lithography.* Since the x-ray resist is exposed by photoelectrons generated by photoelectric x-ray absorption, the same resists used in electron-beam lithography can be used for x-ray lithography. PMMA offers the best resolution and high contrast but low sensitivity. PBS and PGMA are sensitive but low contrast commercial resists developed by Bell Laboratories, as is the chlorine doped resist D Cl PA developed specifically for the 4.4-Å Pd_L radiation (Bowden *et al.*, 1975; Thompson *et al.*, 1975; Taylor *et al.*, 1977). FBM is a positive resist from NTT Labs (Japan) which offers simultaneously high resolution, high contrast, and high sensitivity (Kakuchi *et al.*, 1977). The devel-

* Note also Table 2.7.

opment of sensitive, high resolution resists is an essential part of the research in x-ray lithography because it will contribute to reduction of the long exposure time, which is presently one of the main problems in x-ray lithography.

4. Registration Methods

The registration problem may be solved in different ways according to the intended application. One possible application for x-ray lithography is in noncontact replication over large areas of masks with 2 to 5 μm design rules, requiring 0.25 μm alignment accuracy. For this application, optical alignment with optical microscopes as provided in the most advanced commercial optical proximity mask aligner can readily be adapted to an x-ray replication machine which operates in the same proximity mode. This requires, however, that the x-ray mask be transparent, which is the case with polymer type x-ray masks. Another application is submicron x-ray lithography, where the high resolution capability of x-rays can be fully exploited only when novel methods of registering successive masks with sufficient accuracy can be developed. Alignment of submicron patterns requires alignment accuracy in the 0.05–0.1 μm range. To achieve this kind of accuracy several methods have been proposed or studied. These methods can be classified into two basic groups: those involving detection of x rays and those involving light optics.

a. X-ray registration methods. Several such methods have been proposed, relying either on the transmission of x rays through the substrate or on x-ray fluorescence (Fig. 6.23). The x-ray transmission method (Fig. 6.23a) was originally proposed by Smith *et al.* (1973). In this technique complementary x-ray absorbing alignment masks provide a minimum x-ray signal in the aligned position. The difficulty is the x-ray absorption by the substrate, which would require thinning the substrate to improve the transmission. But even with thinning this method would only be applicable at short x-ray wavelengths, e.g., up to 8.3 Å, and the contrast of absorbing alignment marks would be low at these short wavelengths. The main advantages of this method are that the alignment signal is directly produced by the exposure x rays and that detection can be continuous throughout the exposure.

It has been proposed that harder x rays, such as those present in the continuous spectrum of the x-ray source or, alternatively, produced from an auxiliary short wavelength x-ray source, could be used for transmission alignment (McCoy and Sullivan, 1976). However, alignment mark contrast would again be very low.

Another possible x-ray detection alignment method proposed by

X–RAY DETECTION METHODS

(a) TRANSMISSION   **(b)** FLUORESCENCE

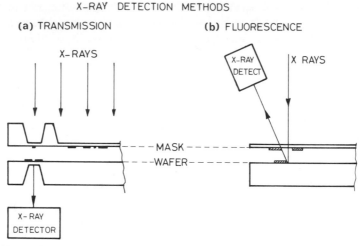

FIG. 6.23   Registration using an x-ray signal in x-ray lithography system: (a) transmission method and (b) fluorescence method.

McCoy and Sullivan (1976) uses fluorescent x rays generated from the wafer surface or from special fluorescent alignment marks. In this case the fluorescence signal is detected back through the x-ray mask (Fig. 6.23b).

   b.   Optical   registration   methods.   These   methods   require   an optically transparent mask substrate, which is the case with polymer, Si_3N_4, or Al_2O_3 mask substrates.

   Some of these methods use the concept of overlapping of single line alignment marks present on both the mask and the substrate combined with harmonic signal analysis to improve the sensitivity to misregistration. One such possible method is derived from an automatic alignment method for wafer steppers (Lacombat and Dubroeucq, 1978). In this case, the image of both alignment marks is projected on the target of an imaging tube. Synchronous detection of the third harmonic video signal of the imaging tube, which is swept at the fundamental frequency, provides the required alignment signal.

   An alternative method of this type was demonstrated at NTT Labs (Japan). It uses mechanical low frequency vibration of the wafer and detection of the fundamental and second harmonic component of the optical signal resulting from the overlapping of the two alignment marks. A registration accuracy of 0.05 μm was obtained in a registration test setup (Yamazaki *et al.*, 1978).

   Another group of optical registration methods makes use of the diffraction of light by alignment marks consisting of periodic line structures or gratings. These methods can provide very high registration accuracy with simple signal detection because they involve collective interference effects taking place between the two diffraction gratings.

The operating principles of these various double diffraction methods can be briefly described as follows. The Moiré method is based on the appearance of Moiré fringes when the mask and wafer gratings have slightly different pitches. King and Berry (1972) have described a visual alignment method using concentric circle geometry alignment marks for which they obtained 0.2 μm registration accuracy, limited only by the difference in pitch of their alignment marks.

Flanders et al. (1977) have demonstrated an alignment method, the principle of which is represented in Fig. 6.24, using two identical gratings. The alignment is determined by measuring the intensities of symmetric multiply diffracted beams (e.g., the +1 and -1 diffracted groups), which for nonblazed gratings are equal by reason of symmetry when the two gratings an exactly aligned. A registration accuracy better than 0.1 μm has been demonstrated by this method (Austin et al., 1978).

Another alignment method of the double diffraction type is the composite grating method, which requires two identical gratings of period p with slit width a greater than the half-period (Torii and Mizushima, 1977).

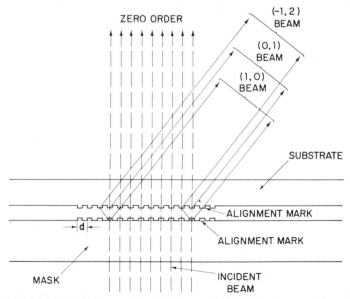

FIG. 6.24 Principle of interferometric alignment technique for the case of transmission through matching grating type alignment marks on mask and substrate. [From Flanders et al. 1977]

When these two gratings are misaligned by exactly one half-period they effectively form a composite grating with a resultant period equal to one-half of the original period.

5. State-of-the-Art in X-Ray Lithography Systems

The first experiments in x-ray replication of high resolution patterns were reported by Spears and Smith (1972). These authors used as the soft x-ray source a modified evaporator gun with an aluminium target producing Al_K x rays of wavelength 8.34 Å (Al_K: K line of x-ray spectrum of aluminum). Silicon membranes 4 μm thick obtained by selective etching (Cohen et al., 1973) were used as mask substrates. Submicron linewidth capability was clearly demonstrated in this initial work.

Systems designed with a production application goal can be built around a conventional optical proximity mask aligner modified so that the illumination head is replaced by an $Al_K(\lambda = 8.34$ Å) x-ray source head. Both medium source power [1 kW, Hughes (1978)] and high source power [10 kW, McCoy (1977)] systems of this type have been reported.

Another interesting system development was reported by Yamazaki et al. (1978) using a very high power (18 kW) silicon target source coupled with a very accurate (0.05 μm precision) alignment stage with registration by optical means. In both cases the exposure chamber is at atmospheric pressure (Helium atmosphere) and 0.25 μm Beryllium window isolates the source from the exposure chamber.

Another approach, pursued by Maydan et al. (1975), is to use shorter wavelength x rays from a palladium target producing a Pd_L line of wavelength 4.37 Å. The x-ray exposure system shown in Fig. 6.25 built at Bell Laboratories by Maydan et al. (1977) can be considered to be the first x-ray replication system that could be used as such on a production scale.

The parameters of this system are the following:

anode characteristics	rotating, water cooled, palladium anode
principal x-ray wavelength	Pd_L, $\lambda = 4.37$ Å
electron gun characteristics	25 kV, 4.5 kW, 3-mm-diameter focal spot
vacuum window	beryllium, 50-μm thick
source to mask distance	50 cm
mask substrate	25-μm-thick kapton (polyimide)
gold absorber thickness	7000 Å
alignment means	optical registration with split field dual focus microscope, accuracy ~ 0.25 μm

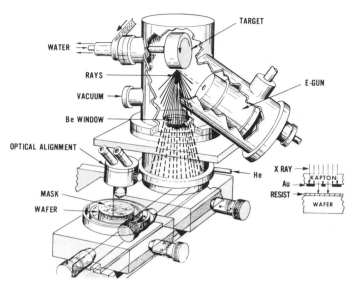

FIG. 6.25 Schematic of a complete x-ray exposure system with alignment. [From Maydan *et al.* 1977]

x-ray flux at wafer	$4 \text{ mJ cm}^{-2} \text{ min}^{-1}$
exposure time with sensitized negative resist	2 min
minimum working linewidth	1 μm
wafer diameter	up to 75 mm

The design emphasis for this system was on exposure speed and convenience of operation rather than on very high resolution.

A medium power (1–5 kW) high brightness x-ray source has been described by Wardly *et al.* (1977). Such a source could be useful for small volume, high resolution fabrication of single masking level devices such as acoustic surface wave or bubble devices.

Finally, for the extreme submicron applications involving several masking levels, practical system realizations do not exist at this time. This subject is still at an early stage of development in the laboratory environment.

X-ray replication using the 44.7 Å carbon K line was shown by Feder *et al.* (1976) to achieve extremely high resolution, with less than 0.1 μm linewidth. At this wavelength, a thin polymer mask substrate can be used; because of the very high x-ray attenuation of gold, the absorber pattern on the mask can also be very thin (less than 0.1 μm) and therefore very accurately defined.

Another x-ray wavelength that has been shown to be suitable for very high resolution is the copper L line of wavelength 13.3 Å (Smith and Flanders, 1977).

Systems designed for this submicrometer application will necessarily be of step-and-repeat mode of operation as a result of mask and wafer stability problems. Extremely high registration accuracy will be required (~ 0.05 μm). Exposure will be made in vacuum.

Synchrotron radiation sources would be ideal, of course, for this application. However, conventional high power x-ray sources could also be used with anode materials such as copper or carbon for long x-ray wavelength ($\lambda > 10$ Å) operation and highest resolution. Future developments in this direction can only be expected to occur when submicron circuits are needed in a large volume.

IV. COMPARISON AMONG THE SEVERAL REPLICATION METHODS

A conclusive comparison between the methods which have just been described is difficult because there is a large number of parameters involved, and the weighting of these performance factors is heavily dependent on the intended use of the replication system. Table 6.5 shows a tabulation of performance and a comparison based on the criteria of resolution and exposure time. Only achieved performance values or reasonable extrapolations have been included in this table.

In order to justify a replication system, as compared to a direct electron-beam writing system of the type described in Chapter 3, the replication system should have a 0.5 μm minimum linewidth capability on various substrates and an exposure time of less than 1 min cm^{-2}. Table 6.5 shows that uv shadow casting, uv refracting optics, 1:1 and n:1 electron projection can all meet these goals.

It is somewhat paradoxical that the research effort is not growing in these areas. An explanation of this research neglect is given for electron projection in Section IV.D, but the main reason is that improved electron-beam scanning systems can reach nearly the same speed with additional features, such as flexibility, distortion correction, registration accuracy, etc. The effort is not growing in the area of uv shadow casting because the contact between the mask and the wafer produces a large number of defects. However, research effort is growing in the area of x rays because this lithography process has the best potential resolution on any substrate, despite the expectation that there will be no dramatic improvement on exposure time. Research effort is also growing in the area of uv imaging systems, especially reflecting optics, although no sig-

TABLE 6.5

Comparison of Various Replication Systems

Replication Method	Minimum linewidth (μm)	Exposure time (s cm⁻²)	Registration accuracy (μm)	Preferred application	Pros	Cons	Status of research
UV contact[a] (Lin, 1975)	0.5	10 (achieved) 1 (extrapolated)		Acoustic and bubble devices	Simplicity	Contact	↑
X ray (Wardly, 1977)[a]	0.2	120		Acoustic and bubble devices	Potential resolution	Low speed	↖
Electron[a] (Lischke, 1977)	1	2.5		VLSI	Speed	Mask, resolution	↗
UV projection (refracting system)[b] (Dubroeucq, 1977)	0.5	12.5		VLSI	Stability, Potential improvement with deep uv	Dependence on substrate	↖
1 : 1 electron projection[b] (Fay, 1974)	0.5	5	±0.2	VLSI	Speed, resolution	Distortion, backscattered electrons	↑
n : 1 electron projection[b] (Heritage, 1975)	0.5	1	±0.1	VLSI	Speed, resolution	Stability	↑

[a] Shadow casting.
[b] Imaging.

nificant improvement beyond 0.5-μm linewidth is expected. Interest is high in this method because it forms an improvement on methods which have been used for a long time in the microelectronics industry that have proven to be simple, reliable, and not too costly.

REFERENCES

Aritome, H., Nishimura, T., Kotani, H., Matsui, S., Nakagawa, O., and Namba, S. (1978). *J. Vac. Sci. Technol.* **15** (3), 992–994.
Austin, S., Smith, H. I., and Flanders, D. C. (1978). *J. Vac. Sci. Technol.* **15** (3), 984–986.
Bassous, E., Feder, R., Spiller, E., and Topalian, J. (1976). *Solid State Technol.* **19,** (9), 55–58.
Binder, H., and Lacombat, M. (1979). *IEEE Trans. ED* special issue on VLSI (to be published). IEEE Trans. Electron Devices, ED-26 (4), 698–704.
Bowden, M. J., Thompson, L. F., and Ballantyne, J. P. (1975). *J. Vac. Sci. Technol.* **12** (6), 1294–1296.
Brault, R. G. (1974). *Proc. Int. Conf. Electron Ion Beam Sci. Technol., 6th* (R. Bakish, ed.), pp. 63–70.
Brochet, A., and Dubroeucq, (1977). *Proc. Int. Conf. Microlithogr., Paris, June 21–24* pp. 239–248.
Cohen, R. A., Mountain, R. W., Spears, D. L., Smith, H. I., Lemma, M. A., and Bernacki, S. E. (1973). Technical Note 1973-38, September 20, M.I.T. Lincoln Laboratory, Lexington, Massachusetts.
De Forest, W. S. (1972). *Proc. NAI Nepcon* **18,** 10.
Dill, F. H. (1975). *IEEE Trans. Electron. Devices* **ED-22** (7), 440–444.
Doniach, S., Lindau, I., Spicer, W. E., and Winick, H. (1975). *J. Vac. Sci. Technol.* **12** (6), 1123–1127.
Dubée; A. (1978). Private communication.
Fay, B. (1974). *Proc. Int. Conf. Electron Ion Beam Sci. Technol., 6th* (R. Bakish, ed.), pp. 527–533.
Fay, B. (1977). *Rev. Tech. Thomson-CSF* **9** (2), 265–284.
Fay, B., Trotel, J., Petroff, Y., Pinchaux, R., and Thiry, P. (1976). *Appl. Phys. Lett.* **29** (6), 370–372.
Feder, R., Spiller, E., Topalian, J., and Hatzakis, M. (1976). *Proc. Int. Conf. Electron Ion Beam Sci. Technol., 7th* (R. Bakish, ed.), pp. 198–203.
Feder, R., Spiller, E., and Topalian, J. (1977). *Polym. Eng. Sci.* **17,** 385.
Flanders, D. C., and Smith, H. I. (1978). *J. Vac. Sci. Technol.* **15** (3), 995–997.
Flanders, D. C., Smith, H. I., and Austin, S. (1977). *Appl. Phys. Lett.* **31** (7), 426–428.
Fuller, C. E. (1977). *ESSDERC, Eur. Solid State Dev. Conf., 7th, Brighton, September.*
Gruen, A. E. (1957). *Z. Naturforsch.* **12a,** 89–95.
Heritage, M. B. (1975). *J. Vac. Sci. Technol.* **12** (6), 1135–1140.
Hiraoka, H. (1977). *IBM J. Res. Dev.* March.
Hughes, G. P. (1978). *J. Vac. Sci. Technol.* **15** (3), 974–976.
Kakuchi, M., Sugawara, S., Murase, K., and Matsuyama, K. (1977). *J. Electrochem. Soc.* **124** (10), 1648–1651.
King, M. C., and Berry, D. H. (1972). *Appl. Opt.* **11,** 2455–2459.
Koops, H., and Bernhard, W. (1975). *J. Vac. Sci. Technol.* **12** (6), 1141–1145.
Koops, H., Möllenstedt, G., and Speidel, R. (1968–1969). *Optik* **28,** 518–531.
Lacombat, M., and Dubroeucq, G. (1978). *Proc. Microcircuit Conf., Cambridge, April.*

Lacombat, M., Gérard, A., Dubroeucq, G., and Chartier, M. (1977). *Rev. Tech. Thomson-CSF* **9** (2), 337–372.

Lin, B. J. (1975). *J. Vac. Sci. Technol.* **12** (6), 1317–1320.

Lischke, B., Anger, K., Frosien, J., Oelmann, A., and Schuster-Woldan, H. (1977a). *Int. Conf. Microlithogr., Paris, June* pp. 163–166.

Lischke, B., Anger, K., Oelmann, A., and Münchmeyer, W. (1977b). *Int. Conf. Microlithogr., Paris, June* pp. 167–170.

Livesay, W. R. (1973). *J. Vac. Sci. Technol.* **10** (6), 1028–1032.

Livesay, W. R. (1978). *J. Vac. Sci. Technol.* **15** (3), 1022–1027.

Maydan, D., Coquin, G. A., Maldonado, J. R., Somekh, S., Lon, D. Y., and Taylor, G. N. (1975). *IEEE Trans. Electron. Devices* **ED-22,** 429–433.

Maydan, D., Coquin, G. A., Maldonado, J. R., Moran, J. M., Somekh, S., and Taylor, G. N. (1977). *Int. Conf. Microlithogr., Paris, June* pp. 195–200.

McCorkle, R. A. (1977). J. Phys. B: Atom. Molec. Phys., 11 (14), L407–409.

McCoy, J. H. (1977). *SPIE Semicond. Lithogr.* **100,** II, 162–171.

McCoy, J. H., and Sullivan, P. A. (1976). *Proc. Int. Conf. Electron Ion Beam Sci. Technol., 7th* (R. Bakish ed.), pp. 536–544.

Mimura, Y., Ohkubo, T., Takeuchi, T., and Sekikawa, K. (1978). *Jpn. J. Appl. Phys.* **17** (3), 541, 550.

Moller, P. (1975). *Wafer Process Seminar, Tokyo.*

Nagel, D. J., Whitlock, R. R., Greig, J. R., Pechacek, R. E., and Peckerar, M. C. (1978). *SPIE Dev. Semicond. Microlithogr.* **135,** III, 46–53.

O'Keefe, T. W. (1970). *IEEE Trans. Electron. Devices* **ED-17,** 465–469.

O'Keefe, T. W., Vine, J., and Hardy, R. W. (1969). *Solid State Electron.* **12,** 841–848.

Scott, J. P. (1974). *J. Phys. E* **7,** 574–578.

Scott, J. P. (1975a). *J. Vac. Sci. Technol.* **12** (6), 1309–1312.

Scott, J. P. (1975b). *J. Appl. Phys.* **46,** 661–664.

Scott, J. P. (1975c). *IEEE Trans. Electron Devices* **ED-22,** 409–413.

Scott, J. P. (1978). *J. Vac. Sci. Technol.* **15** (3), 1016–1021.

Sedgwick, T. O., Broers, A. N., and Agull, B. J. (1972). *J. Electrochem. Soc.* **119** (12), 1769–1771.

Smith, H. I. (1974). *Proc. IEEE* **62** (10), 1361–1387.

Smith, H. I., and Flanders, D. C. (1977). *Jpn. J. Appl. Phys. Suppl. 16-1,* **16,** 61–64.

Smith, H. I., Spears, D. L., and Bernacki, S. (1973). *J. Vac. Sci. Technol.* **10** (6), 913–917.

Sommerfeld, A. (1954). "Optics." Academic Press, New York.

Spears, D. L., and Smith, H. I. (1972). *Electron. Lett.* **8,** 102–104.

Speidel, R. (1976). *Workshop on VLSI, 1st, Aachen, November.*

Spiller, E., and Feder, R. (1977). "X-ray Optics, Application to Solids" (H. J. Queisser, ed.), Chapter 3, pp. 35–92. Springer Verlag, Berlin and New York.

Spiller, E., Eastman, D. E., Feder, R., Grobman, W. D., Gudat, W., and Topalian, J. (1976). *J. Appl. Phys.* **47** (12), 5450–5459.

Stevens, G. W. W. (1957). "Microphotography," p. 30. Chapman and Hall, London.

Sullivan, P. A., and McCoy, J. H. (1976). *IEEE Trans. Electron. Devices* **ED-23,** 412–418.

Taylor, G. N., Coquin, G. A., and Somekh, S. (1977). *Polym. Eng. Sci.* **17,** 420.

Thompson, L. F., Ballantyne, J. P., and Feit, E. D. (1975). *J. Vac. Sci. Technol.* **12** (6), 1280–1283.

Torü, Y., and Mizushima, Y. (1977). *Opt. Commun.* **23** (1), 135–138.

Van den Berg, H. A. M. (1978). *ESSDERC, Eur. Solid State Dev. Conf., 8th, Montpellier, September.*

Wardly, G. A. (1973). *Rev. Sci. Instrum.* **44,** 1506.

Wardly, G. A. (1975a). *J. Vac. Sci. Technol.* **12** (6), 1313–1316.
Wardly, G. A. (1975b). *IEEE Trans. Electron. Devices* **ED-22,** 414–417.
Wardly, G. A. (1977). *Int. Conf. Microlithogr., Paris, June* pp. 217–220.
Yamazaki, S., Nakayama, S., Hayasaka, T., and Ishihara, S. (1978). *J. Vac. Sci. Technol.* **15** (3), 987–991.
Yu, A., and Spicer, W. E. (1968). *Phys. Lett.* **169,** 497.

Index